REFUGE IN HELL

REFUGE IN HELL

How Berlin's Jewish Hospital Outlasted the Nazis

DANIEL B. SILVER

HOUGHTON MIFFLIN COMPANY

BOSTON   NEW YORK

2003

For information about permission to reproduce selections
from this book, write to Permissions, Houghton Mifflin Company,
215 Park Avenue South, New York, New York 10003.

Visit our Web site: www.houghtonmifflinbooks.com.

Library of Congress Cataloging-in-Publication Data
Silver, Daniel B.
Refuge in hell : how Berlin's Jewish hospital outlasted
the Nazis / Daniel B. Silver.
p.   cm.
Includes bibliographical references and index.
ISBN 0-618-25144-8
1. Jüdisches Krankenhaus (Berlin, Germany)—History—20th century.
2. Hospitals—Germany—Berlin—History—20th century. 3. Jews—Germany—Berlin—History—20th century. 4. Jews—Germany—History—1933–1945. 5. Jews—Medical care—Germany—Berlin—History—20th century. 6. Medical policy—Germany—History—20th century. 7. Holocaust, Jewish (1939–1945)—Germany—Berlin—Personal narratives. 8. Berlin (Germany)—Ethnic relations. I. Title.
RA989.G34B477 2003
362.1′1′094315509044—dc21   2003047896

Printed in the United States of America

Book design by Victoria Hartman

QUM 10 9 8 7 6 5 4 3 2 1

For Sybil, with love
For Ernie, in loving memory

Contents

Preface   ix

1. *Nichts Juden. Juden Kaputt*   1

2. The Hospital and the Berlin Jews   14

3. The Beginning of the End, 1938–41   31

4. The Nazis' Intermarriage Quandary   46

5. The Deportations   59

6. The Assault on the *Gemeinde* and the
   Hospital, 1942–43   77

7. Making a Life for Oneself in the Hospital   93

8. The Factory Raid and the *Frauenprotest*   119

9. The Continued Assault on the Hospital   140

10. Prisoners and Survivors   159

11. The Work of the *Reichsvereinigung*
    and the Hospital, 1942–45   177

12. The Twilight of the Nazis 190

13. The Trial of Dr. Dr. Lustig and
Other Questions 209

Afterword 242

Notes 253

Bibliography 279

Glossary 284

Acknowledgments 290

Index 296

Preface

The Story Behind the Story

In AUGUST 1945, Ernie Mayerfeld, a nineteen-year-old GI stationed in Berlin, received a letter from his father in New York asking him to undertake a mission for a family friend.

Until 1938 the elder Mayerfeld had been a prosperous leather distributor in Frankfurt. Even as the Nazi persecution mounted in Germany, it had seemed inconceivable to Herr Mayerfeld that the family's comfortable life would be disrupted permanently. After all, the family's roots in Germany and Austria went back hundreds of years. (The residence of one ancestor, the Baron Eskeles, whose wife was a patroness of Mozart, today serves as the home of Vienna's Jewish Museum.) And after the Nazis took power in 1933, he still could not foresee the worst. Had he not received a medal for his service at the front in World War I, accompanied by a letter of thanks signed by Der Führer himself? Not even the 1938 *Kristallnacht* pogrom, in which Herr Mayerfeld narrowly escaped arrest, had convinced him to emigrate. Only in the ensuing months when his suppliers would no longer sell him the merchandise needed for his business was he finally persuaded to flee.

And so, virtually at the last possible moment and aided by a large dose of good luck, the Mayerfelds escaped and eventually made their way to New York, where fourteen-year-old Ernst turned himself into Ernie, an American teenager. Five years later, after fighting in the Battle of the Bulge, he returned to the country of his birth as one of the occupying U.S. troops.

His father's request was one of many that Ernie had received asking him to look for surviving relatives of German Jewish émigrés in the United States. Frequently, the searches were unavailing. But in this case, Herr Mayerfeld's friend was certain that his sister, Johanna Frank, had survived the war as a nurse in the Berlin Jewish Hospital. He sent a package of foodstuffs to be delivered to her.

And so one day Ernie made his way through the rubble and devastation of occupied Berlin to 2 Iranischestrasse in the Wedding district. There he found a spacious compound of seven buildings set in a large garden. Carved in stone over the main entrance on Iranischestrasse, in the pediment of the administration building, was the name *Krankenhaus der Jüdischen Gemeinde*, or Hospital of the Jewish Community. Johanna Frank was indeed there, attending to her nursing duties.

"The buildings were all still standing," Ernie remembered, "although some of them had taken hits in the bombing. Inside, though, it was unbelievable. Doctors in white coats and nurses in clean, starched uniforms bustled through spotless corridors and rooms, attending to their patients."

It was as if the twelve years of Nazi horror had never happened. Astounded by what he found, Ernie asked *Schwester* Johanna and her coworkers how it was possible that this hospital, full of Jews, had made it through the Nazi period. All agreed that it was a miracle, but no one had a coherent explanation to offer.

More than half a century passed, filled with marriage, family, and a successful career as a CIA officer and later as a lawyer in the CIA's Office of General Counsel. From time to time Ernie thought about his strange experience at the Berlin Jewish Hospital and wondered about the story that lay behind it, but he had no time to make inquiries.

At a dinner party in the late 1970s or early 1980s, about the same time that Ernie and I became legal colleagues at the CIA and grew to be close friends, I met Klaus Zwilsky, a charming and ebullient man, then in his fifties, who spoke with a slight German accent. Over the years we continued to see each other. One night over dinner, the talk turned to how it must feel to live under the constant threat of bombing. I don't remember how the topic arose; probably we were talking about Beirut or one of the world's other perennial hot spots.

Klaus listened for a while and then volunteered a comment, describing his own emotions as a child in Berlin in 1944 and 1945, cowering fearfully in the cellar while Allied bombers attacked the city.

"But, Klaus," someone said. "I don't understand. You're Jewish; your parents were both 100 percent Jewish. How could you have been living in Berlin during the last years of the war?"

"My father worked at the Jewish hospital," Klaus explained, "and we all lived there." He said a few more words about his experience of the Allied air raids, and the conversation moved on to other things.

In this way I too learned that a Jewish hospital in Berlin had remained open throughout the entire Nazi era and that Jewish doctors, nurses, administrators, and patients had survived there. The fact astonished me. I thought I knew a good deal about the Nazi persecution of German Jews. I had read widely on the subject of the Holocaust. I was aware that a handful of Jews had survived in Germany, some in hiding, some "protected" by marriage to non-Jews. But I also knew — or thought I knew — that the Nazis had ruthlessly extirpated every trace of Jewish life in Germany. They had destroyed the synagogues, desecrated the cemeteries, dissolved the Jewish organizations, prohibited Jewish worship, driven two-thirds of Germany's Jews into exile, and then deported all but a handful of those who remained — the "lucky" ones to the ghetto established in Theresienstadt in what had once been Czechoslovakia, and the rest to the death camps of Eastern

Europe. How, then, was it possible that a Jewish hospital operating openly under the name *Krankenhaus der Jüdischen Gemeinde* had continued to exist in Berlin throughout the war? How was it that Klaus and his parents, full Jews with no apparent form of "protection," could have survived the war living in that hospital?

The question kept recurring through the next two decades of a life that, like Ernie's, was too busy to permit further investigation. Klaus, who had been only a child during the war years, was reticent about his experiences and volunteered no further explanation. I could find nothing written on the subject in English-language sources. Years went by, years during which from time to time I would say to myself, "Someday I need to find out about the Jewish hospital," and then move on to whatever preoccupation was more pressing.

Finally, the day came when circumstances made it possible for me to begin serious research on the Berlin Jewish Hospital during the wartime years. My immediate thought was to ask Ernie Mayerfeld if he would be interested in joining me.

"Did you know that there was a Jewish hospital in Berlin that operated all the way through World War II?" I asked.

His response took me by surprise. Everyone else to whom I mentioned this fact reacted with astonishment. Ernie looked sheepish.

"Not only do I know that," he said haltingly. "I was there." He proceeded to tell me the story of his 1945 visit.

We agreed that we would set out together to find out how and why this hospital, alone among all of Germany's Jewish institutions, had survived when everything else associated with German Jewry was being destroyed. Our initial objective was to satisfy our own curiosity. As we found out more, however, we agreed that we should write something that would bring this astonishing story to the public's attention. Our determination to do so was strengthened when we discovered that the only Internet reference we could find was on a scurrilous neo-Nazi, Holocaust-denial Web site where the fact that the Berlin Jewish Hospital operated throughout the war was adduced as "proof" that the Nazi atrocities had never occurred.

Our research quickly revealed that the essential facts relating to the Berlin Jewish Hospital were not unknown in the small circle of scholars who have devoted themselves to the study of the German Jewish experience during the Nazi era. Indeed, many facts pertaining to the hospital's survival from 1938 through 1945 have been recorded in two German-language publications — in a small monograph devoted to the 1938–45 period and in portions of a larger history of the hospital. Both were the products of extensive archival research and of interviews with war survivors. The findings of the monograph were summarized in English in an article in a scholarly journal, the *Leo Baeck Institute Year Book*. Passing references to the hospital also could be found in other scholarly books on German Jewry during the Nazi era. Thus we found that the task of preserving the record for the scholarly community had largely been completed.

Nor had the existence of the hospital in the war period completely escaped the attention even of authors who wrote for a more popular audience. Fleeting references to it gave evidence that they knew it was there. For example, in a fascinating book, *The Last Jews in Berlin*, Leonard Gross tells the stories of several Jews who survived the final years of the Nazi period in hiding in Berlin. A passing reference makes clear that he knew that the hospital was in operation throughout this period, but nothing more is said about the institution and the large number of Jews who were living there openly.

None of the scholarly or passing accounts, we felt, satisfactorily addressed two important questions. Again and again we asked ourselves, "How could this have happened?" So, too, has almost everyone who has encountered the simple fact of the hospital's survival. Another question that the barest outline of the facts about the hospital urgently raises is: "What was it like to live and work in such circumstances?" And so we set out to do two things. First, we wanted to supplement the existing historical record as much as possible, knowing that the number of living witnesses already had been greatly diminished by the passage of so many years. Second, we decided to write this book, and in so doing, to attempt to answer our two questions.

Sources

In pursuit of the first objective we turned to something new, the Internet, and something traditional, a newspaper. We posted an appeal for information on the Internet Web site of the German Special Interest Group of the Jewish Genealogy Net, and we published an advertisement in the newspaper *Aufbau*, the German-language periodical of the German Jewish émigré community. It was Ernie who remembered that his parents had read *Aufbau* avidly in his youth. It was a surprise to us both to find that it still was being published. It was an even greater surprise, in the weeks and months that ensued, to receive e-mail messages, letters, and telephone calls in response both to the Internet posting and to the *Aufbau* advertisement, although primarily the latter. The communications came from all over — mostly from the United States, but also from Germany, Israel, Brazil, Australia, Canada, and France. In some instances, we were contacted directly by people who had been in the hospital, either as patients or as members of the staff. In other cases, friends and relatives gave us information on how we might be able to find former hospital patients or employees whom they knew. The total number of people still alive who once had worked or lived at the hospital was not huge — fewer than twenty — but, in light of the passage of more than half a century since the end of the war, it was more than we had dared hope for.

We called and wrote to the people who seemed most likely to have useful information and began to conduct interviews. One of these never took place; the subject died before the date of our appointment. Another was canceled when the subject, a former hospital prison patient from 1944 to the end of the war who initially had been enthusiastic about telling his story, called in a state of agitation and said that he was afraid that our visit would awaken unpleasant memories. We desisted, but Ernie gently managed to gather the essential information over the telephone.

Not long after we returned from a trip to New Jersey and New York to speak with the first three wartime survivors, my beloved friend Ernie Mayerfeld died suddenly of a heart attack, leaving an enormous void in many lives, including mine. He also left me with the determination to complete the research and write this book as a tribute to him. I continued interviewing as many surviving individuals as I could find.

All of the survivors I was able to locate and interview were women. Every interview followed the same pattern. I tried to schedule my visit for a time when no one would feel obligated to provide a meal. Nonetheless, regardless of the time of day, on arrival I would find the table set and a bountiful display of food laid out. The first order of business always was to eat. Only then, with the imperatives of German Jewish hospitality fulfilled, were my hostesses ready to talk about their experiences. Without exception, the people I met were delightful, charming, vivacious, and intelligent. One could easily discern, more than half a century later, the qualities of strength and spirit that had kept them alive and sane through years of persecution, loss, and terror.

In researching and writing this book, I have relied heavily on the work of scholars who have investigated the history of the Berlin Jewish Hospital during the 1938–45 period. Rivka Elkin, the Israeli historian, deserves great credit for having written the definitive monograph on the hospital during that period, *Das Jüdische Krankenhaus in Berlin zwischen 1938 und 1945*, the contents of which were ably summarized in her article in English in the *Leo Baeck Institute Year Book*. Equal recognition is due to Dagmar Hartung-von Doetinchem and Rolf Winau, editors of *Zerstörte Fortschritte*, a 1989 history of the hospital from 1756 to modern times that includes a lengthy and excellent chapter by Ms. Hartung-von Doetinchem on the wartime period, and to

Daniel Nadav and Manfred Stürzbecher, the authors of that book's chapter on the hospital's director, Dr. Walter Lustig. (Full references to all of these books and to Ms. Elkin's article can be found in the Bibliography.)

I have gone back to original sources whenever it seemed appropriate. Some of the most important were personal histories of people who were at the hospital during the relevant period. Of particular interest are the written memoirs in German of Hilde Kahan, Dr. Lustig's secretary, and a videotaped interview of Ms. Kahan in English, both found in the archives of Yad Vashem in Jerusalem. Similar memoirs exist (in some cases published in whole or in part in German or English, or both) that were written by others who lived or worked at the hospital. I have paid particular attention to all of these personal histories because I wanted to describe the texture of daily life in the hospital and to reconstruct the drama of living under an intense and continual pressure that differed from what other European Jews experienced in the ghettos, labor camps, and death camps.

I have also had recourse to a variety of other archival materials — in particular, to war crimes trial transcripts and to the records of the wartime central organization of German Jews, the *Reichsvereinigung*. With the assistance of historical research consultants, I searched the captured German government records housed in the National Archives in College Park, Maryland. This search failed to turn up any new material relevant to the hospital. Finally, I examined and used certain materials that were not used by earlier researchers, largely personal papers of people who were at the hospital. It has been particularly gratifying that two holders of important personal papers asked me to help them find a suitable repository where these materials would be preserved and made available to researchers. (One collection ultimately was entrusted to the Leo Baeck Institute Archives located in the new Jewish Museum in Berlin. The ultimate home of the other is still under consideration.)

Relying on Memories

The body of archival material relating to the hospital — records of the hospital and of the *Reichsvereinigung* and the Jewish community, war crimes trial pleadings and judgments, a few records of the Gestapo and of Adolf Eichmann's department in the *Reichssicherheitshauptamt* (RSHA), or Reich Security Main Office, which had formal jurisdiction over the hospital — reveal amazingly little, at least in any transparent way, about what is really interesting. One cannot determine from official, bureaucratic documents how and why the hospital managed to stay open when, by all the logic of the Nazi racial policy, it should have been eliminated. Nor does the formal record preserve the infighting, conniving, ambitions, deals, backbiting, double-dealing, skullduggery, and luck that must have contributed to that outcome.

So, too, it is surprising how little information the archival record truly provides about day-to-day conditions in the hospital, particularly in the chaotic circumstances that prevailed during the final months of the war. The principal source of information on daily life is witnesses' recollections — those of the former inhabitants of the hospital who were interviewed by Elkin or Hartung-von Doetinchem or more recently in the course of conducting research for this book, witnesses who testified at war crimes trials, and hospital survivors who wrote memoirs or letters describing their experiences. These accounts provide invaluable documentation of the hospital's story, but, to the same degree, they are subject to the inherent uncertainties and limitations of human memory. Several points should be kept in mind.

First, although some of the firsthand accounts were written or collected shortly after the end of the war, many of the memories reflected in this book were already old at the time they were recorded. That is especially the case, obviously, of those that were collected specifically for this book in interviews held during the past several years. It would be oversimplifying to assume that time has caused these recollections to dim. For many of the people who lived or worked in the hospital, the last years of the war were the most unforgettable of their lives. Yet, time and postwar life have a way of transforming even the most vivid of memories and blurring the details. Even Hilde Kahan, who as secretary to the hospital's director had an intimate view of what transpired, gives slightly different accounts of the same events in her written memoir and in her videotaped interview, which occurred years after the memoir was written.

Second, for every person in the hospital, the horrifying things that were witnessed and experienced must have had a powerful psychological effect. Everyone in the hospital underwent years of constantly intensifying Nazi persecution. For each, it was a time of loss, as relatives and friends disappeared in the deportations, and a time of fear. The haven the hospital provided was at best fragile and ephemeral. Again and again, those who survived saw others around them seized and taken away. No one ever knew who would be next. Not a single person at the hospital could have felt truly safe. Thus, for many, life at the hospital was perceived, and has been remembered, through a filter of strong emotion. In some cases a survivor's account is so divergent from other reports that it is clear that powerful emotions essentially reshaped the way events were remembered.

An interesting example of how easily memories can be distorted is given by Holocaust scholar Beate Meyer in a November 2000 paper describing her research on the *Reichsvereinigung*, the central organization of Jews in Germany that functioned from 1939 until 1943 and then, in a "rump" form, to the end of the war headquartered in the hospital. She recounts the experience of interviewing a Jewish woman, a survivor from Hamburg, about Max Plaut, who directed the *Reichsvereinigung* district office in northwest Germany. The interviewee spoke with great certainty about two Plauts, the father, Raphael, whom she described as a man of integrity, and the son, Max, whom she described as dishonest. In reality, this woman had never known Max Plaut's father. Her memory of Max Plaut in his earlier years as an upright community leader was inconsistent with her recollections of him from 1938 on, when she perceived that he exercised his official role in a corrupt manner. Faced with this cognitive dissonance, her memory had played a trick on her and divided the single individual into a "good" father and a "bad" son.

A prime example of the same kind of phenomenon is the journalist Cordelia Edvardson's account of her brief stay as a teenager in the orphanage section of the hospital, where, for some reason, the Gestapo placed her before later deporting her to Auschwitz. In her memoir, *Burned Child Seeks the Fire*, she depicts the hospital as a lawless hellhole where promiscuous sex abounded and a black market flourished in drugs and cigarettes. In the context of a memoir that is written in a poetic and highly impressionistic style, it makes sense for the hospital environment to serve as a metaphor for the horror and confusion that beset a traumatized adolescent. Yet, although others' accounts confirm that sexual liaisons occurred in the hospital, no one else substantiates Edvardson's orgiastic description to the same degree, and virtually all other sources gainsay what she says about drugs and cigarettes.

Hartung-von Doetinchem records a similar discrepancy. One of the survivors she interviewed provided a vivid description of how, when the war with Poland broke out, the Nazis began to loot the hospital every few weeks, taking away its medical supplies and equipment and leaving it almost completely devoid of what it needed to continue functioning. The informant goes so far as to say that the Gestapo even emptied the kitchens and loaded their contents onto trucks. Yet numerous other witnesses describe the hospital in 1939 as well organized and functioning normally. Hartung-von Doetinchem notes that the story of looting cannot be reconciled with the information provided by other informants. Nor can it be squared with the accounts I collected. Except for the one woman interviewed by Hartung-von Doetinchem, everyone described the hospital, right through to the end of the war, as a functional medical institution, short of some items as the war neared its end — as no doubt every hospital in Germany was — but by no means stripped of medical equipment or supplies.

It is hardly surprising that someone whose life suddenly descended into hell should remember the hospital in terms as hellish as the death camp to which she was sent. It is equally comprehensible that another woman who may well have gone through her post-Holocaust life burning with anger at the Gestapo for the uncounted acts of looting it committed elsewhere should "remember" one that, however plausible, did not occur. No overarching point needs to be made with respect to these discrepant memories. Where they arise, I have chosen to accept as most probable the story that emerges from the greatest number of accounts, while noting that divergent recollections exist. With respect to the entire account of life in the hospital that is based in survivors' memories, it is sufficient to note that, although perceptions undoubtedly were colored, and in some details perhaps even distorted, by emotions and personal reactions, what the survivors have to tell us is largely accurate and is as close to reality as we ever will get.

Jews and Aryans: A Note on Terminology

Anyone who writes about the Nazi period faces at least two issues of terminology: who is encompassed in the term *Jew*, and what word should be used to describe non-Jewish Germans? In both cases, with reluctance and with apologies to anyone who may find this usage offensive, I have adopted the terms the Nazis used — clearly not out of any sympathy with that usage but because, in writing about the perverted world of Nazi racial ideology, those terms most accurately and succinctly express the relevant ideas.

For the Nazis, a "Jew" was anyone they decided was Jewish, based on a notion of racial Judaism that had nothing to do with either anthropology or the Jewish religion. An elaborate calculus was developed, under the Nuremberg Laws in particular, for the "racial" classification of the population. It categorized as Jews thousands of people who did not consider themselves to be Jewish and would not have been considered Jewish under Jewish law. These included converts to Christianity and the children of converts, as well as children born to mixed marriages in which the mother was not Jewish and had not converted to Judaism. The same categorization excluded people whom Jews would consider Jewish, such as children born to a mixed marriage in which the mother was Jewish and had not converted to Christianity but whose names had been left off the register of an official Jewish community *(Gemeinde)* because of parental decision or mistake or clerical error.

In this book I use the term *Jew* to refer to those who were so categorized by the Nazis and suffered accordingly, without distinguishing between those who were legally Jews under Jewish law and those who were not. I do so because I am writing about a population that was subjected to persecution and threatened with annihilation because they were Jews in Nazi eyes, and about the way in which hundreds of people among that population found an improbable refuge in the hospital. In this context it seems irrelevant to worry about how their religious affiliation might have been judged in other circumstances.

In referring to Germans who were not Jewish in Nazi eyes, I have decided similarly to remain within the frame of reference provided by Nazi doctrine, without thereby intending, in any way, to give credence to a totally abhorrent ideology. The fact is that there is no good way to describe non-Jewish Germans during the Nazi era. The survivors whom I interviewed generally used the term *Christian*, but that strikes me as unsatisfactory and misleading.

First, it glosses over the fact that the Nazis made a distinction based on the fiction that Jews were racially different from the rest of the population. Although in practice the Nazis found themselves compelled, for want of an alternative, to refer to the religious registration of an individual's grandparents in categorizing people of mixed ancestry, in theory they never deviated from their racial ideology. To use a religious term to refer to the Nazis' imagined racial construct thus seems inappropriate.

Second, to use the term *Christian* in this context seems an insult to Christianity. Although there is no doubt that fifteen hundred years of anti-Semitic teachings by the Christian churches set the stage for the Holocaust and that both the Catholic and Protestant churches in Germany by and large betrayed the central moral principles of their faith in the face of Nazism, it goes too far to equate *Christian*, a term properly applied to a believer in the Christian religion, with the Nazis' odious concept of a master race, especially in light of the Nazis' own hostility to the Christian religion.

The term *non-Jew*, in addition to being awkward, is imprecise. Not everyone in Germany who was non-Jewish shared in the privileged status accorded to what the Nazis called the German "racial people." Gypsies and Eastern Europeans of non-German stock were also deemed inferior, and the Gypsies were subjected to persecution similar to that visited on the Jews. To apply the term *Germans* to the so-called racial people is also distasteful, since it implicitly accepts the Nazi assumption that no Jew could ever be truly German, no matter how fully that Jew participated in or contributed to German culture. The same issue is alive in Germany today with regard to the status of Turks and other immigrants, as well as Jews. I cannot bring myself to join modern-day German racists in using the term *German* to denote what the Nazis would have called "Aryan."

In Nazi ideology and the earliest anti-Jewish legislation, *Aryan* applied to those deemed to belong to the master race. In later Nazi legislation, the term *Jewish blood* was also used, but to refer to non-Jews as "those not of Jewish blood" is not only awkward but, in my eyes, no less offensively redolent of the Nazi racial ideology than the term *Aryan*. So, in the end, I have chosen to use the term *Aryan* to mean what the Nazis intended it to mean, just as I have used the term *Jew* in the same sense the Nazis gave it.

REFUGE IN HELL

1

NICHTS JUDEN. JUDEN KAPUTT

"You are jews? Not possible," the Russian soldier said in his own language and then in broken German: *"Nichts Juden. Juden kaputt."* "You can't be Jews. The Jews are all dead."

It was April 24, 1945, and victorious Soviet troops, fighting street to street against a last-ditch SS defense, had just succeeded in wresting from Nazi control a stretch of Iranischestrasse in the outlying Berlin neighborhood called Wedding. There, in several battle-scarred but still handsome buildings set in a spacious garden, the Soviets found a hospital that sheltered hundreds of people — doctors, nurses, patients, nonmedical staff, and a disparate assortment of others.

A spokesman stepped forward to speak for the inhabitants. He had been coached in a few halting words of Russian by one of the patients, a Russian Jew, who was cowering, panic-stricken, upstairs in his room. Years before, he had fled from Soviet communism to safety in Germany. Then his place of refuge had turned into a deathtrap. Yet by some miracle he had survived, living for years in these buildings. Now that the Nazis finally had been vanquished, he found himself out of the frying pan and back in the fire, frightened that when the Russians discovered his original nationality they would ship him back to face the fate he had eluded years before.

"This is the Jewish hospital," the spokesman said. "We are Jews."

The claim defied credulity. The Soviet soldiers, some of them Jews themselves, knew of the extermination of Europe's Jews, of the slaughters perpetrated by the invading German troops in Eastern Europe, and of the death camps. Surely, they thought, all of Germany's Jews were dead. Yet here, in the very heart of the Nazi capital, they encountered what appeared to be a fully functioning medical facility filled with people who claimed to be Jews. It took considerable effort before the occupants, using the few halting words of Russian they had been taught, were able to convince the liberators that they were in fact Jewish survivors, not Nazis in disguise.

There were some eight hundred Jews on the hospital's premises that day. They represented a significant proportion of Germany's remaining identifiable Jews as so categorized by the Nazis. In a room on an upper floor of the administration building, Hilde Kahan, secretary to the *Reichsvereinigung*, the rump administration of what once had been Germany's central Jewish organization, had been carefully filing away reports on the last remnants of Berlin's Jewish population. These reports came to her boss, Dr. Walter Lustig, the head of the *Reichsvereinigung* and the hospital's medical director, from across the garden. There, behind barbed wire in what until 1944 had been the hospital's pathology pavilion, the Gestapo had maintained Berlin's last *Sammellager,* a temporary holding camp where Jews awaiting deportation were kept until their number was large enough to fill a transport to a concentration camp. In the *Sammellager,* Fräulein Raphael, a young Jewish woman, had been keeping meticulous count for the Gestapo, month by month, of how many known Jews remained in Berlin. The tally on February 28, 1945, stood at 6,284, broken down into the categories assigned by the Nazi racial regulations:

Full Jews living in "privileged" mixed marriages
Full Jews living in "nonprivileged" mixed marriages

to who we were. They in turn directed us to the old Jewish Hospital, where they would help us. We walked to the Hospital, which was not damaged. I was surprised that it looked as if nothing had happened, the world was at a complete standstill. A Jewish nurse in a clean starched uniform greeted us, directed us to a room with clean beds and told us that they were able to furnish us with room and board.

Coincidentally, it was also in August 1945 that a nineteen-year-old American GI, Ernie Mayerfeld, paid his visit to the hospital to deliver the package that a fellow German émigré in New York had sent for his sister Johanna, a Jewish nurse. (Who knows? Perhaps *Schwester* Johanna was the very nurse who greeted Harry Rosenthal; perhaps Ernie and Harry Rosenthal passed each other in the hospital's lobby.) Like Harry, Ernie was astonished by what he found: "I asked people there how this was possible. The only answer I received was a shrug and the statement 'We don't know.'"

From 1945 to the present, incredulity has been the typical reaction of those who have stumbled across the fact that the Nazis permitted an identifiable Jewish institution, and especially one like the Jewish hospital, to continue in existence in a city that in 1943 Goebbels had declared *Judenrein* (cleansed of Jews). Only one other Jewish facility continued to operate in Berlin during the same period, the Jewish cemetery at Weissensee. There, a handful of Jewish employees remained on duty to care for the cemetery and occasionally to dig a grave for one of the small number of Berlin Jews who, for one reason or another, had remained in Germany long enough to die there.

The survival of the Weissensee cemetery is less astonishing than that of the hospital. The cemetery served a category of events that the Nazis were only too happy to see occur, Jewish deaths. The hospital stood at the opposite pole. Its vocation was to preserve Jewish lives. Yet in April 1945 the hospital was still functioning as a center of medical treatment in which Jewish doctors and nurses were still caring for Jewish patients. Despite repeated Gestapo incursions that had sent many hundreds of other patients and staff members to their deaths, the remaining people in the hospital had managed to survive the Nazi terror. The Jews whom the Soviet troops found in the hospital on April 24, 1945, had good reason to wonder that they were alive at all. A few figures tell the story. When Hitler came to power in 1932, more than 500,000 people in Germany were registered as members of an official Jewish *Gemeinde* (community), about one-third of whom belonged to the Berlin Jewish *Gemeinde*. As the statistics kept by Fräulein Raphael and stored in Hilde Kahan's file cabinet attested, at the end of the war the total number of registered Jews in Berlin was slightly more than 6,000. Of the missing 160,000 or more, somewhat fewer than two-thirds had emigrated. The lucky ones made it to the United States, England, or some other country that escaped German occupation. However, many German Jews (perhaps the best-known example being the family of Anne Frank) fled to other places on the European continent. There, most enjoyed only a brief respite before their place of refuge was overrun by the Germans. Almost all of the German Jewish refugees who fell into German hands in this manner were sent to the death camps in Eastern Europe, and few survived.

By April 1945, the vast majority of those Berlin Jews who had not managed to emigrate before it was too late were dead. They had disappeared in a variety of ways. Some had been victims of the growing Nazi brutality in Germany between 1933 and 1941, killed on the streets or arrested and murdered by the police, the SS, or the Gestapo in barracks, police stations, or jails. Some had been sent to concentration camps located in Germany, such as Buchenwald, Ravensbrück, Dachau, and Sachsenhausen, and had died or been murdered there. Finally, beginning in 1941, the Germans had deported most of Germany's remaining Jewish population to the East, where in overwhelming numbers they had become victims of the German killing machine. Almost sixty thousand Berlin Jews were murdered in this fashion. A graphic summary of the Nazis' accomplishments appears in a 1946 photograph that shows a few of the surviving hospital staff marching through streets lined with ruined buildings toward a demonstration in the public park known as the Lustgarten. Two Jewish nurses who survived the war in the hospital, Meta Cohen and Erna Westheimer, march under a banner emblazoned with two six-pointed stars and the words (in translation): BERLIN JEWISH HOSPITAL: WE HONOR THE DEAD VICTIMS OF FASCISM. Another poster in the same procession proclaims the grim statistics: BERLIN JEWISH COMMUNITY. 1933: 186,000 MEMBERS; 1945: 5,100 MEMBERS.

At the war's end, in addition to the some six thousand registered Jews, there were a number of Berlin Jews living "underground," in hiding or with false identity papers. It has been estimated that ten to twelve thousand Berlin Jews attempted to escape persecution and deportation by assuming false identities or going into hiding, or both, and that only about twenty-five hundred to three thousand actually made it to the end of the war. The rest died of natural causes, were killed in the Allied bombings or the final battle for Berlin, or were caught by the Nazi authorities and sent to be murdered in one of the death camps.

Although in April 1945 the hospital's buildings were scarred, they essentially were intact and looked more or less the same on the outside as they had in 1938 — the same, that is, if one could overlook the damage and debris from bombs and shells, the fact that the former manicured grounds had been turned into vegetable gardens and a cow pasture, and that barbed wire still surrounded the pathology building. Any returning Berlin Jew could recognize the hospital, if only by the words carved high above the main gate. They read, as they still do today, KRANKENHAUS DER JÜDISCHEN GEMEINDE (Hospital of the Jewish Community). As an institution, however, the hospital in 1945 had been sharply reduced from its prewar proportions. A very large percentage of its medical staff had disappeared, and even the physical facility had shrunk.

At the time of liberation, three of the seven main buildings
that had been part of the Jewish hospital complex at the beginning of the war no longer formed part of the hospital. The nurses'
residence, or *Schwesternheim*, and the buildings that had housed
the gynecology department and the infectious disease department had been expropriated in late 1942 by the Wehrmacht for
use as a military hospital, known to everyone as the *Lazarett*. In
addition, in 1944 the Gestapo had confiscated a corner of the
hospital grounds containing the *Pathologie*, the hospital's pathology laboratory, and an adjacent gatehouse and fenced them off to
serve as Berlin's last *Sammellager*. This came at a time when the
Germans were running low on Jews to deport and the special
trains to Theresienstadt or Poland were becoming less frequent
than in 1941–43. Earlier, there had been several *Sammellager* in
different places in Berlin, but now a single and smaller facility
sufficed.

When the Soviets arrived, the vestiges of the organizational
structure of a functioning hospital remained, but the repeated
Nazi deportations of doctors and nurses since 1942 had reduced
it to minimal proportions. The surviving medical staff was working indefatigably, doing its best to care for patients. There were
many sick and wounded to look after, but exactly how many is impossible to determine given the chaotic circumstances in the final
days of the war. Among them were Aryans, the first to be treated
in the hospital since the Nazis decreed in 1938 that Jewish medical facilities could only treat Jews. Now, in the desperate conditions of early 1945, Germans who were wounded while fighting
in the vicinity of the hospital were willing to make an exception to
their bigotry, defy Nazi law, and get treatment wherever it was
available.

By April 24, 1945, the Gestapo officers had fled from the
Sammellager. So too had the handful of renegade Jews who lived
there with them. Their role, about which more will be said later,
had been to track down Jews who had gone underground and dis-

appeared into a shadow existence, trying to evade their captors through the use of false papers and such hiding places as they could find.

The eight hundred or so people who remained to greet the Soviet liberators were a heterogeneous assortment. The historical record tells us how they ended up there and who they were — at least by category; for many, there is no record of their names. Knowing how these groups of people came to be at the hospital, however, does not explain the riddle of why the Nazis allowed a Jewish medical facility to remain in operation throughout the Final Solution.

Included in this final number were patients and members of the medical, nursing, and support staff who had taken up residence in the hospital at various times, either because they had been bombed out or evicted as Jews from their former homes or because they were slave laborers assigned to work at the hospital. Also on hand were the remnants of groups of Jews who had been transferred to the hospital when the Nazis closed other Jewish institutions in Germany, such as orphanages and old age homes. Most of these unfortunates had been deported before the war ended, but some remained in April 1945. Among them were a handful of abandoned children who were suspected of being fully Jewish but whose "racial" status had not been definitely determined. The Nazis had used the hospital as a kind of ghetto to which they consigned Jews who had nowhere else to live or whose status was ambiguous. These included Jews of foreign nationality and Jews who were being held there as potential bargaining chips in negotiating exchanges for German nationals captured in Palestine. The authorities also used the hospital to house Jews who had been brought to Berlin from other cities in Germany as part of a Nazi effort to separate them from their Aryan spouses. This was intended as a first step in overcoming the political and legal barriers to the deportation of Jewish men who lived in mixed marriages and whose Aryan spouses refused to divorce them despite Gestapo pressure to do so.

Some of the "patients" who gained their freedom that day were not really sick. Among them, housed in the special ward known as the *Extrastation*, were a small number of Jews who were not receiving medical treatment but who were being protected from deportation by the patronage of one or another prominent Nazi — in some cases probably because of bribery, in other cases for reasons at which we can only guess. In addition, since 1941 one unit of the hospital had been the so-called *Polizeistation*, or police ward. This was where Jews were incarcerated who had fallen ill while already in the hands of the police, Gestapo, or SS — in a police station, prison, or concentration camp in Germany or in a *Sammellager* awaiting transport to the East. Why the Nazis sent these people to be restored to health is unclear; perhaps, from time to time, a virtually instinctive German sense of bureaucratic order came to the fore and was applied unthinkingly, even in the midst of mass murder. With the connivance of the medical staff, some of the police prisoners, like Bruno Blau, a Jewish lawyer whose extensive memoirs became a major record of the hospital's wartime experiences, managed to remain there, pretending to be ill long after they had actually recovered.

In addition to being a medical facility, the hospital thus had become a prison — twice over. First, there was the locked police ward that housed patients who were benefiting from a temporary respite on their way to be killed. Second, there was the *Sammellager* in the former pathology pavilion, filled with prisoners condemned to the same fate but without the excuse of illness or injury to delay its execution. The last transport of Jews had left Berlin in March 1945 as the Russians were closing in on the city. Many of the death camps in the East had already been liberated or evacuated. But so determined were the Nazis in their campaign of extermination that, even as defeat became inevitable, they were willing to expend scarce resources on deporting the handful of Jews remaining in the Reich. When it no longer was possible to send them to Poland, they sent them to concentration camps in the *Alt Reich*, Germany as it existed before Hitler began his war of aggrandizement. So it was that on the day of liberation there were Jews in the hospital who, until the Gestapo guards had fled days before, had been incarcerated in the *Sammellager* awaiting shipment to a concentration camp.

As always, Hilde Kahan was at work that day, ready to throw herself into the job of reconstruction. With her elderly mother, whom she had kept out of Gestapo hands by audacity and determination, she lived in a room at the hospital. Both position and force of character made her a significant personage in the hospital community. Seen in a videotaped interview filmed when she was in her seventies, she is a compelling presence, projecting an air of intelligence and competence. She appears tough and assertive, hardened by her wartime experiences and by having been forced since girlhood to make her way in the world unaided. Yet, from time to time, when her severe expression softens and a smile fleetingly appears, one realizes that the somewhat forbidding exterior hides a person with a sense of humor and considerable charm.

Like her boss, Dr. Lustig, and many other Jews in Berlin, Kahan came to Berlin from East Prussia, where she was born in Königsberg (now Kaliningrad, Russia) in 1911. Her father died when she was fourteen, and her widowed mother, a dentist, was ruined when the Nazis refused to allow her to practice under the national health insurance scheme. Burdened with the need to care for her mother, Hilde started work at the age of seventeen as a stenographer and continued doing office work from then on, with a brief interlude as a seamstress. After 1933, she experienced long periods of unemployment when successive Jewish employers went out of business. When her last private Jewish employer sold out to an Aryan, however, the new owner of the business surprised her by keeping her on and treating her kindly, even in the face of threats by the railroad administration to deny him the railcars he needed for his business if he kept a Jew on his payroll. *Kristallnacht* put an end to that happy relationship. Her employer reluctantly decided that it was unsafe for both of them for her to continue working in his business. Only her good luck in eventually finding work with the Jewish *Gemeinde* saved Hilde and her mother from destitution.

After a period of unemployment, Kahan was hired by the *Hilfsverein*, the section of the Jewish communal administration that assisted Jews in emigrating from Germany. In 1941, as the mass deportations began, the Gestapo closed the *Hilfsverein*, signaling an end to the Nazi policy of ridding Germany of its Jews by encouraging emigration. Only about one-third of the *Hilfsverein* employees were absorbed by other sections of the Jewish organization. Of the rest, one-half had to report to the government's Jewish Labor Bureau for assignment to forced labor in factories or on the railroad, and the other half were deported. Kahan had the good fortune to be in the one-third for whom the Jewish administration found other work. She became a secretary to Dr. Lustig, then head of the health department of the *Reichsvereinigung* and the Berlin Jewish *Gemeinde*, the two organizations having effectively become one. She stayed with him throughout his career at the hospital.

Hilde Kahan's job was her life. As secretary to the man who served not only as director but also as head of the *Reichsvereinigung*, she was a figure of authority in the hospital community. That earned her, however, a measure of the fear and dislike with which that community regarded her boss, Dr. Lustig.

Lustig himself — the central figure in the drama of the hospital's final years under the Nazis, the ultimate survivor and artful dodger — apparently was nowhere to be found when the Soviet troops arrived. Although he often slept at the hospital, being married to an Aryan meant that he had been able to retain his apartment in the western part of the city. Perhaps he was at home on the day of liberation; perhaps he was somewhere on the hospital grounds but staying prudently in the background, waiting to see how things sorted themselves out. Wherever he was, the hospital's Jews had to find another spokesman to persuade the Soviet troops that they were not Nazis in disguise, a task that was made harder by the presence within the same walls of the *Lazarett,* the military hospital filled with German soldiers and military doctors.

Most in the hospital population were half-Jews or spouses of Aryans. As such, they had been protected from deportation by Nazi rules that everyone knew could be changed at any time. Their relief at being saved from the Nazis' hands was great, but it was outstripped by that of the few "full Jews," especially the handful of Jewish couples with children. For the most part, these were people who had participated in life at the hospital right through the years of the greatest danger, from the time the deportations had begun in 1941. Dr. Helmuth Cohen, the director of medical services, together with his wife Meta, a nurse, and their preteen daughter, Eva, could only wonder in mixed relief and sadness that they had escaped the fate of so many of their friends and professional colleagues. Similar emotions swept over Ehrich Zwilsky, Lustig's adjunct in administering the *Reichsvereinigung,* his wife, and his thirteen-year-old son, Klaus, playmate to Eva Cohen. For Klaus liberation now meant that he would be able to celebrate his Bar Mitzvah, the time for which was at hand. Unmarried nurses like Lisa Meyersohn, bachelor doctors like Heinz Elkan, who lived at the hospital with his mother, and married couples both of whom were full Jews, like the hospital's administrative director, Selmar Neumann, and his wife, marveled at having escaped deportation even though they were not protected by living in a mixed marriage. Devoutly religious, Neumann thanked God for sparing them the fate that had claimed so many others like them.

While relief and thankfulness must have been the prevailing emotions felt by those who were on the hospital's premises on April 24, 1945, other emotions were also in play. For some, there still was fear — fear of the Russians, or fear that their former colleagues who had been deported would seek to punish them for cooperating too closely with the Nazis. Others felt the first pangs of the survivor's guilt that would haunt them for the rest of their lives. For many there was hope that loved ones who had disappeared in the transports would return alive. Sadly, these hopes were destined to be disappointed in most cases. A few looked forward to reestablishing the comfortable lives they had enjoyed in pre-Nazi Germany. Others, probably the majority, were determined as quickly as possible to leave the country that had rejected them as evil subhumans and try to rebuild their lives elsewhere. And, for several couples, liberation represented the chance to start lives together openly, for even in the hospital men and women had found room for romance.

Those among the hospital population who had not been formally under arrest still had been prisoners, their lives hemmed in by innumerable restrictions and humiliations, with no guarantee from one day to the next that their turn to be deported would not arrive. Now they were to be safe and free. By 1945, those among them who were not children had lived through more than twelve years of Nazi persecution that had grown in cruelty and intensity until it matured into full-blown genocide. They had seen their lives and families uprooted, their loved ones taken from them and sent into oblivion. Many had suffered unspeakable indignities and privations. They were conscious that their hospital community constituted the sole living Jewish institution in a country from which everything Jewish was supposed to have been extirpated. More than fifty-five years later, those who are still alive can find no entirely convincing explanation for their survival. Almost every survivor says the same thing:

"It was a miracle."

2

THE HOSPITAL AND THE
BERLIN JEWS

AM YISRAEL CHAI. "The people Israel lives."
In recalling the worst days of their numerous martyrdoms throughout history, Jews often chant these words to a sad melody, drawing hope from the fact that through all the vicissitudes of exile from the Holy Land, despite persecutions and pressures to convert and assimilate that under any reasonable expectation should have extinguished Judaism at many junctures during the last two millennia, Jewish identity and the Jewish religion have endured. In retrospect, the survival of the hospital also symbolized the principle of *Am Yisrael Chai*. In the heartland of history's most vicious and relentless campaign to destroy the Jews, not just as a religion and culture but physically as a people, a Jewish communal organization had persisted and a nucleus of Jews had survived openly. Yet, for a variety of reasons (discussed in Chapter 13), the survival of Berlin's Jewish hospital never became such a symbol — not to the people who were there and even less to the rest of the world, which has remained largely unaware of the hospital's story.

In any event, few, if any, of the hospital's inhabitants were thinking of symbolism in April 1945. For years their preoccupation had been survival. Friends and colleagues among the hospital staff, patients in the wards, children in the orphanage, all had disappeared. To all but the most obtuse, it had been clear for a long time that the hospital and its remaining inhabitants were caught up in a race against time. At some point the war would end with victory for the United States and England. But in the meantime the Nazi killing machine was laboring implacably to destroy Europe's Jews.

Liberation removed the omnipresent threat of extinction, but it soon was replaced with other concerns. One was fear of the liberators. The Soviet troops who captured the hospital did not completely exempt the Jewish survivors from the depredations they visited on the rest of Berlin. Then there was the chaos and poverty of immediate postwar Berlin, not to speak of the shortages of food and fuel, the bitter cold of the winter of 1945–46. It took all of everyone's time just to stay alive and to carry out the tasks of daily existence. And there was the frantic, and too often unavailing, attempt to find out what had happened to family members who had been deported, to see if anyone had survived. Struggling to remake their own lives and to care for the displaced Jews who were trickling into Berlin from the camps, broken in mind and body, the hospital's staff in the aftermath of liberation had neither time nor inclination to reflect on the significance, symbolic or otherwise, of the fact that the hospital had made it through the entire Nazi period without losing its vocation as a place of healing or its identity as a Jewish institution.

That vocation reflected a centuries-old tradition. Although the hospital's formal origins date back to the eighteenth century, when the Jews in Berlin established the precursor of the organized Jewish community that existed at the time the Nazis came to power, its roots can be traced almost to the beginning of Jewish settlement in medieval times. The hospital's history in fact mirrors the story of Jewish life in Berlin.

The founding of the city of Berlin dates to sometime late in the twelfth century. Although Jews had been trading in the region long before that, the history of Jewish settlement there started shortly after Berlin emerged as an identifiable town. The first known Jewish burial occurred in 1244; the official establishment of the Jewish community is put at 1295.

The early history of Jewish life in Berlin followed the tragic patterns prevalent in so much of Europe. In 1349 the black plague reached the area and triggered an outbreak of violence against the Jews. This ended only in 1354 when the reigning Margrave of Brandenburg reestablished the right of Jews to live in the city and a synagogue and Jewish school were founded. The centuries that followed were marked by recurrent cycles of toleration and anti-Semitism, acceptance and expulsion. In 1510, thirty-eight Jews were publicly burned and the remaining Jewish population was expelled from the Brandenburg realm. In the 1570s other expulsions occurred. It was only with the Enlightenment that the status of Jews in Berlin became established on a more solid footing, one that lasted until the Nazis. In 1650 the process started when the "Great Elector" Frederick William invited a small number of Jews into Brandenburg. In 1651 he issued an edict permitting fifty Jewish families to enter the realm and to settle wherever they wished. This example of toleration attracted other Jews, including some wealthy families who had been expelled from Vienna.

In the reign of Frederick the Great, the position of the Jews improved even further. In 1750 Frederick issued an edict on the position of Jews in the Kingdom of Prussia that granted them control over their own schools, synagogues, and cemeteries. It was in this period, a few years later, that the Jewish hospital in its modern form was founded.

The true origins of the hospital, however, go much farther back in time. The maintenance of hospitals had been a traditional function of organized Jewish communities in Germany at least since the Middle Ages. Caring for the sick in a separate building, in turn, grew out of the tradition of maintaining a hostel for traveling Jews, called a *Hekdesh*, as an adjunct to the synagogue, a practice that can be traced back at least as far as the Hellenistic period in the Holy Land before the destruction of the Second Temple. Over time, it appears, the hostel for traveling Jews evolved into a place for the care of the sick; perhaps the need to care for ill travelers led to the idea of using the same premises to care for sick members of the community. Another Jewish tradition that contributed to the development of Jewish hospitals was that of organizing a communal fellowship devoted to visiting and caring for the sick, the *Bikur Cholim*, and one devoted to the proper burial of the dead, the *Chevra Kadishah*.

Even before the sixteenth-century expulsions of the Jews from the territory of the Margrave of Brandenburg, the Berlin Jewish community had maintained a *Hekdesh*. In 1703 the *Bikur Cholim* and *Chevra Kadishah* of the restored community built a new *Hekdesh* where medical care was provided both to sick Jewish travelers and to members of the community who had no one to care for them at home. The organizations employed a doctor to visit the sick and a barber to perform operations. In the ensuing half century, the building became dilapidated and proved inadequate for the demands of a rapidly growing community. In 1753, the two associations with the help of some wealthy Berlin Jews joined in erecting a new building at 7 Oranienburgerstrasse near the central offices of the Jewish community. This building was expanded in 1821, at which time the Jewish community took over its administration and management from the *Bikur Cholim*. It was further enlarged in 1840, when it included a staff of six doctors and a midwife.

Twenty years later, the growing number of patients and the location made even the enlarged original premises inadequate. By the middle of the nineteenth century, the city had grown up around the once peaceful site and the hospital now stood on a noisy street. Moreover, the property lacked amenities that other Berlin hospitals enjoyed, such as piped water, appropriate heating facilities, and an operating theater. To remedy these deficiencies, in 1861 the Jewish community decided to move the hospital to a new and larger facility at 14 Auguststrasse.

The second half of the nineteenth century found Berlin in the full bloom of an economic and industrial expansion in which Jewish financiers and industrialists played a central role. Indeed, as a leading chronicler of Berlin's history has noted, the tragedy of the Holocaust is particularly bitter in the context of Berlin, whose economic and financial ascendancy was due largely to its entrepreneurial Jewish population.

The success of Jewish businessmen in the city, which has been estimated as accounting for as much as one-half of the city's economic activity, attracted other Jews, until by the 1870s some 80 percent of all Prussia's Jews had moved there. A large and prosperous Jewish community built institutions worthy of both its status and its aspirations. Jews were prominent not only in commerce, industry, and finance, but increasingly in the city's intellectual life and in the professions, including medicine and law. They had full political rights and were free to live anywhere they wished in the city or its environs. Only the influential Prussian military remained essentially closed to them. Many Jews felt that they had succeeded in becoming fully integrated into German society, with only residual elements of anti-Semitism hampering their complete acceptance.

It was, of course, precisely at this moment and in response to Jewish success that anti-Semitism again began to grow. It took an ominous form: it was a "racial" anti-Semitism that preached hatred for Jews on grounds that they were inherently evil, regardless of their level of assimilation, regardless even of conversion to Christianity. Moreover, for the first time in German history, anti-Semitism became a political movement. Racial and political anti-Semitism persisted through the early twentieth century and World War I. In the aftermath of World War I it ripened into the Nazi movement and eventually into genocide.

It was in the flush of Berlin's mid-nineteenth-century economic expansion that the Jewish community, enjoying a dramatic increase in both numbers and prosperity, built on Auguststrasse one of Berlin's first general hospitals and one of the largest of its type, primarily to serve the needs of the Jewish population. The new hospital was set in gardens and was furnished with the most up-to-date facilities and equipment. Over the next eighteen years it was further expanded by the addition of new facilities, including a clinic for pulmonary therapy and an outpatient department. As the years passed, however, even this structure, considered both large and ultramodern at the time of its construction, proved to be inadequate. The Jewish community decided to replace it with a new facility in the outlying Wedding district of Berlin, while retaining the Auguststrasse premises for outpatient clinics that would serve the Jewish population in that neighborhood. The new hospital was to be located on a large plot bordered on one side by what is now Iranischestrasse and on the other side by Schulstrasse.

In 1913 the current hospital opened on the site it occupies today. At that time, Berlin's Jewish community was in a phase of building showcase institutions, including impressive synagogues. Even the new Jewish cemetery at Weissensee was a landmark. The new Jewish hospital was a fitting expression of the community's wealth and self-confidence. It was designed on the block principle, in which various departments were housed in separate pavilions rather than being strung out along corridors as in the old building. The capacity was increased from the 100 beds in Auguststrasse to 230 beds.

There were seven principal buildings, together with ancillary structures. Along Iranischestrasse, a tree-lined residential street, the main administration building stretched for almost a block from the intersection of Iranischestrasse and Schulstrasse. It was an imposing stone structure built in a neoclassical style with a large central entrance. (It is also the only one of the hospital's buildings to remain basically unchanged since the war.) High above the entrance is a triangular pediment bearing the hospital's name carved in stone. Until it was destroyed in the war, a wooden clock tower stood in the center of the roofline. Continuing down Iranischestrasse, next to the administration building but separated from it by a garden, was the *Schwesternheim*, or nurses' residence, a solid, freestanding structure of five stories under a mansard roof. This housed both the nursing school and the dormitories for nurses and nursing students. Across Iranischestrasse from the *Schwesternheim* was a Jewish old age home. Also part of the social services network run by the Berlin Jewish *Gemeinde*, it was an independent institution but had a close working relationship with the hospital.

Behind the main administration building, enclosed by walls, fences, and outlying structures, lay spacious grounds landscaped with lawns, flower beds, and towering trees. Directly opposite the administration building, across a broad stretch of lawn and gardens, were the principal medical buildings. At one end of the administration building, opening onto the garden on the interior side near the *Schwesternheim*, was the hospital's synagogue, recognizable to this day by the Stars of David set into the round windows. The main part of the hospital was composed of a series of interconnected pavilions, with the principal buildings arranged in a U-shape around three sides of the central garden. There also were a number of outlying structures. At the basement level all these buildings were linked together by a massive series of corridors. Designed originally to enable patients to be transported from one building to the next without having to be taken outdoors, they served during the war as the hospital's bomb shelters.

The pavilions were solid and unmistakably Germanic in architecture. Everything bespoke solid middle-class values, a sense of order, cleanliness, and serenity. The physical setting was an appropriate framework for what had become, and continued until the Nazi era to be, one of the city's premier medical institutions — a source of medical care for Jew and non-Jew alike, a center not only of medical treatment but also of teaching, research, and medical progress.

The hospital's survival first came into doubt the moment the Nazis ascended to power. Adolf Hitler was sworn in as chancellor of the German Reich on January 30, 1933. The Nazis moved quickly to consolidate their control over the German state through a combination of legal and illegal means, aided by President von Hindenburg's dissolution of the Reichstag and call for new elections. The arson of the Reichstag building on February 27, 1933, provided Hitler with the pretext to issue an emergency order suspending civil rights. Although the Nazi Party won only 44 percent of the vote in the March parliamentary elections, the Nazis took control of the country and began a campaign of anti-Jewish measures, including economic boycotts and acts of terror. Storm troopers attacked Jewish-owned department stores on March 11, 1933. On March 20, the first concentration camp opened at Dachau, near Munich. A Nazi-sponsored boycott of Jewish businesses was mounted on April 1.

There soon followed a flood of legal measures directed against the Jews. The 1935 Nuremberg Laws, which deprived German Jews of their citizenship and prohibited sexual relations between Jews and Aryans, have become the notorious symbol of the Nazis' anti-Semitic legislation, but they were only part of a long succession of decrees by which Germany's Jews were socially isolated and economically despoiled. April and May 1933 saw the issuance of a large number of such decrees, beginning with the Law for the Restoration of the Professional Civil Service, which expelled from public employment anyone who was not an "Aryan" as defined in the so-called Aryan clause — that is, anyone who had any non-Aryan (especially Jewish) parent or grandparent. Some exceptions, which were in force for a relatively short time, allowed civil service jobs to be retained by people who had been employed on or before August 1, 1914, had fought for Germany or her allies at the front during World War I, or had had a father or son killed in action during that war.

These measures had an immediate impact on Jewish doctors and on the hospital. In Germany, then as now, a large proportion of medical treatment was financed by the national health insurance system. Under the Nazi measures, a significant percentage of Jewish doctors lost their affiliation with the national system and thus found their practices substantially reduced. However, even where formal affiliation was not terminated, both public and private health and welfare organizations put pressure on their members not to patronize Jewish doctors. Jewish physicians were also expelled from German professional organizations, further marginalizing their professional standing.

One of the most highly placed Jewish doctors to lose his job as a result of the Law for the Restoration of the Professional Civil Service was Walter Lustig, who was defined as a Jew under the Aryan clause even though he had been baptized and was married to an Aryan woman. Lustig attained prominence in 1941–42 because he was forced to aid in the deportations of Berlin Jews. He emerged as the hospital's leader in the crucial final years of the war. From at least 1942 onward, Walter Lustig was arguably the most powerful figure of German Jewry and the absolute master of the hospital — subject always to the control of his Nazi keepers in the RSHA and the Gestapo. Yet it is surprisingly difficult to get a feel for Lustig as a person, to understand and judge the man who was more important than any other Jew in the hospital's survival and who became the overlord of the pitiful remnants of German Jewry.

Walter Lustig was typical of the class of successful, assimilated Jewish professionals whose apparent success in integrating into German society had been shattered by the rise of Nazism. Slight of stature, he affected a large moustache and, by all accounts, acted more Prussian than the Prussians. Holder of both a medical degree and a doctorate in philosophy, he adhered strictly to the German tradition of using both titles, insisting that people address him as "Herr Dr. Dr. Lustig."

Lustig was born in 1891 to the Jewish merchant Bernhard

Lustig and his wife, Regina (maiden name Besser), in Ratibor, Upper Silesia (now Raciborz, Poland). He graduated from the local gymnasium in March 1910 and enrolled in the University of Breslau in October of the same year, where he pursued a course of medical studies specializing in surgery. He received his medical degree and license in the spring of 1915. Commentators on Lustig's character consider it significant that, as a young man in Breslau, he reportedly played a role in a group that opposed the revolutionary Spartacist movement, led by Rosa Luxemburg and Karl Liebknecht, which mounted an uprising after the Armistice. They conclude from this that Lustig was inherently loyal to authority and also was unusually sensitive to which way the political wind was blowing — qualities, they say, that explain his later cooperation with the Nazis. There seems, however, to be more than a little 20/20 hindsight in this conclusion. Given Lustig's middle-class background, his professional ambitions, and the effort he had made in educating himself for advancement within German society, it is not surprising that his political views were not radical or leftist. In respecting established authority, he did no more than share the ingrained obedience of the vast majority of middle-class Germans (a habit of mind that was to cost German Jews dearly).

Lustig's political activities were soon overwhelmed by wartime duties. He was drafted and put to work as a military doctor. While serving in the army, he managed to complete his work for a Ph.D., also in medicine, and received that degree only a year and a half after his medical degree was awarded. Lustig performed his military service in Breslau, where he treated the sick and wounded from the World War I eastern front. His military work impressed his superiors.

After leaving the army, Lustig went to work for the public administration while at the same time maintaining a private medical practice. During his entire career he worked principally as a medical administrator. Lustig also was a prolific writer on medical subjects. He had a lengthy bibliography of published works, including *The Theoretical Basis for Practical Health Care: A Nurse's*

Textbook in the Form of Questions and Answers. Another of his works, popularly known as *Der Kleine Lustig* (The Little Lustig), constituted an "indispensable handbook for medical administrators" during the period between the two world wars. During his years in Breslau, Lustig's duties included collecting information on public health matters and reporting it to the Prussian Ministry of Health. By any standard, he maintained an extraordinary level of activity, combining a full-time job in public administration with a private practice and a steady outpouring of medical literature. He clearly was a man driven by a compelling desire for professional advancement.

Seeking an even wider arena for his ambitions, Lustig moved to Berlin in 1927. There he made two almost simultaneous changes to his life, both of which would have far-reaching consequences. The first was to marry Dr. Annemarie Preuss, a non-Jewish physician. The second was to take a job with the Berlin police. His marriage to a non-Jew provided him, in the 1940s, with protection against being deported. His career with the medical department of the Berlin Police Presidium taught him the inner workings of the German bureaucracy and brought him into contact with some of the same people who, as officials of Adolf Eichmann's Department IV B 4 in the RSHA, later would preside over the fate of the hospital and its inhabitants. In particular, during his years at the Police Presidium he became acquainted with both Fritz Wöhrn and Rolf Günther, who eventually became Eichmann's two key aides in overseeing the hospital.

Until the Nazis took power, Lustig was active both politically and professionally. During his tenure in the Berlin police department he was aligned politically with the Social Democrats. He made a name for himself with his many publications and advanced within the police hierarchy until in 1929 he was appointed to the position of director of the Police Presidium's medical affairs department. He held the prestigious bureaucratic titles of *Oberregierungsrat* (chief administrative counselor) and *Ober-*

medizinalrat (chief medical counselor). The police department in Berlin had broad administrative authority that extended well beyond mere criminal matters. Lustig's responsibilities in his position thus included supervising health matters in schools, institutions, and group care facilities, as well as conducting occupational training for medical personnel. All this brought him into contact with many senior government officials and leading figures in the private medical sector.

The Nazis' ascent to power put an end to Lustig's public career in October 1933. His reaction to losing his job also may be indicative of his character. As noted, the so-called Law for the Restoration of the Professional Civil Service made exceptions for Jewish veterans who had served at the front. These exceptions were sparingly applied and in any case were not in force for long, but Lustig tried strenuously to avail himself of them on the basis of his service as a military doctor in Breslau. The effort was unsuccessful, since serving as a doctor in his hometown did not qualify as service at the front. Nonetheless, he was not fired outright; instead his dismissal took the form of a forced retirement, even though his age was only forty-two, which left him with a pension of almost five hundred marks a month. This stubborn unwillingness to give up a position of authority seems to have been a salient characteristic, one that was to come to the fore again at the end of the war and lead him into trouble, possibly to his death.

At some time, probably in 1933 or shortly thereafter (no one knows exactly when, except that it could not have been later than 1935), he entered the employment of the health department of the Berlin Jewish *Gemeinde*. He worked under the director of the health department, Erich Seligmann, a former professor of hygiene. What Lustig did initially is as unknown as the exact date he began to work for the *Gemeinde*, but, whatever his official title, he began to become active in matters relating to the hospital even while he was conducting a private practice. Over the course of

time, Lustig was to prove as adept at surviving and rising in the
official Jewish bureaucracy as he had been in the pre-Nazi police
department.

Lustig was an elusive and protean figure, so elusive that not a
single photograph of him can be found. His physical appearance
must have been unexceptional, since few of those who knew him
firsthand can recall anything about how he looked, other than the
fact that he was small, "only a little man." To Margot Neumann, a
young forced laborer in the hospital's laundry, he was a "small,
delicate person" who seemed like an old man. Lustig's most
memorable feature was his "sharp" eyes. *Schwester* Carry remembers them as "cold stabbing eyes — terrible eyes." Another
forced laborer, Ruth Graetz, remembers him as very Germanic in
appearance, a man who "looked like a major from the First World
War," with spectacles and a big moustache.

For many, Lustig's name evokes predominantly negative feelings. According to one source, "The name Walter Lustig awak-
ens even today vigorous aversion among Jewish witnesses of the
events." Yet even his detractors give grudging credit to his talents
and to his accomplishment in keeping the hospital open through
the final years of the Nazi regime. His contemporaries describe
him in wildly differing terms — turncoat and Gestapo collaborator; savior of the Jewish hospital; the man who sent hundreds of
Jews to their death; the man who saved hundreds of Jews from the
camps; a protector of children; a lecher.

One of the harshest criticisms of Lustig is that he was unsym-
pathetic to the plight of his fellow Jews, an anti-Semite, who
"never felt himself connected to Judaism." According to some,
his interest in the Jewish community was minimal until rising
anti-Semitism and the advent of Nazism made it clear that he
might have to look within that community for a career. He is said
to have "fiercely avoided" his fellow Jews prior to the time in the
early to middle 1930s when he contacted the organized Jewish
community and found employment there. The head of the hospital's neurology department, who worked under him, describes

him as "totally unburdened by Jewish awareness." This depiction of Lustig rises to an even graver accusation in the report of
Hildegarde Henschel, who worked with Lustig at the hospital
during the time of the deportations. She describes Lustig as "an
unscrupulous anti-Semite." As a young man he had himself baptized, a step often taken by Jews with little religious or communal
identity who hoped to ease their progress in German society. He
married a non-Jewish woman.

Among the conflicting views, only a few points of commonal-
ity emerge. Everyone describes Lustig as somewhat overbearing
and typically formal and correct. He had a "querulous and autocratic nature," was easily offended, and was distant and reserved
in his relations with professional colleagues and the other inhabitants of the hospital. But that reserve had its exception in Lustig's
proclivity toward sexual predation. No one who describes the
man fails to mention this aspect of Lustig's conduct or his affairs
with young nurses, one of whom he shared with the commandant
of the Gestapo contingent at the hospital. A woman always had to
be careful with Lustig. In the words of Hilde Fischer, who was
married to a doctor on the hospital staff and who worked there as
a nurse, "It was good not to be pretty." Another nurse, *Schwester*
Carry, remembers Lustig even before he became the hospital's director. As head of the health department of the *Reichsvereinigung*,
he exercised responsibility for nurses' training during the period
when she was a student nurse in 1938–40.

> He was famous for having us young nurses come to his office in the
> Nurses' Residence for "physicals." And we had to strip completely.
> And, stark naked, we had to stand there and lie down on a table. And
> we hated the thought of it, when we had to come down there. And he
> stared at us and he had eyes that were just piercing. We couldn't
> stand that man. He was absolutely a horror.

In her written memoir, Hilde Kahan, who worked perhaps
more closely with Lustig than anyone, describes him in guarded
terms, acknowledging his bureaucratic talents and giving him

credit for efforts to protect the orphaned children who were sent to the hospital. She says little about his human side, nor does she describe her own relationship with him except in the most formal terms. Indeed, she rarely refers to Lustig by name at all, calling him instead "Dr. L" or "the Boss." She makes it clear that his intervention saved her and her mother when they were already in a *Sammellager* awaiting deportation, yet even this recollection is devoid of any affection, and her testimony in the war crimes trial of SS officer Fritz Wöhrn, one of the hospital's overseers, was instrumental in leading the Berlin State Court to publish a gratuitous and devastating appraisal of Lustig.

And yet, in an oral recollection of Lustig many years later, Kahan is much more positive. "He was a very courageous man," she says. "In my eyes, he was a genius." She credits him with saving the hospital by playing one Nazi organization against another. According to her, his personal courage, the only characteristic of a Jew for which the Gestapo, she says, had any respect, enabled him to stand up to the Nazis.

A more nuanced view is given by Ruth Beleski, a young woman who in 1943 was sent as a forced laborer to work in Lustig's office: "He was a very intelligent, very efficient person. And he was aware of his position, his power too. And he could be very charming."

Finally, Ruth's sister, Eva, a secretary in the hospital's admissions office who was sometimes pressed into service to type for the director, remembers Lustig engaged in what remains his archetypal act: compiling lists at the Gestapo's orders of hospital staff members to be deported:

> Everybody lived in absolute dread of him. . . . He was very clever, a very clever man. But he wasn't terribly liked — because of the temper. We had to type these lists out of the people who were going to be taken away. And one mistake and he was in a rage.

An event that occurred years before Lustig's emergence as the head of the hospital, his dismissal from public service early in the Nazi regime, ended up serving him well by impelling him to cast his lot with the organized Jewish community, which kept him employed throughout the 1930s. As already noted, the Nazis, through unremitting crude propaganda, strong-arm tactics, and acts of terror, continually agitated to prevent the Aryan population from patronizing Jewish businesses and professionals, including doctors and hospitals. Private insurance and welfare organizations enthusiastically fell into line. As a result, most Jewish doctors faced professional ruin, and the pressures that threatened their livelihoods also affected the status of Jewish hospitals, including the Berlin Jewish Hospital. During the five-year period from the Nazi takeover in 1933 until 1938, the number of non-Jewish patients using the hospital decreased dramatically, and both the hospital and its staff were seriously underutilized. Even as early as July 1933 only 180 of the hospital's 380 beds were occupied, and a cry of alarm was raised in the *Gemeindeblatt der Jüdisches Gemeinde zu Berlin*, the official gazette of the Berlin Jewish *Gemeinde*. A bold headline proclaimed: THE JEWISH HOSPITAL IN DANGER! Below, there appeared a lengthy recitation of the hospital's past glories as a center of high-quality medical care for Jews and Christians alike, together with a description of its present woes. High among the latter was a recent order of the city administration that prohibited the hospital from treating public welfare patients even if they were Jewish. Caring for indigent Jewish patients, whose treatment was paid for by the municipal welfare system, had been an important part of the hospital's activity and a major contribution to its budget. Now, the announcement declared, as a result of the city's prohibition the hospital's facilities and staff were underutilized and the already inadequate training possibilities for Jewish doctors and nurses faced further reduction.

The broadside ended with an appeal to the Berlin Jewish community to support the hospital:

That is why we expect you to come to our hospital when your medical condition requires you to be hospitalized. That is why we expect Jewish doctors to send patients needing hospitalization to our hospital. As before, you will be received here and cared for with a warm heart. The equipment of the hospital is in top shape. Experienced doctors, loving nurses, stand at the ready. . . .

Please, all should help carry this message from mouth to mouth:

The Jewish Hospital Must Be Saved!

The irony is that the *Gemeinde* itself was destined to disappear. But the hospital survived the Nazis, as did the enigmatic Dr. Lustig.

3

THE BEGINNING OF
THE END, 1938–41

ON THE NIGHT of November 9, 1938, flames, screams, and the sound of breaking glass heralded the beginning of the final phase for German Jewry, although three more years would pass before the awful shape of the Nazis' ultimate plan would become apparent. From the beginning the Nazi state had condoned and engaged in limited violence against Jews. But in November 1938 the violence escalated suddenly and dramatically when the government cynically organized a nationwide campaign of anti-Jewish mob violence on a massive scale. The pretext for this carefully orchestrated assault against Germany's remaining Jews was the assassination of a German diplomat in Paris by a deranged young Jew whose Polish parents had been expelled from Germany in brutal circumstances. The November 9 pogrom came to be known as *Kristallnacht*, "the night of crystal," for the massive amounts of broken glass that littered the streets of German cities. Synagogues, Jewish institutions, and Jewish businesses throughout Germany were attacked and destroyed. Hundreds of Jews were killed or injured; as many as 20,000 Jewish men were arrested and mistreated in jails and concentration camps throughout the country.

The *Kristallnacht* pogrom served as a wake-up call to many German Jews who had believed that they would be able to continue their lives in Germany and that conditions would someday improve. There was a feverish scramble to escape after November 1938. Although by then the possibilities for emigration were sharply reduced, about 78,000 Jews still managed to emigrate in the single year of 1939. Under the pressure of Nazi persecution, some two-thirds of the 500,000 Jews who lived in Germany in 1933 had emigrated by the time the war began in 1939. Nevertheless, in 1941 there remained 167,000 Jews in Germany living under extremely severe conditions. Most were desperate to leave the country, but the doors virtually had closed against them all over the world. The entry of the United States into the war in December of 1941 would lock those doors, among other things by cutting off the contributions from American Jews that up to then had been the major source of funding for emigration.

For the Jews who stayed behind in Germany, life during the period from *Kristallnacht* to 1941 increasingly was hedged about with persecution and restrictions. Jews were forbidden to participate in almost every form of employment and business activity, and the Jewish community was plundered by decrees that required Jewish firms and assets to be transferred to Aryans in forced sales at derisory prices and that compelled Jews to deposit their cash and other liquid assets in blocked accounts under government control. From that point on, unless they had illegal resources on which they could draw (an undertaking that could be fatal if one were caught), German Jews were financially dependent on the vagaries of a merciless government.

A series of post-*Kristallnacht* decrees consigned Jews to a deliberately contrived form of social death. They were prohibited from access to public places, including parks and even certain streets in the city, and from entering any restaurant, theater, movie house, or concert hall that served Aryans. In 1939 Jewish men were compelled to adopt the middle name *Israel* and Jewish women the middle name *Sara* if they did not have first names that were deemed identifiably Jewish. These middle names had to be listed in the telephone directory and used on all official documents. This public "racial" labeling was a precursor to the infamous racial badge that was to come two years later.

Following *Kristallnacht*, Jewish political organizations and publications were suppressed. A government-controlled and government-censored publication, the *Jüdisches Nachrichtenblatt*, became the sole permitted organ of communication and served primarily to announce new repressive anti-Semitic measures. The same function was served by the religious services that were held at the few synagogues that remained in operation, those that had not been destroyed during *Kristallnacht*. The decrees followed one another in an unabated torrent of measures that were designed, with sadistic ingenuity, to make life as miserable as possible. Jews had to turn in their radios. They had to surrender their typewriters. They had to give up their cutlery, except for one knife, fork, and spoon per person. They were prohibited from buying clothing. When the war began in 1939 and rationing was instituted, Jews were given special ration coupons overprinted with the letter *J* in red ink and were restricted to inferior rations. Ultimately they were limited to shopping during a single hour, 4:00 P.M. to 5:00 P.M., a time when the shops usually had been stripped bare of anything desirable.

Yet, despite the terrible circumstances in which Berlin's Jews existed, there subsisted at least a spurious appearance of continuity with the past. Certain Jewish communal organizations continued to exist, albeit under strict control of the authorities. Among them was a central organization of German Jews and, in Berlin, the organized *Gemeinde*, or Jewish community (although, as we shall see, the status of the *Gemeinde* became clouded after 1938). These organizations operated such religious and social welfare institutions as the Nazis permitted the Jews to retain, among them the hospital. Jewish religious observance continued as well as it could in such difficult circumstances. Rabbi Leo Baeck, the revered head of the German Jewish community, passed up the opportunity to emigrate so that he could minister to those who remained in Germany. Despite continual Nazi harassment, he and other German rabbis and rabbinical students who remained behind managed to keep Jewish worship alive, even to import supplies of kosher meat for observant Jews. (The Nazis had banned kosher slaughter of animals in Germany shortly after taking power.) There even was Jewish entertainment for a segregated Jewish public under the aegis of the *Jüdische Kulturbund*, or Jewish Culture Association, where Jewish musicians, actors, and other performers expelled from all other employment in Germany found an outlet in performing for solely Jewish audiences; however, they were forbidden to play the music of Aryan German composers.

Social welfare was a major preoccupation of organized Jewish existence during this period. Emigration increasingly had stripped the German Jewish community of its younger and more productive members and had left behind the old, the sick, and the poor. In addition, the Nazi confiscations and economic restrictions had impoverished even those Jews who had managed to hold on economically through the pre-*Kristallnacht* period. Among healthy Jews of employable age who remained in Germany, increasing numbers were forced out of public employment and the professions and then out of commerce through the forced "Aryanization" of their businesses. Young men and women who would have gone on to higher education were barred from educational institutions and had few or no job opportunities. Once unemployed, Jews were required to register with a special Jewish Labor Bureau and had to perform forced labor wherever they were assigned. By 1941 most able-bodied Jewish men and women, including teenagers, were at forced labor, primarily in the many war-related industrial plants in and around Berlin.

Some German Jews may have thought that things could not get any worse, but in 1941 they did. In September 1941, the Nazis promulgated regulations that required persons classed as Jews to wear the infamous racial badge: a yellow six-pointed cloth star with the word *Jude* written across it, to be firmly sewn onto the individual's clothing over the left breast. The Jews were required to purchase their yellow stars from the authorities. The yellow star evoked intense emotions among German Jews: shame and humiliation, as well as the fear that it would mark them even more clearly as targets for harassment and violence when they ventured outside their homes. The premier diarist of the Nazi era, Victor Klemperer, a Jewish former university professor living in Dresden with his non-Jewish wife, Eva, described his reaction on September 18, 1941: "The 'Jewish star,' black on yellow cloth, at the center in Hebrew-like letters 'Jew,' to be worn on the left breast, large as the palm of a hand, issued to us yesterday for 10 pfennigs, to be worn from tomorrow. . . . For the time being at least Eva will take over all the shopping. I shall breathe in a little fresh air only under shelter of darkness."

An even worse blow fell in the following month. In October, the German authorities began to implement their plan to "resettle" Germany's Jews in conquered territories to the East. The authors of this plan intended "resettlement" as a euphemism for murder. This was not the first time the Germans had used deportation as a means of getting rid of Jews. There had been several isolated instances earlier, including the deportation of Polish Jews in 1938. (It was the suffering of the parents of Herschel Grynzspan in that deportation that led the young Polish Jew to assassinate the German first secretary Ernst vom Rath at the German embassy in Paris. This provided the Nazis with the pretext for the November 1938 pogrom.) In 1940 groups of Jews from Stettin were deported to Poland, and others from Baden and the Rhine Palatinate were sent to France. The 1941 deportations were the first, however, to be mounted against German Jews living in major population centers. They unmistakably announced that the Jews were finished in Germany. The lack of any public opposition made it clear that, as far as the German public was concerned, the forcible disappearance of Germany's Jews was acceptable. Indeed, when the decree imposing the racial badge took effect, many Aryans professed amazement that there still were so many Jews around. Until the yellow stars began appearing on the streets, many Germans had assumed that most Jews had left the country.

———

To understand the hospital's situation after *Kristallnacht,* we must look at the tangled organizational structure of the Jewish community. In a pattern that prevailed in Germany long before the Nazis and that still exists today, every religious denomination in Germany was organized into a *Gemeinde* (translated, depending on context, as community, municipality, congregation, or parish). In the case of the Jews, the *Gemeinde* encompassed either a single city like Berlin or, in areas with smaller Jewish populations, one of the German states (*Länder*). Children were registered at birth as members of the local *Gemeinde* of their parents' religion. Converts and products of mixed marriages could register in a *Gemeinde* different from that of one or both of their parents. (For certain mixed Jewish-Christian marriages, the Nazi racial laws turned decisions the parents had made years before on how to register their children, or even mistakes made by the registrars, into issues on which life or death could turn.) The government collected taxes for the support of religious institutions from the citizenry and passed the proceeds on to each *Gemeinde* in accordance with the number of adherents officially registered on its rolls. The *Gemeinde,* in turn, used these funds to support religious and social welfare institutions.

The Berlin *Gemeinde* thus was the official embodiment of the Jewish religion in Berlin and the recipient of the religion taxes levied on the city's large and, until the Nazi period, largely affluent Jewish population. It supported a broad array of religious, educational, and social welfare activities, among them a health department, which included the hospital. Under the pressures imposed by the rise of Nazism, the Berlin *Gemeinde*'s social welfare activities, especially assistance to those seeking to emigrate and those left unemployed or impoverished by the anti-Semitic decrees, moved to the forefront.

The hospital had been built on land owned by the *Gemeinde* and was financed at least in part with funds that the *Gemeinde* provided, although it also had an independent endowment fund, the Jubilee Fund. The hospital's directors were answerable to the *Gemeinde*'s elected assembly. The clarity of this organizational structure, however, began to blur in 1938, and by 1941, like most things relating to Jewish life in Germany, what appeared on organization charts and what happened on the ground were not always congruent.

In the tidal wave of repressive measures that followed *Kristallnacht*, the government had terminated the legal status of every Jewish *Gemeinde* in Germany. Jews were no longer members of their local *Gemeinde*, nor did the state collect taxes on behalf of the Jewish communities for redistribution to the Jewish agencies. Thus the focus of Jewish communal activity shifted to the national organization.

The existence of a central Jewish organization at the national level was a recent development. For years, even though the rise of political anti-Semitism made it obvious to many Jewish leaders that the Jewish community needed to unite in self-defense, German Jewry had been unable to agree to form a single umbrella organization. Opposition to the idea came from various sources. Some felt that a unified political body would only feed anti-Semitism. Then there were the omnipresent rivalries that split apart the Jewish community. The Zionists and the anti-Zionists were suspicious of each other. So, too, were the Orthodox and the non-Orthodox. The *Gemeinde* in the smaller cities and *Länder* resisted the formation of a central body for fear that it would be dominated by the Berlin *Gemeinde*, which before the Nazi era represented a third of Germany's Jewish population. It was only after the Nazi takeover in 1933 that the pressure of events finally overwhelmed these fears and rivalries. An organization was formed called the *Reichsvertretung der deutschen Juden*, or Central Representation of German Jews. (In 1935 the government forced it to drop the term "German Jews" and instead use "Jews in Germany.")

Rabbi Leo Baeck became president of the *Reichsvertretung*. He commanded almost universal respect among German Jews and was regarded by both Jews and non-Jews as Germany's most prominent Jewish leader. He had devoted his professional life to writing and speaking to the broadest possible audience in defense of the validity and worth of the Jewish religion and to seeking intellectual rapprochement between Judaism and Christianity. His intellectual powers, skills as a public speaker, tolerance for diversity of religious and political views within the Jewish community, and outstanding personality had brought him to a position of pre-eminence. When Germany's Jews at long last joined in creating a national organization to deal with the threats posed by Nazism, Dr. Baeck was the obvious choice to become its president. His personal courage and self-sacrifice in the difficult years that followed amply justified his selection and established the saintly reputation that attaches to his name today.

The *Reichsvertretung* took on the task of trying to represent the Jewish community vis-à-vis the Nazi state. It also undertook, with significant financial assistance from abroad, a massive program aimed at alleviating the suffering of Germany's Jews. This included maintaining schools for Jewish children who had been expelled from the public schools and running vocational training programs for Jews excluded from the professions to retrain them for occupations they could follow in Germany or to prepare them for emigration. There also were welfare programs to care for the growing percentage of the Jewish population that was made up of the poor and elderly.

When on March 13, 1938, the Nazi government terminated the legal status of the *Gemeinde*, Baeck issued a call to German Jews to continue to support their local communities and, in particular, to pay directly to the community offices the taxes that previously had been collected by the state. To some extent this appeal was successful. With the voluntary contributions of German Jews, foreign contributions, and money from other sources, the Berlin *Gemeinde* continued to operate until the authorities finally dissolved it in 1943. Increasingly, however, as more and more of German Jewry became concentrated in Berlin, the activities of the *Gemeinde* overlapped those of the *Reichsvertretung*. At the same time, many officials began to hold parallel positions in both organizations, so that the distinction between the Berlin *Gemeinde* and the central organization increasingly became more a question of theory than reality.

The next step in the bureaucratic saga following on the heels of *Kristallnacht* was the Nazi government's dissolution of the *Reichsvertretung*. The Nazis, however, soon repented of their decision. They still wished to encourage the emigration of as many Jews as possible, and the central Jewish organization had been more effective in bringing this about than government agencies could be. In addition, there were a variety of other administrative matters that could more effectively be handled through the intermediary of the Jewish community. In this, the Nazis were acquiring experience they soon would put to deadly use in the annihilation of Jewish communities in conquered territories and ultimately in Germany itself. So, the government ordered the Jews to organize a new central organization, substituting the word *Reichsvereinigung* (central organization) for *Reichsvertretung* (central representation). This change reflected the fact that the new organization no longer represented Germany's Jews in their relations with the government. Instead, it became a government instrument for controlling the Jewish population. Membership in the *Reichsvereinigung der Juden in Deutschland* was made compulsory for every Jew as defined by the Nuremberg racial laws, except for Jews living in "privileged" mixed marriages — primarily Jewish women married to Aryan men. Each local *Gemeinde* became a branch of the *Reichsvereinigung*. The organization operated under close Gestapo supervision.

So it was that by 1941 the hospital functioned under the organizational umbrella of the *Reichsvereinigung*, although, through the *Gemeinde* health department, it still maintained a formal relationship to the Berlin *Gemeinde*. The most important aspect of the new arrangements that began in 1938 was that, through the *Reichsvereinigung*, the hospital was placed under the direct supervision of Department IV B 4 of the RSHA. Originally this had been the department in charge of "Jewish emigration and evacuation." By 1941 it had become the department for "Jewish affairs and evacuation," emigration having been largely abandoned as a Nazi objective. Its head was Adolf Eichmann, the bureaucratic mastermind of the Final Solution.

All of this organizational upheaval, not to speak of the November 1938 *Kristallnacht* pogrom, made a less visible impact on the hospital than on most other Jewish institutions in Germany. However, it could not escape being significantly affected by what was happening to the community it served and in particular by the repressive decrees that dealt with the medical profession.

Unlike many Jewish institutions, the hospital was spared physical damage during *Kristallnacht*. Indeed, the fact that the carefully orchestrated violence of the November pogrom bypassed the hospital was viewed by many as a sign that the institution probably would be allowed to remain unharmed. Although 1938 was a year of disaster for other Jewish institutions, in a perverse sense it could be viewed as a strong year for the hospital. The underutilization that had plagued it during the preceding five years ceased to be a problem.

In June 1938 a decree banned Jewish doctors from treating Aryan patients. At around the same time the hospital as a whole was prohibited from treating Aryans and was thus limited to accepting only Jewish patients. A photograph of the Gynecology Outpatient Clinic in 1939 shows over the door a sign in large letters announcing "From 1 October 1938 *only* Jewish patients will be handled." Yet the hospital's services were still very much in demand because the non-Jewish hospitals in the city were turning away Jewish patients, who were then forced to use the hospital. And, it must be remembered, the Nazi racial laws defined as Jews large numbers of people who may have had Jewish parentage but otherwise had no sense of identification with the Jewish community, including people whose parents had converted to Christianity and who had been brought up their entire lives as Christians. Thus the racial laws and the 1938 measures affecting medical treatment forced people to use the hospital who might never otherwise have chosen to do so on the basis of any sense of communal affiliation.

Another reason why the hospital found itself busy during the period beginning in 1938 was that the authorities elsewhere in Germany were engaged in an assault against Jewish medical and welfare institutions that ultimately led to the closure of all of them other than the hospital itself. As medical facilities in other German cities were forced to close, their patients and, at least to some extent, their staffs were transferred to the Berlin facility. This transfer occurred at the same time as increasing numbers of Germany's Jews became concentrated in Berlin. The pressures of anti-Semitism and Nazi repression were felt most acutely in smaller communities, where Jews were more isolated and where Jewish schools and cultural institutions were not available to fill the gap when Jews were excluded from German life. Jews responded by fleeing. Those who could not emigrate, or did not want to, went to Berlin and sought safety in numbers. Thus the Jewish population of Berlin on June 30, 1941, which stood at approximately 72,000 people, represented about 43 percent of Germany's 167,245 remaining Jews, while at the onset of the Nazi regime in 1933 the city had held only 32 percent of the country's Jews.

An additional explanation for the heightened call for the hospital's services in 1938–39 was the high level of physical violence against Jews in the Berlin area and throughout Germany. Hundreds of people were injured in the November 1938 pogrom. Indeed, the consequences of *Kristallnacht* made it necessary to add 150 beds to the surgical department. Moreover, of the thousands arrested and incarcerated in nearby concentration camps like Sachsenhausen and Oranienburg, many, when eventually released, were battered and in poor health. During the years that followed *Kristallnacht* until the deportations effectively had been completed, instances of Gestapo and police violence against Jews continued, creating a continual need for the hospital's services.

Another call on the hospital arose from the practice, applied intermittently and with no apparent rationale or pattern, of sending injured or sick Jewish prisoners to the hospital to be treated, even though the Nazis intended that the patient ultimately would die at their hands. The Gestapo required the hospital to establish a *Polizeistation*, or police ward, which was a locked ward in the main hospital building. Certain ill or injured Jews who were in police, SS, or Gestapo custody, including inmates incarcerated in concentration camps in the Berlin area, were brought to the hospital for treatment. They were kept under guard in the prison ward until the authorities deemed them well enough to return to the concentration camp or to be shipped out to the death camps in the East.

The measures taken against Jewish professionals in 1938 had a profound effect on the composition of the hospital's professional staff as it stood in 1941, on the threshold of the most intense phase in the hospital's fight for survival. In 1933 Jewish doctors had been deprived of their positions in public hospitals under the Aryan clause, and then they had been pushed out of jobs in private non-Jewish clinics by the Nuremberg racial laws in 1935. The final blow came with a decree of July 25, 1938, that stripped all Jewish physicians, of whom there were some three thousand in the Reich, of their medical licenses. In September, the law was amended to allow about seven hundred Jewish physicians to engage in the occupation of *Krankenbehandler*, or "carer for the sick," but they were restricted to dealing with Jewish patients or working in Jewish institutions.

Walter Lustig was one of the beneficiaries of this provision.

Having decided not to try to emigrate, possibly because of the protection he counted on deriving from his marriage to an Aryan but more likely because he seems to have been marked by a serene self-confidence, he benefited from others' departures to rise in the Jewish hierarchy. When his boss in the *Gemeinde/Reichsvereinigung* health department, Erich Seligmann, left Germany for the United States in 1939, Lustig took over his position. In July 1939, the *Jüdisches Nachrichtenblatt* (Jewish chronicle) described him as the person who henceforth would be responsible for health matters within the *Reichsvereinigung*. In that capacity, he played a key role in filling vacancies that opened up at the hospital because of the emigration of members of the medical staff. At some point in 1940 or 1941 (exactly when is unclear), he was appointed as the *Gesundheitsdezernent*, or chief of the health department, and thus became a member of the governing board of the *Reichsvereinigung*.

The misfortunes of Germany's Jewish physicians were not without positive consequences for the hospital. The country's highest concentration of unemployed Jewish doctors was in Berlin, and many were renowned experts in their fields. The hospital attempted to give employment to as many as possible, as well as to find jobs for newly qualified doctors whose internships elsewhere had been interrupted by the 1938 decrees. Thus the hospital was able to enrich its staff with the pick of Germany's remaining Jewish medical figures. But the negative aspects of the situation were significant as well. Many staff members were trying to emigrate, and some were successful. Others fell prey to the constant risk of being picked up by the Gestapo for one reason or another and sent to a concentration camp in Germany. In addition, as we shall see, once the mass deportations started, the medical staff was constantly threatened with deportation, both collectively and individually. The result was a high level of turnover and instability in the medical departments. Indeed, after *Kristallnacht*, during the spring and summer of 1939, month after month, the *Jüdisches Nachrichtenblatt*, the sole remaining legal Jewish publi-

cation, carried advertisements placed by the hospital seeking candidates to fill senior-level medical positions.

The number of *Krankenbehandler* and their distribution
among localities in Germany were strictly controlled by the authorities and were the subject of ongoing negotiations between
the Jewish community and the government. "Negotiation" is
perhaps a misleading word, since it is clear that all the power lay
on the government's side. The most the Jews could do was try to
convince the Nazis that a result sought by the Jewish community
was consistent with Nazi policy. In this, the Berlin community
was relatively successful as regards the hospital.

The German health authorities were persuaded that the hospital's staff physicians should not be counted in the quota of 175
Krankenbehandler who were authorized in 1938 to treat Jews in
Berlin. An additional 27 physicians for the hospital were approved on the basis of a list of names submitted by the Berlin
Gemeinde. The attempt by the *Gemeinde* to have this list expanded
apparently gave rise to criticism that the Jews were trying to exploit the situation to obtain more than the spirit of the law envis-
aged. The representatives of the *Gemeinde* hastened, in correspondence with the authorities, to create a list of reasons why this
was not the case. They cited the need for increased medical services to deal with the rising Berlin Jewish population resulting
from the Nuremberg Laws and other decrees. They stressed the
public health risks that could result from epidemics among the
Jews in the city, a danger exacerbated by the Jews' worsening economic situation. These arguments, especially the fear of epidemics, were successful in persuading the authorities to maintain the
permitted complement of physicians for the hospital. The authorities also were persuaded to authorize the hospital to conduct
some activities from which Jews had been barred completely,
such as performing certain laboratory tests. The alternative, the
Nazis apparently feared, was that Aryan laboratories might have
to perform such tests for Jews or that Aryan hospitals might have
to treat Jewish patients.

Thus, on the eve of the mass deportations, the hospital was a busy, overcrowded institution, the focal point of medical treatment not only for the Berlin Jewish community but increasingly for all of German Jewry as emigration and forced closures destroyed Jewish hospitals and clinics in other cities. In 1940 there were almost 70 percent more operations performed than in 1925–27, when the hospital also had been full, and in 1941 the number of surgical procedures rose by another 50 percent.

Nurses' training was another major activity at the hospital. Despite the Nazi repression in all other aspects of the medical field, the hospital's school of nursing continued to function. Even though Jewish doctors had been expelled from the medical profession and fewer than 25 percent of their number permitted to practice ghettoized medicine under the degrading *Krankenbehandler* title, the education of nurses continued undisturbed. Nurses' training courses were given until 1941. Even in that year of intense official persecution of the Jews, final examinations for the hospital's nursing students were held in the presence of government representatives, and the nurses' certificates of qualification were signed and stamped by the Berlin police chief.

The fact that Jewish nurses were allowed to qualify and receive German state certificates is a puzzling anomaly. One of the hospital's nurses, Charlotte Holzer, explains how she exploited this unusual situation on behalf of her mother, who otherwise would have been assigned to forced labor:

> I . . . then created several multi-year care-taking certificates for my mother, signed with the names of Jews who had emigrated. Night after night I took my mother along to the ward and taught her as much as I could about nursing care. And I believe that my mother in this fashion became a really good nurse. She received the state diploma and worked, starting in 1940, in the Jewish nursing and sick home, which at this time was located on the premises of the Jewish Hospital.

Unfortunately, in the end this ploy did not protect Holzer's mother from being sent to Auschwitz, where she died.

4

THE NAZIS' INTERMARRIAGE
QUANDARY

ROSEMARIE H., ONE OF a number of young half-Jews who were sent to reinforce the hospital's staff in 1943 after the mass deportation of most of Berlin's remaining full Jews, retells a story she heard from her mother. When Rosemarie's mother introduced her fiancé to the family, her brother, Rosemarie's *Onkel* Fritz, was horrified.

"Our parents will turn in their graves if you marry that Jew," he said.

From that time on he maintained virtually no relationship with his sister, even less with her husband and children. His daughter, Rosemarie's cousin, married a Nazi who had something to do with a concentration camp. The two families stopped speaking to each other. In 1943, Rosemarie's brother escaped the roundup in which Jewish forced laborers were arrested and deported to the East, but before long he was arrested on spurious charges and imprisoned in the Sachsenhausen concentration camp near Berlin. His Jewish father, broken by forced heavy labor for which he was unsuited and wearing the humiliating yellow star, further humbled himself by begging his Nazi brother-in-law for help in getting his son released. He was met with insults and a stark refusal.

"I wouldn't lift a hand to help a Jew," *Onkel* Fritz said.

Rosemarie's mother's sister could not have been more different from their brother Fritz. She lived on terms of close intimacy and affection with her Jewish and half-Jewish relatives. The two families had apartments in the same building. Food was in short supply for everyone as the war progressed, but Jews, their special ration cards overprinted with a big red *J*, got less than everyone else. Rosemarie remembers that her aunt would slip her treats, such as hoarded bits of chocolate, to make up for the deprivations that the Jews were suffering. As she did, the aunt would commiserate with her on the harsh life led by half-Jews like Rosemarie.

"Oh, you poor child," she would say. "You poor child." The aunt's husband was in charge of the air raid shelter for the building. Jews were not allowed in the shelter, but when there was a particularly heavy bombing he insisted that his Jewish relatives come downstairs into the shelter. "I take the responsibility," he said. "This is inhuman. Something might happen to you."

Rosemarie's story is typical of situations that could be found all over Germany, although nowhere so frequently as in Berlin, prewar Germany's center of culture and sophistication and a place where Jews had achieved a high level of assimilation into German society. During the period of World War I and the Weimar Republic, despite rising anti-Semitism, intermarriage had risen to significant levels. By 1927, 25 percent of Jewish men and 16 percent of Jewish women were marrying outside the Jewish religion. Thus, when the Nazis began their anti-Jewish measures in 1933, there were thousands of part-Jewish families and thousands of people who considered themselves entirely assimilated into the Christian community but had one or more Jewish grandparents. The prevalence of Jewish-Aryan couples and their part-Jewish offspring, coupled with the Nazis' indecisiveness in their regard, became a key factor in the hospital's fate during the period of the Nazi genocide. This issue was so central to what happened to the hospital that, in order to understand how the hospital survived to the end of the war, it is necessary to look in some detail at the tangled history of the Nazis' attempts to deal with it.

Intermarriage and part-Jewish Germans posed a constant dilemma for the Nazis and were a source of internal debate that never was resolved. On the one hand, the Nazis' anti-Semitic mania was based on the racial theory that Jewishness was in the blood. By this reasoning, a German with Jewish ancestry was a Jew regardless of his or her religious affiliation. On the other hand, Hitler and many of the other Nazi leaders feared that to subject every part-Jewish German to the fate reserved for full Jews would engender a political risk.

Even a totalitarian regime that ruthlessly suppressed political opposition by terror operated on the premise that it was desirable to retain mass political support among the German people. In calculating how far it could go in moving against intermarried families, the regime had to take account of the fact that Aryan Germans did not share a single and predictable attitude toward their Jewish or part-Jewish spouses, children, grandchildren, nieces, nephews, cousins, and other relations. Some, like Rosemarie's *Onkel* Fritz, put anti-Semitism above any claim of kinship. Others, like her aunt and her uncle by marriage, even if they believed generally in the Nazis' anti-Semitic tenets, remained loyal to their Jewish kin.

The maintenance of close family ties between Jews and their Aryan relatives was a common phenomenon. For example, one of the hospital employees from 1943 to 1945, Ruth Graetz, the daughter of a Jewish father and an Aryan mother, remembers continuing to enjoy affectionate and supportive ties with her mother's family. They had welcomed her mother's marriage to a Jew, not an uncommon attitude in pre-Nazi Berlin, where, she notes, a Jewish husband was considered a "catch" for many non-Jewish girls since he could be counted on not to drink and to treat his wife with consideration. On occasion, the wartime support offered by Aryan relatives went far beyond kind words and gifts of food. The hospital's Dr. Hans Knopp, a half-Jew, was hidden by his Aryan relatives in Mainz from the time he went underground in 1943 until the end of the war.

If the debate within Nazi circles had been resolved in favor of a ruthless elimination of everyone in Germany who could not prove unblemished Aryan ancestry, the hospital could not have remained in existence long enough to be saved by Germany's loss of the war. Fortunately, however, the outcome of the Nazis' uncertainty over mixed marriages and ancestry approached, but never reached, a decision in favor of total elimination. Hitler hesitated to take a step that could turn a sizable portion of the population against the regime while the war was going badly. He deferred action until things improved, which never happened. As a consequence, a minimal Jewish presence remained in Germany until the end of the war. That presence does not entirely explain the hospital's survival, but there can be no doubt that it was a necessary condition for it.

At the outset of the Nazi regime, the question of defining who was a Jew and what exceptions, if any, would be made to the anti-Jewish measures was easier for the Nazis to handle than it became in the 1940s, when the move to mass murder made fine distinctions assume enormous importance. In their first measures against the Jews, eliminating Jews from public employment, the Nazis adopted the Aryan clause, under which anyone with at least one Jewish grandparent was considered non-Aryan. This clause was enthusiastically embraced by a vast range of nongovernmental associations, including professional groups, cultural entities, and social organizations. Indeed, so rapidly and widely was the Aryan clause applied in the private sector that Jews found themselves largely excluded from the professions and from virtually every aspect of German social and cultural life even before the regime took formal action to that end. Nazi Party and German government organizations imposed even more stringent requirements on membership and employment, requiring candidates to be able to prove untainted Aryan ancestry for themselves and their spouses as far back, in some cases, as the eighteenth century. Although thousands of intermarried Jews and people of part-Jewish ancestry were affected by these measures, the popularity with which they were received and the lack of any significant opposition to them by the German public showed that even those Aryans who had Jewish relatives were prepared to tolerate this level of official anti-Semitism.

The next significant increase in the severity of the government's anti-Jewish measures occurred with the promulgation of the Nuremberg Laws of 1935. These included two main enactments. The first, the Reich Citizenship Law, deprived Jews of German citizenship. It created a new category of state subject, *Staatsangehöriger*, a person subject to the jurisdiction of the Reich but not entitled to participate in political life by voting or holding office. Political rights and full German citizenship were reserved for the *Reichsbürger*, a status accorded only to those of "German blood," the equivalent of "Aryan" in earlier Nazi usage and legislation. The second piece of legislation, the Law for the Protection of German Blood and Honor, prohibited marriage and sexual relations between Jews and subjects of the Reich who were of German blood. The ban on sexual contact was reinforced by a prohibition against employment in a Jewish household of any female domestic servant of German blood under forty-five years of age. Significantly, however, the law did not render illegal those marriages that already existed between Aryans and Jews. There was no lack of support within the government for carrying the matter to this extreme, but political considerations intervened. To have dissolved existing marriages would have conflicted with traditional German notions of the sanctity of marriage and constituted a challenge to the beliefs of both Protestant and Catholic churches.

The Nuremberg Laws, which were hastily drafted in time for Hitler to proclaim them at the Nazi Party Congress in Nuremberg, left unresolved the question of who was to be considered Jewish. Debate on how to implement them in this regard continued for some time. Eventually, the implementing decrees defined a person as Jewish if he or she had at least three fully Jewish grandparents. The law created a new category of *Mischling* (plural: *Mischlinge*). The term, which can be translated as mongrel, hybrid cross or half-caste, was intentionally pejorative and was used to describe persons of mixed Jewish ancestry with fewer than three Jewish grandparents. There were two categories of *Mischlinge*. "Second-degree *Mischlinge*" were those with no more than one Jewish grandparent. For most purposes they were to be treated as equivalent to Aryans. The situation became much more complicated with respect to people with two Jewish grandparents. Such a half-Jew was categorized as a "first-degree *Mischling*" if he or she had neither married a Jew nor ever been enrolled as a member of the Jewish religious community. Although barred from many occupations, first-degree *Mischlinge* generally were exempted from the anti-Semitic legislation that followed the Nuremberg Laws. Any half-Jew who was legally registered as a Jew or had chosen to marry a Jew was defined as a *Geltungsjude* (meaning "person counted as a Jew"). *Geltungsjuden* were subject to all the humiliations and restrictions that the Nazis imposed on full Jews. Thus half-Jews, although they had the same degree of Jewish ancestry, were divided into two classes that were treated in widely different ways. In the immediate aftermath of the Nuremberg Laws the restrictions imposed on full Jews and *Geltungsjuden* included the loss of all civil and voting rights and, for those who up to then had kept their jobs in the public sector because they were World War I veterans, loss of employment. As time went on, the implications of being classed as a full Jew became worse and worse.

The decree implementing the Law for the Protection of German Blood and Honor created a bewildering set of permitted and forbidden marriages. Full Jews (including *Geltungsjuden*) could marry only other full Jews or first-degree *Mischlinge*. First-degree *Mischlinge* could marry each other or they could marry full Jews and thereby become *Geltungsjuden* themselves. They could not marry Aryans. Second-degree *Mischlinge* could marry Aryans but could not marry someone in the same category as themselves. They were forbidden to marry first-degree *Mischlinge* unless they obtained a special exemption from the minister of the interior or the deputy führer. Except as expressly permitted, sexual relations and marriage between persons of German blood and Jews were classed as *Rassenschande*, or racial defilement.

These rules represented a compromise between the desires of the Nazi hard-liners, who wanted to treat all *Mischlinge* as full Jews, and those in the Nazi Party and in the government who feared the social and political repercussions of such a radical approach. No one knows precisely how many people there were in Nazi Germany who had either one or two Jewish grandparents or, although not Jews themselves, were married to Jews. Estimates range from as many as several hundred thousand to perhaps close to one million. Even at the low end of this range, there existed a large number of Aryan Germans who had some tie of relationship by marriage or blood with a full Jew or a part Jew. The political ramifications of this fact did not leave Hitler unmoved. As Nathan Stoltzfus has emphasized in his magisterial study of German-Jewish intermarriage during the Nazi period, for all of Hitler's fanaticism on the subject of Jews, he subscribed to a theory of power that required a consensus of the "racial people," that is, the Aryan population. "In Nazi theory, terror was a means for controlling the fringe once the majority was amenable." This is why propaganda and manipulation of the masses played such a major role in the Nazi program, even (perhaps especially) after the Nazis had succeeded in initially seizing power through a combination of political success and terrorism.

It is not surprising that the Nuremberg Laws and implementing decrees, as a product of reluctant compromise between fanaticism and political reality, were riddled with inconsistencies and ironies. Nazi dogma was that Judaism was a racial rather than a religious identity. Nazi literature is full of allusions to the ineradicable stain that even a small quota of Jewish blood would create. A "full Jew" under the Nuremberg Laws was no less a Jew if he or she converted to Christianity or even had been baptized in that faith at birth and had never known any other religious identity.

This situation was not uncommon. Jewish emancipation in Germany had led to a strong trend toward assimilation. Substantial numbers of people who had been born Jewish had decided in the late nineteenth and early twentieth centuries that social and economic advancement was worth a few drops of holy water. Thus many fledgling Jewish doctors (like Walter Lustig) and Jewish lawyers converted, at least nominally, to Christianity on entering professional life, knowing that by doing so they could lower the heavy barriers that lay in the way of their finding employment. Likewise, numerous Jewish couples had had their children converted and had raised them as Christians to ensure for them a brighter educational and vocational future. In some cases these children were devout members of a Christian denomination, especially when the conversion had occurred a generation back. Under the Nazis they found, first, that their religion was immaterial if their grandparents had been Jewish and, second, that almost all the Aryan members of their faith no longer were willing to worship in their company. One of the saddest aspects of the Holocaust was the situation of these "racial Jews" of Christian faith. For, although stigmatized by Nazi law and by the bigotry of their fellow Christians, they were also coldly received by a Jewish community that had more than it could handle just dealing with the impoverishment, misery, and fear of people who had been enrolled as members of the Jewish *Gemeinde* all their lives.

As the Nazi persecution grew steadily more fiendish in the months that followed *Kristallnacht,* the distinctions created by the Nuremberg Laws took on an ever increasing importance in the lives of persons with "Jewish blood." For those Jews who were married to Aryans, an important distinction was also created between ordinary mixed marriages and "privileged mixed marriages." This arose first in the context of the April 30, 1939, Law on Rental Leases with Jews. The law essentially deprived Jews of rights as tenants and was part of the government's drive to expel thousands of Jews, especially in Berlin, from their apartments and concentrate them in *Judenhäuser,* or Jew houses. The law contained an exemption for "privileged" intermarried households, those in which the children had not been enrolled in a Jewish *Gemeinde* as of September 1935 or in which the husband was Aryan. Jews in these marriages were exempt from compulsory membership in the *Reichsvereinigung* and from a host of invidious restrictions, such as the requirement to wear the yellow star and the prohibition on using public transportation. They received the same food rations as Aryans, as well as rations of clothing and tobacco, which were unavailable for other Jews. The distinctions among mixed marriages, which created greater hardships for Aryan women married to Jewish men than for Jewish women married to Aryan men, can be seen as a reflection of a Nazi misogyny and male chauvinism that attributed a higher status to males.

The effect of the "privileged Jew" rules for intermarried couples of Jewish men and Aryan women and their children was to make everything turn on whether the child had been listed on the register of a Jewish *Gemeinde* on September 15, 1935. Up to that point, as Bruno Blau, the eminent statistician of twentieth-century German Jewish life and an inmate of the hospital's prison ward, notes, there had been no reason to take too seriously the registration of children with the *Gemeinde*, and many mistakes had been made. Children who had been baptized were not withdrawn from the official registry of Jews; children who were raised as Jews were left off. Yet the rules on privileged mixed marriages were inexorable; the registry governed. Some unassimilated Jewish men with Aryan wives whose children had been left off the register by mistake found themselves living as privileged Jews. Some thoroughly assimilated Jews who had baptized their children in their Aryan wives' Christian religion but had failed to effect a change in the children's registration found themselves subjected to all the indignities and risks of unprivileged status.

One apparent effect of these rules was to foster identification with Judaism among children of nonprivileged mixed marriages even if they were not Jews. Under Jewish law a person born of a

Jewish mother is Jewish, regardless of the father's religion. The Nazi rule for mixed marriages ran in the opposite direction, and it appears, based on anecdotal evidence, that most children of Jewish mothers and Christian fathers were raised as Christians. Given German social beliefs that ascribed primacy to the male spouse, this probably would have occurred even without the impetus of Nazism and the invention of the privileged Jew concept. On the other side, however, the Nazi persecution of "Jewish households" that arose from mixed marriages between Jewish men and Aryan women virtually precluded the children in those families from identifying religiously with the Christian half of their parentage, as did the refusal of most Christian congregations to worship with Christians of Jewish ancestry. Treated as *Geltungsjuden*, these children effectively were forced into feeling Jewish. Almost all of the *Geltungsjuden* interviewed for this book who lived through the Nazi period in Germany manifest a strong sense of Jewish identity, regardless of whether their mothers had converted to Judaism, as would have been required to make them Jews in the eyes of Jewish law. Most themselves married Jews and raised their own children as Jews. Given the strong trend toward assimilation in pre-Nazi Germany, one can doubt whether this would have occurred to anywhere near the same degree in the absence of the Nazi persecution.

In some cases, the racial laws and privileged Jew regulations tore families apart and set parents against children. One of the most poignant examples was Cordelia Edvardson, a *Mischling* child who spent several months in the hospital's *Kinderunterkunft*, or orphanage (although she was no orphan), before being sent to Auschwitz. As a survivor in postwar Sweden, Cordelia Edvardson (her married name) wrote a searing account of her experiences, as mentioned earlier, in which she gave a hellish depiction of life in the hospital.

Edvardson's mother was a half-Jew who bore Cordelia out of wedlock as the result of an affair with a full Jew. Thus, by Nazi racial calculus, Cordelia, with three Jewish grandparents, was a full

Jew. All this was unknown to the child, who grew up as a Catholic in a household comprising her mother, her mother's husband, an Aryan, and the children of that marriage, who, with only one Jewish grandparent, counted as second-degree *Mischlinge* and were safe. She was shocked when the Gestapo appeared and claimed that she was a Jew and was required to wear the yellow star and to abide by all the other anti-Semitic measures. Her stepfather and half siblings distanced themselves from her. Her mother tried various stratagems to save her daughter, including an attempt to arrange for the adoption of the girl, by now a teenager, by a Spanish couple. The Gestapo intervened and accused the mother of violating the law. They summoned mother and child to a Gestapo office, where the Nazis presented them with an ultimatum. The mother would go to prison for her alleged infractions unless the daughter signed a paper acknowledging that she was a Jew, subject to whatever fate Germany reserved for full Jews. Her mother begged Edvardson to sign. Profoundly shocked by her mother's unwillingness to risk imprisonment to save her own child's life, Edvardson acceded and began a descent into hell from which she emerged at the end of the war with psychological scars.

Privileged Jews were supposed to be exempt from the requirement to wear the yellow star, from the host of sadistic repressive measures imposed by the government after *Kristallnacht*, and from deportation. In theory, the unprivileged Jews in mixed marriages and their children, while subjected to everything else, also were supposed to be protected against deportation. None of these rules could be counted on, however. They were grudging concessions that had been adopted at the highest levels of the Nazi government only as a temporary expedient and were intended to avoid creating grounds for social unrest at a time when the deteriorating war situation already risked doing so. The underlying Nazi hatred of Jews and part Jews had not abated, and mixed marriages were especially abhorrent to devout rank-and-file Nazis, since they involved "racial defilement." Consequently, many civil government officials, as well as members of the SS and

Gestapo, tried to evade these rules and limit their applicability whenever possible. Since the protection afforded by a mixed marriage lasted only so long as the Aryan partner was alive and the marriage endured, the Gestapo pushed for divorces of mixed couples and waited eagerly for the demise of intermarried Aryans so that their Jewish spouses could be arrested and sent to the East.

Frustrated by the continued presence of Jews in the Reich, officials throughout the German bureaucracy agitated continually for new legislation that would permit the deportation of Jews living in mixed marriages and their half-Jewish children. They proposed legal measures that would dissolve mixed marriages so that the Jewish partners could be deported. In this, however, they encountered opposition from within the German legal establishment and the churches. This opposition was not founded in any compassion for the Jews or their Aryan spouses. Rather, as we have seen, it arose from concern about the damage that compulsory divorce might do to the essential principle that the marriage bond was sacrosanct.

While waiting for the regime to permit them to unleash the full savagery of anti-Semitic oppression against the intermarried Jews and the *Mischlinge*, Nazi officials did their best to destroy the Jews who they feared might elude their grasp. (As will be seen, the efforts to break up intermarried couples had their effects on the hospital.) Aryan men with Jewish wives lost their jobs. Aryan women married to Jews were treated with contempt and often brutality. Together with their husbands and children, they were crowded into *Judenhäuser* with "Jewish households" like their own. These minighettos were visited often by Gestapo officers, who committed acts of psychological and physical brutality against the inhabitants, often singling out the Aryan wives for special contempt. Ruth Beleski, who worked at the hospital from 1943 through the end of the war, remembers when she and her sister, as *Geltungsjuden*, first were summoned to the Jewish Labor Bureau, the *Arbeitsamt*, to be assigned to forced labor. Her mother accompanied them, thinking that as an Aryan she could protect her children. The director of the office, however, only raged at Mrs. Beleski, calling her a "whore" for having married a Jew, and assigned both girls to undesirable jobs at an I.G. Farben factory.

Intense official harassment directed at Aryan spouses of Jews was frequently accompanied by heavy family pressure. Not only were family members often fiercely anti-Semitic, but they were also frightened for themselves. The presence of Jews and *Mischlinge* in the extended family, at a minimum, was an embarrassment and, even worse, could be a roadblock to career advancement. For relatives who were members of the SS, the Gestapo, or the Nazi Party hierarchy, it was a particular problem. Although many Aryan relatives of intermarried Germans remained supportive, many others wanted nothing more than to see the marriages dissolved and to have the Jewish "taint" disappear from their families. They worked on the intermarried family member, trying to use blandishments, threats, or insults as a means to encourage a divorce.

In the face of both official and familial pressure, it is remarkable how many Aryans remained loyal to their Jewish spouses. This was particularly true of Aryan women married to Jewish husbands. While many Aryan men divorced their Jewish wives when it became clear that remaining in the marriage would doom their careers, relatively few Aryan women divorced their Jewish husbands. By remaining true to their marriages, these women in most cases managed to protect their husbands and children from extermination, even if they could not shield themselves and their immediate families from the remaining pains of Nazi persecution.

5

THE DEPORTATIONS

IT WAS YOM KIPPUR day 1941. Even after the terrors of *Kristallnacht*, the arrests, the detentions and murders of Jews in concentration camps throughout Germany, the expulsion of Jews of Polish nationality, and the frantic scramble of many Jews to emigrate, some sixty to seventy thousand Jews still lived in Berlin. Hundreds of them crowded into the Levetzowstrasse Synagogue, the only large synagogue to have survived the November 1938 pogrom, to observe the holiest day in the Jewish year. They prayed with special fervor. Many must have wondered what sins they possibly could have committed that would warrant the miseries to which they had already been exposed and the even worse fate that most of them feared lay ahead.

The services, the last Yom Kippur services to be held in Nazi Berlin, were conducted by Rabbi Leo Baeck. Only days before, Baeck had been called upon to exercise his rabbinical judgment in favor of Jewish survival. The Nazis had issued yet another in the seemingly unending series of anti-Jewish decrees that were reducing the Jewish population to despair. This time the order was a ban on the possession of radios; it required all Jews to surrender their radios at their local police station on a specific day, Yom Kippur. As Germany's chief rabbi, Dr. Baeck had to decide whether it was permissible to comply even if it meant desecrating the holiest of Jewish holidays. Although in earlier years he had defied Nazi decrees affecting the High Holidays, this time he bent to reality. Knowing that the Nazis would use noncompliance as an excuse for further arrests and brutality, he told his congregation that they could turn in their radios on Yom Kippur.

But a worse fate than being deprived of radios awaited Berlin's Jews that day. At the end of the services the Gestapo arrived and demanded the keys to the synagogue. A message was sent to Dr. Baeck: Berlin's Jews were to be "resettled" in the East, and the Levetzowstrasse Synagogue was to be converted into a *Sammellager*, a holding camp for Jews awaiting transport. The official Jewish organizations, the Berlin *Gemeinde* and the *Reichsvereinigung*, were ordered to cooperate in carrying out the deportation. They were told that if they withheld their cooperation the treatment of the unfortunate deportees would be even harsher.

The leaders of the Jewish community spent that night in agonized debate. Should they cooperate and thereby possibly ease the fate of their people, or should they refuse to be a part of this monstrous scheme? They knew all too well, from reports that had filtered back from victims of earlier small-scale deportations, that conditions for deportees were appalling. In the end, despite Baeck's misgivings, they opted for cooperation.

Earlier, by threatening to resign in protest, Baeck had thwarted the Gestapo's attempt to insert a Jew who was widely regarded as a Gestapo collaborator into the governing board of the *Reichsvertretung*. No such ploy seemed possible, however, by Yom Kippur 1941. At this point in the deteriorating saga of German Jewry, Baeck's personal prestige no longer mattered to the Nazis. A threat to resign would have been unavailing.

Although Baeck had disagreed with the decision to cooperate with the authorities, he maintained a discreet reticence when their decision encountered postwar criticism and took upon himself the responsibility for agreeing to use Jewish *Ordner*, or "police auxiliaries," in the roundup and transportation of the deportees. "When the question arose whether Jewish orderlies should help pick up Jews for deportation," he wrote, "I took the position that it would be better for them to do it, because they could at least be more gentle and helpful than the Gestapo and make the ordeal easier. It was scarcely in our power to oppose the order effectively."

In calling on the organized Jewish community to help carry out the deportations, the Nazi authorities were applying a policy they already had begun to implement successfully in Poland and other captured territories and were to apply in most of the countries that fell under their sway. Volumes have been written on the extent to which such cooperation made the Holocaust possible, and many have been harshly critical of the Jewish communal leaders who participated, not excluding Baeck. Hannah Arendt, in her controversial study of the Eichmann trial, asserted that Eichmann received cooperation from Jews "to a truly extraordinary degree." She writes, "Without Jewish help in administrative and police work — the final rounding up of Jews in Berlin was . . . done entirely by Jewish police — there would have been either complete chaos or an impossibly severe drain on German manpower. . . . To a Jew this role of the Jewish leaders in the destruction of their own people is undoubtedly the darkest chapter of the whole dark story."

Controversy over the role and alleged culpability of European Jewish leaders has endured to this day. It played out in courtrooms as a handful among the few Jewish leaders who survived were subjected to criminal prosecution. It has agitated the world of Holocaust scholarship, engendering mountains of contending paper. This is not the place in which to judge the actions of Berlin's Jewish leaders. What is important is that the decision of the *Gemeinde/Reichsvereinigung* to play the part the Nazis assigned had enormous consequences for the hospital. On the one hand, it dragged the hospital directly into the deportation maelstrom and turned it into a key institutional adjunct to the deportation process — to such a degree that in the last years of the war the hospital's grounds housed the center of the Germans' mop-up campaign against those Jews who remained in Berlin and were not exempt from deportation. On the other hand, the fact that the Nazis saw the hospital as playing a useful role in the large-scale deportations contributed in large measure to the institution's survival during a period in which the Nazis were eliminating all Jewish organizations and institutions elsewhere. Thus the hospital's part in the deportations became a significant factor in its survival and kept alive a number of Jews who otherwise would have been deported and almost certainly would have perished.

As we have seen, the Nazis' tightening control over all Jewish communal institutions had converted the hospital into a subsidiary unit of the *Reichsvereinigung*. On paper the hospital's subordination to the national Jewish organization followed two routes. One was through direct reporting to the health section of the relief and welfare department of the *Reichsvereinigung*. The other was through the hospital's continuing theoretical status as part of the Berlin *Gemeinde*. However, the *Gemeinde* had become a unit of the *Reichsvereinigung* like every other *Gemeinde* in Germany. Moreover, these were distinctions without a difference, since the same man was in charge of health matters for both the *Reichsvereinigung* and the Berlin *Gemeinde*. This was Walter Lustig.

Lustig's conflicted and powerful personality had its first full opportunity to occupy center stage as the result of the Nazis' decision to provide medical deferments from scheduled deportations. The medical deferment program (which is described more fully later in this chapter) appears to have been part of a Nazi policy applied in the initial stage of the mass deportation process to conduct the deportations in a manner that would enlist maximum cooperation from both the Jewish communal organizations and from the victims themselves. For this purpose, it was necessary to conceal the true nature of the operation from both the Jews and the general public. Thus the deportations were described as a program of "resettlement" through which the Jews would be relocated in communities in the East, where the able-bodied would be required to work. That it was intended to work these Jews to death and immediately exterminate the others was kept a secret. At the outset, Berlin's Jews widely assumed that the Nazis' intentions were as proclaimed and that families that were deported together would be "resettled" together. As a result, there were numerous hasty marriages, as well as many instances in which family members who had not yet been selected for deportation volunteered to accompany those who had. "We were standing in line to be married. . . . Everybody got married. Because we all thought: young will be together in camps and old will be together. Young will be separated from the old. We never expected that they would separate male and female. People married to have somebody to go with."

As time went on, the true nature of the deportations became apparent — sooner to those Jews who were prepared psychologically to confront an unspeakable reality, later to those who were less well informed or had greater powers of self-delusion. To the strong-minded, there was no doubt that a horrible fate awaited the German Jews sent to the East, possibly excepting those sent to Theresienstadt, which the Germans portrayed as a "privileged" place of "resettlement" for elderly or eminent German Jews. Well into the last years of the war, the Nazis successfully deluded most remaining German Jews into believing that this ghetto in the former territory of Czechoslovakia was a relatively benign, self-governing Jewish community whose residents were safe from further deportation. The reality was far grimmer. Although Theresienstadt was not itself a death camp, most of the German Jews sent there either died from disease and privation or later were transported to the killing camps in Poland.

Dr. Hermann Pineas, who was director of the hospital's neuropsychiatry department from 1939 to 1943 until he and his wife went underground, was among those who perceived very early what was going on. He lived in the same house as another Jewish doctor, Jules Moses, who had been a Social Democratic member of the Reichstag during the Weimar government. In 1941 Moses showed Pineas a letter that one of Moses's former Reichstag col-

leagues, who was not Jewish, had received from yet another former Social Democratic Party member who was serving in the
army on the eastern front. The letter described atrocities perpetrated in Russian towns, where the writer had witnessed Jewish
women being forced to dig their own graves. Lined up with their
children, they then were shot in front of the graves they had dug.
Although the details of genocide directed at deported German
Jews, and especially the gassings in the death camps, were not yet
known, what Dr. Pineas read in that letter and what he shortly
thereafter heard directly from an Aryan friend who had been at
the front alerted him to the true nature of the deportations and
led him and his wife, two years later, to make the fateful decision
to go into hiding.

Over the course of time, as similar stories about German
atrocities in the East filtered back from German troops, knowledge about the terrible fate that awaited Jewish deportees became
increasingly diffused among both Jews and non-Jews. So too,
with the passage of time, did the Nazis' approach to the deportation of Berlin Jews become more and more openly brutal. By
1943 the Nazis largely had given up the pretense of "resettlement" and, with the decreasing supply of Jews to be deported,
had abandoned medical exemptions. In 1941, however, a veneer
of bureaucratic regularity helped maintain the fiction that Berlin's Jews were merely being resettled to segregate them from the
Aryan population and give them an opportunity to rehabilitate
themselves through labor.

The deportation process proceeded, in an eerily bureaucratic
fashion, largely through the instrumentality of the *Gemeinde/
Reichsvereinigung*. The Jewish authorities were required to compile lists of Berlin Jews from the communal records and then to
select from those lists the names of individuals to fill the number
required for a rail transport to the East, usually around one thousand. Transports left Berlin at the rate of about one a week. The
housing office of the *Gemeinde* would send notices by mail to the
selected deportees informing them that they were required to

vacate their rooms or apartments and that they should pack no more than twenty-five kilos (fifty-five pounds) of luggage and prepare to be picked up for "resettlement" on a date several days in the future. The actual collection of the deportees generally took place at night (presumably to minimize public attention) and was done by a Gestapo officer and an officer of the Berlin Criminal Police. These two officers usually were assisted by one or more Jewish (usually half-Jewish) *Ordner*, or police auxiliaries, supplied by the *Gemeinde*. In using Jewish *Ordner* to help in the roundups, the Gestapo was applying a technique that came to be widely used in the occupied countries and in the death camps. However, although there are accounts of Jewish *Ordner* who behaved cruelly toward their fellow Jews, especially in the death camps, accounts of the Berlin deportations generally do not suggest that the Berlin *Ordner* behaved with any degree of conspicuous cruelty.

The deportees were loaded into closed trucks; furniture vans were often used for this purpose. They were driven to a *Sammellager* and held there until the Gestapo had assembled the entire quota required to fill the transport. This could be a time-consuming process, since not every Jew notified of impending deportation was prepared to wait passively until the Gestapo came. Some ran away and went underground, trying to survive in hiding. Others killed themselves, or at least attempted to.

The *Sammellager* were set up in buildings confiscated from the Jewish community, starting with the Levetzowstrasse Synagogue and later including a former Jewish old age home on Grosse Hamburgerstrasse and several other Jewish community buildings throughout the city. There, out of sight of the public, the Jews were held, often for several days, in crowded conditions of great discomfort, with inadequate food and sanitary facilities and a lack of beds or even chairs on which to sit. The *Gemeinde* was required to provide food for them. The principal agent in this regard was the *Jüdischer Frauenbund*, or Jewish Women's League, which made sandwiches in a former Jewish school under close Gestapo supervision using food supplies that the Gestapo meted out in ungenerous proportions. These women, many of them wives of *Gemeinde/Reichsvereinigung* officials, numbered about forty at the beginning. As the deportations took their toll, the number shrank, and only about eight were serving in 1942, when the Gestapo put an end to the role of the *Frauenbund* in preparing food for deportees. Staff members recall that the hospital's kitchen was often called upon to provide sandwiches for deportees, especially as time went on and the membership of the *Frauenbund* dwindled. After the Gestapo cut off the *Frauenbund* in 1942, the hospital's kitchen became the principal source of food for Jews who were in the process of being deported.

The hospital was intimately involved in the deportations in several ways. When, on Yom Kippur 1941, the leaders of the *Gemeinde/Reichsvereinigung* received orders to cooperate in establishing a *Sammellager* in the Levetzowstrasse Synagogue, one of the first steps was to establish a first-aid unit there staffed with doctors and nurses from the hospital. This activity continued throughout the deportations, with the hospital providing doctors and nurses to do medical inspections in the *Sammellager* and to provide first aid at the railroad stations when the deportees were being loaded into trains for their journey.

The most tragic aspect of the hospital's involvement in the deportations began soon after the first transports, when the Gestapo started to require that the hospital furnish doctors and nurses to accompany the transports on the journey to the East. While ostensibly this was an assignment only to perform medical duties, it soon became clear that it probably was a death sentence, since none of the nurses and doctors assigned to accompany a transport ever returned.

The Nazis' involvement of medical personnel in the deportation process was not from benevolent motives. Everything was driven by one purpose, to effect the elimination of the Jews as rapidly as possible and at the lowest cost to the German government. The inclusion of doctors and nurses aboard the transports seems to have been done partly to eliminate Jewish medical personnel. Probably the main rationale, however, was that the presence of Jewish doctors and nurses at the collection points, on the railroad platforms, and to some degree in the transports themselves was a way of bolstering the false impression that the deportations were in fact a "resettlement" program. In reality, given the crowded and chaotic conditions that prevailed, there was little effective medical help that the doctors and nurses could provide either aboard the trains or after arrival in the camps. Their presence, however, might have calmed the deportees' fears and helped keep them docile, thus enabling relatively small numbers of SS, Gestapo, and police officers to keep control over large numbers of frightened Jews.

Herta Pineas, Dr. Pineas's wife, worked in the food supply service of the *Frauenbund* and often found herself in the *Sammellager* or on the station platform distributing food. She describes a Jewish doctor of her acquaintance whom she encountered at the railroad station. He was dressed in his summer coat and straw hat for a journey that was taking place in the winter. He had been arrested in the summer for listening to a foreign radio station and was being brought from prison, presumably in the clothes he had been wearing when arrested, to become the physician assigned to a transport. A neurologist, he was given a small box of instruments and medication that had been brought from his apartment. Mrs. Pineas comments bitterly on how little this doctor, a specialist without much experience in emergency medicine and furnished with inadequate and inappropriate supplies, would be able to care for someone who collapsed from exhaustion on the platform.

In December 1941 the Gestapo ordered the *Gemeinde/Reichsvereinigung* health department to establish a *Transportreklamationstelle* (transport claims service), a board to examine claims that Jews were too ill to be deported. This activity, under Lustig's direction, engaged the hospital until the end of 1942, when the Nazis halted medical deferments, and it constitutes perhaps one of the most complex and haunting passages in the hospital's wartime history. Accounts of the deferment process have been left by two of the secretaries who recorded the board's findings and recommendations, Hildegarde Henschel and Hilde Kahan.

In the perception of Hilde Kahan, whose roles as one of the board's secretaries and as Lustig's personal assistant gave her an intimate view of the deferment process, the German government had no moral scruples about deporting the ill and bedridden, on stretchers if need be. She attributed the authorities' action to the difficulties of transporting seriously ill people, not to humanitarian feelings. But difficulties of transportation may not have been the only reason for allowing medical deferments; indeed, that probably was not the real reason at all. On its face, the deferment program seems at odds with other Nazi policies. While it is not entirely clear how the Nazis decided which Jews should be deported earlier rather than later, in general it appears that an underlying aim was to get rid of the sick and aged first, leaving behind — at least temporarily — those Jews whose labor could contribute to the war effort. Thus, granting medical deferments contradicted the objective of deporting those incapable of working. However, the propaganda value of the deferment program vis-à-vis the Jews outweighed its costs. Exemptions were to be granted only in the most severe cases and were unlikely to add up to a significant number. There were still more than 160,000 Jews in Germany when the deportations started, a number large enough to permit a few deferments for exemplary purposes without really affecting the flow of Jews toward the East.

Making the Jews believe that seriously ill people would not be transported contributed to the Nazis' ability to hide the true nature of the deportations and thus prevent Jewish resistance. So, too, did the existence of a medical review procedure carried out by Jews and therefore necessarily more humane, even under unfavorable conditions, than if it had been conducted by Nazi officials. It is not surprising that, by the time a year had passed, the medical deferment possibility had disappeared in the face of several changes in circumstances. One was that the nature of the deportations had become much clearer to Berlin's Jews, as tens of thousands of their friends and relatives disappeared and were not heard from again. Another was that the supply of Jews to be deported was becoming smaller. Large numbers of Jews were "cheating" the Nazis by committing suicide or going underground. Consequently, it was not as easy to find another person to fill the place on a transport that might have been vacated by a Jew granted a medical deferment. Against the preeminent imperative of keeping the trains filled, any small advantage derived from granting medical deferments had to give way. In addition, as time went on, the attitude of the German authorities to the Jews and the way they treated them became increasingly harsh, perhaps stimulated by the indifference the German public showed to the disappearance of their Jewish neighbors, possibly also by Nazi contempt for the ease with which Germany's Jews had been induced to cooperate in their own destruction.

The offices of the medical examination board were situated in the *Schwesternheim*, the nurses' residence of the hospital. The board was staffed by six physicians from the hospital, six secretaries, and six assistant nurses. The doctors represented a broad range of specialties. Two additional doctors visited bedridden patients who were too sick to come to the hospital. In the evening they would return and dictate their findings. If the initial result supported deferring the deportation, the bedridden patient had to be brought to the hospital by ambulance for a second, official examination.

The workload of the board was overwhelming because, according to Hildegarde Henschel, "the Gestapo was behind in the processing of cases." As a result, the board worked from 8:00 A.M. to 11:00 P.M. Everything was done with Germanic order and precision. The doctors' findings were reduced to written reports typed in triplicate. The original went to the Gestapo, one copy was filed in the board's registry at the hospital, and the other was sent to the *Gemeinde* headquarters on Oranienburgerstrasse. The two possible outcomes of the examination were no objection to deportation or a recommendation for a three-month delay. Dr. Lustig had to approve all recommendations for delay, and he personally examined each patient in that category.

On occasion, Henschel says, the examination resulted in the applicant's being admitted to the hospital for treatment or even for an operation to render him or her more mobile or able to work. If this was the case, it must reflect how little the hospital's staff understood, in the period from October 1941 to late 1942, about the fate that awaited the Jews in the East. Perhaps the saddest sentence in all of Henschel's description of the board's work is the comment that pregnant women could be exempted from deportation only if they were at the point of giving birth. Even then, after six weeks the mother and newborn infant were sent on a transport.

In a curiously unreflective appraisal of the board and its work, Henschel seems to take pride in the bureaucratic correctness of the proceedings: "I was a secretary and never was able to find any irregularities," she boasts, apparently oblivious to the hellish nature of the task the board was asked to perform. Hilde Kahan's recollections of her parallel experiences reflect a clearer view of what was going on. She describes the burden of work as overwhelming, but she attributes it, more plausibly, to the desperation that gripped Berlin's Jews once the deportations began. To the vast majority, even the miseries to which they had been reduced seemed preferable to being uprooted and sent to an unknown fate in a foreign country. Anyone who had any hope of making a case for medical deferment applied for one, and the board conscientiously examined each such application. The cases poured in. At times, as many as thirty ambulances stood in the street outside the hospital waiting for applicants who had been brought in on stretchers for their medical examinations.

For Kahan, the board's work was anguishing. It counted among her most terrible memories.

During the medical examinations, we had, in the presence of the patient, to write our findings for the Gestapo, after the doctor whispered the results of his individual examination to us. Nothing was left undone, no special examination was missed, if one could hope for a result that was favorable for the future of the sick person. Blind people came and cripples, epileptics and people suffering from tuberculosis, and on account of the large number they had to be standing for hours waiting for their examination. It was most hard when we had to go through the waiting areas and were seen by friends and acquaintances who pleaded with us to do something for them, although they knew themselves how powerless we were in the face of this devilish work.

Applying for a medical deferment was obviously an act of desperation. Many who did so must have known that their medical condition probably was not bad enough to warrant a deferment but hoped that the Jewish personnel who staffed the review board would be sympathetic enough to give an exaggerated report that would sustain a deferment. Was the medical board in fact entirely powerless, or did the doctors find ways to help people avoid deportation?

Henschel hints that the latter may have taken place on occasion. She describes Lustig as having "conscientiously tried to take an interest in those scheduled to be evacuated. He knew how to prevent the Gestapo from learning that the [medical examination] section worked in the interest of the Jews." She attributes his ability to deceive the authorities to his "possibly too intimate" contact with the Gestapo. It was Lustig who appeared with the board's medical report and recommendations, and it was rare that the Gestapo reached a decision that did not reflect the medical board's recommendations.

Some Jewish doctors may have resorted to unnecessary surgery to help patients escape, or at least postpone, deportation. The number of operations performed in the hospital in 1941 reached an all-time high. And there is some evidence that bogus or unnecessary operations were performed after the deportations had started. For example, the hospital's ophthalmologist, Dr. Hirschfeld, who was known to have helped Jews living "underground," performed an unusually large number of eye operations after the deportations began — twice as many in December 1941 as his earlier monthly average.

But if any altering of the truth was done in the interest of saving Jews from deportation, it could only have been carried out on a limited and circumscribed basis. As Hilde Kahan remarks, "The Gestapo's guidelines were very rigorous and cruel." Everything that went on in the *Gemeinde/Reichsvereinigung* and its subsidiary units was under constant Gestapo surveillance. Moreover, in many cases Aryan government doctors were called upon to give a second opinion when the Jewish board had recommended a deferment. Lustig and his colleagues surely knew that any significant and discernible departures from honest diagnoses stood a great chance of being detected. Detection would likely have spelled the end of a Jewish-staffed medical review board and probably would have led to the immediate deportation of the doctors and nurses involved. Thus the board's staff had every incentive to ensure the probity of their work, both for reasons of personal safety and to preserve the activity itself. Yet even those, like Hildegarde Henschel, who ended up describing Lustig in the most pejorative terms, seem to have believed that in some fashion Lustig contrived to skew the proceedings so as to preserve at least some Jews from immediate deportation and managed to keep the Gestapo from finding out what he had done. None of those who were involved suggest that, in doing so, Lustig acted out of venal motives. It is in this light that one must understand two of Mrs. Henschel's statements that otherwise would appear inconsistent. On the one hand, she says that Lustig exploited his close ties to the Gestapo in favor of the people scheduled for deportation and, on the other hand, that there were no "irregularities" in the board's proceedings. By "irregularity" she must mean a distortion of the patient's medical status committed for a corrupt reason instead of a benevolent purpose.

By the end of 1942 the work of the medical review board was at an end, for several reasons. In May 1942, an order was issued prohibiting Jews from using public transportation. The only exception was that Jews with jobs more than seven kilometers (slightly over four miles) from their homes could get special permission to use public transit to travel to and from work. However, this exception did not permit the hospital's staff to travel by bus, tram, or rail to visit patients in their homes, and the availability of ambulance services for Jews had been drastically curtailed. Thus examinations of bedridden patients who were confined at home virtually ceased. Moreover, despite the limited delays resulting from the medical deferment program, the Nazis had been busy dragging off the elderly and infirm. By the end of 1942, most of the remaining Jewish population in Berlin consisted of able-bodied people who were performing forced labor in war production factories.

The desperation that led hundreds of Jews to besiege the medical board with claims for exemption also gave rise to an unprecedented wave of suicide attempts. The rate of suicides rose dramatically as time went on, peaking at the height of the deportations in late 1942 and early 1943. Bruno Blau estimates that as many as one-quarter of all Jewish deaths within Berlin in 1942–43 were due to suicide. As many as seven thousand Jews killed themselves in Berlin during this period. One hospital nurse remembers that information about the true character of the death camps began to become known to Berlin Jews in about 1942:

> Until then one imagined life in a ghetto — that was where the transports were allegedly sent to — to be harder because of less food, less accommodation and other physical hardships. After the news about the camps seeped through the rate of suicides went up terribly always about two or three days before a transport was due to leave. There was a well-organised black market in opium and other lethal drugs.

Although Jews killed themselves in all sorts of ways, by far the predominant method was the ingestion of a poison such as potas-

sium cyanide or an overdose of an opiate or sedative, most often Veronal. However, these measures did not necessarily bring
about immediate death. While thousands died in their homes, in
many cases the patient lapsed into unconsciousness but lingered
long enough to be given medical attention. Some could be revived, and some no doubt took an amount insufficient to kill
them. Indeed, *Schwester* Carry, remembering the onslaught of
suicide cases, concludes that many Jews who attempted suicide
were ambivalent about whether they really wanted to die. Some
took an overdose in the hope that it would ward off deportation
and somehow ameliorate their situation without actually leading
to death.

> At that time we had beds all in the hall, on both sides. You could
> barely pass. Absolutely everywhere you put your foot was a bed with
> somebody who had tried to commit suicide. The poor people; they
> didn't really want to die. I mean they wanted to escape the deporta-
> tion. Of course, I can see that. But anybody who commits suicide and
> wants to die and asks the nurse to close the window or she'll get
> pneumonia, cannot really mean it. . . . I mean, deep in the heart.

At the height of the deportations, all the available beds were
full. Then the hallways filled up with suicide cases on stretchers. Finally, additional patients on stretchers had to be placed in
the bathhouse. In some cases it was not immediately apparent
whether the patients were dead or alive. The staff pumped their
stomachs, only to discover in many cases that they had already
died.

The suicide victims who arrived at the hospital with a chance
for survival posed an acute dilemma for the staff. The Nazis were
determined that no Jew should deprive them of the opportunity
to commit murder on their own schedule. Attempted suicide was
therefore a crime. Any patient who was saved had to be transferred to the locked police ward to recuperate and, when able to
be transported, was then transferred to the *Sammellager* and deported to the East.

Doctors and nurses were tempted to allow the suicide victims, especially those who were unconscious and not in agony, to die in peace. However, two considerations militated against doing this. One was the Hippocratic oath; the other was fear of the Gestapo. In the end, different staff members found different solutions. One nurse never withheld treatment from a suicide patient because she felt that her professional responsibility was to preserve life regardless of who the patient was. In addition, in the case of young patients, she had the hope that they would survive the concentration camp. Other doctors and nurses embraced the same view regarding young patients. One describes an incident in which she revived a sixteen-year-old boy who had taken sleeping pills. When he awoke, she exhorted him to try to survive and extracted from him a promise to do so. There seems little doubt, on the other hand, that on occasion doctors and nurses surreptitiously withheld treatment from older suicide victims and let them die. Obviously, no records were kept of such occurrences, so it is impossible to estimate how often this happened.

As time passed, the increasing harshness of the Nazis' measures against Berlin's Jews alleviated the hospital of some of the burden imposed by suicide cases — not because Jews stopped committing suicide, but because the ambulance services stopped providing services to Jews, thus making it impossible for many critical cases to be brought to the hospital. Hilde Kahan remembers, as one of the most harrowing of her experiences during a long litany of horrors, a specific suicide case that shook her immensely, for, as she says, "although we had seen such a terrible degree of unhappiness, we were not completely numbed."

She received a call from a man who wanted an ambulance sent for his widowed mother. Scheduled for deportation, the old woman had been out of the house when the police came to pick her up the preceding day, but neighbors had told her what had happened. That evening, preferring to die in her familiar surroundings, she had taken poison, probably an overdose of Veronal. She was lying in their apartment unconscious. Ambulance services having been cut off for Jews, the only available transport was an old truck that had belonged to the Jewish *Gemeinde* and formerly had been used for transporting files. Now, it was fitted out with a stretcher, and the hospital used it as a makeshift ambulance, when they could get hold of it; the Gestapo had confiscated it for use by the *Sammellager* and made it available only on specific occasions. In order for the hospital to obtain access to the truck, the Gestapo had to be supplied with an attestation of medical necessity by a *Krankenbehandler*. With such an attestation in hand, the hospital usually had to wait several hours to get the truck, even in cases of accidents.

Kahan gave the son the address of a *Krankenbehandler* in his neighborhood and told him that the *Krankenbehandler* could give the necessary attestation by telephone to speed things up. Throughout the day, the son called the hospital repeatedly and spoke to Kahan. Clearly conflicted, he did not summon the *Krankenbehandler*, but he wanted to report that his mother still lingered in life, unconscious, and to talk about his fear that if he got medical help for her she might be revived and then suffer more severely at the Nazis' hands. Kahan warned him that the hospital's telephones were often bugged and that he could be putting himself in danger of a murder prosecution by what he was saying. Nonetheless, the man persisted in sharing his agony with her over the telephone, until finally he called in the afternoon to report that the old woman had died.

Thus, remarks Kahan, a file was closed that failed even to get a transport number.

6

THE ASSAULT ON THE *GEMEINDE*
AND THE HOSPITAL, 1942–43

OCTOBER 20, 1942. In the early morning dark, hundreds of Jews, prohibited from using the streetcars, the S-Bahn and the U-Bahn, could be seen making their way through the streets of Berlin. Only the yellow stars sewn to their coats over the left breast provided a note of color in the monochromatic dawn scene. On Gestapo orders, they were on their way to the *Gemeinde* building on Oranienburgerstrasse.

Already, earlier in the year, the senior officials of the *Gemeinde* and the *Reichsvereinigung* had been warned. The shrinking number of Jews left in Berlin no longer warranted maintaining the staffs of the communal organizations, including the hospital, at current levels. Since then, each transport to the concentration camps had included a certain number of employees of the *Gemeinde/Reichsvereinigung*, slowly reducing the size of those organizations. Now, however, the ax was about to fall on a grand scale. The *Gemeinde* had sent orders to all Jewish communal employees to assemble at the *Gemeinde* offices at 7:00 A.M. sharp. The employees were warned that the only acceptable excuse for failing to appear was serious illness attested to by a doctor's certificate and that anyone who justified absence on the basis of a doctor's certificate would be subjected to a second medical examination (presumably by the Gestapo's own medical staff). Such strict orders could only have resulted from heavy pressure from the German authorities.

The bulk of the employees who gathered that morning in the offices on Oranienburgerstrasse, some three hundred in number, worked for the old age home, the health department of the *Gemeinde/Reichsvereinigung*, or the hospital. Among them was Walter Lustig. Only a skeleton staff had been left behind at the hospital to care for the patients.

As 7:00 A.M. came and went, hundreds of men and women milled around in the main meeting room of the Oranienburger-strasse offices, but no one arrived from the Gestapo or the SS. The frightened Jews waited for hours. Knowing that the threat of disaster hung over them, their distress mounted as the hours passed. Finally, at about 1:00 P.M., a commotion was heard in the hallway. SS *Sturmbahnführer* Günther, accompanied by other SS officers, came into the room "like a whirlwind," Hilde Kahan says. He turned to Walter Lustig.

"One hundred people must be deported. You choose them."

Lustig demurred.

Günther pulled a young girl with blond hair out of the crowd and sent her to the side of the room. Her only crime, apparently, was looking too Aryan. Then he singled out a number of obviously disabled or crippled employees and sent them to the same place. Then he began calling out names. People answered in "voices muted by fear." The people whose names were called had to line up in a corner of the room. According to one account, as Günther called out names, he shouted accusations of wrongdoing:

"Yesterday you were in the street without your star."

"You used the streetcar."

After Günther had pulled a handful of victims from the crowd in this fashion, he turned to Lustig. "That's how it's done," Günther said. "Can you do the rest?" This time Lustig complied. From among his fellow employees and colleagues he selected the remaining names until the list came to ninety-nine. Then the

Gestapo man himself chose the last person. It was Dr. Schönfeld, who had been serving as the hospital's director. Any lingering doubt as to the fate of the one hundred individuals who had been selected was quickly dispelled when Günther told them to go home and prepare to leave in a few days on a transport to the East. That meant Auschwitz, they knew, rather than Theresienstadt.

Everyone knew that each of these people, together with all of his or her immediate family members still living in Berlin, was doomed. Berlin Jews still thought that, if "lucky," they would be sent to the "privileged" ghetto at Theresienstadt. Transport to Auschwitz meant disappearance into a silence that it was becoming increasingly clear meant death.

After the selection, the entire group was dismissed. Those who had escaped selection — this time — went back to work. The unlucky communal employees returned home to prepare for the transport. Before they left, the SS issued a threat: if anyone on the deportation list failed to report at the assigned time and place, hostages would be taken and punished and another employee would be chosen to take his or her place. Notwithstanding these warnings, in the next several days eighteen of those assigned to the list disappeared into hiding. As a result, eight communal leaders — four officials of the *Gemeinde* and four members of the *Reichsvereinigung* board — were taken and summarily shot. In addition, eighteen more *Gemeinde* employees were chosen for the transports to take the place of the men and women who had gone into hiding.

Dr. Schönfeld left Oranienburgerstrasse and went home. There he and his wife killed themselves. The Gestapo appointed Walter Lustig to take his place as the hospital's director and chief of medicine.

The deportation of the one hundred *Gemeinde* and *Reichsvereinigung* officials in October 1942 was the second major deportation of communal officials. A similar mass arrest and deportation had occurred on June 19, 1942. On that date, the Gestapo had occupied the *Reichsvereinigung* headquarters building on Oranien-burgerstrasse at 8:00 A.M. Some fifty employees arrived late for work and were arrested, apparently on that basis alone. Then another fifty were designated for deportation. Some senior officials were included in this group, but the highest levels of the organization, the members of the *Vorstand,* or governing body, including most notably Rabbi Baeck, were not taken. Months after these two 1942 raids, in January 1943, the role of the *Gemeinde* and the *Reichsvereinigung* as entities even remotely representing the interests of the Jewish community effectively came to an end when the three senior officials, Leo Baeck, Paul Eppstein, and Philipp Kozower, were deported to Theresienstadt, together with their families. With Leo Baeck no longer in Berlin, no one could view the communal organizations as anything more than instruments of the Nazi authorities.

The *Gemeinde* continued in nominal existence until June 10, 1943. On that date, both it and the *Reichsvereinigung* were formally declared dissolved by the German authorities. The *Reichsvereinigung* soon was revived de facto, although not in formal terms, when the Nazis discovered that they still had a use for it. The *Gemeinde,* however, was gone for the rest of the Nazi period; it was reestablished only after the liberation of Berlin. Of the preexisting structure of the Jewish communal organizations, only one department remained in operation, the health department, and only one senior official passed unscathed through the succession of arrests and deportations, its head, Walter Lustig.

The reality was that for some time Lustig, as head of the health department of the *Gemeinde/Reichsvereinigung,* had been the effective master of the hospital — or, more accurately, the chosen channel through which the RSHA and Gestapo directed the hospital's affairs. Other than in the October 1942 roundup, it is not known how much of a part, if any, he played in choosing deportees before his appointment as director. It is hard to believe, however, that he played none.

Berlin's Jews gave a name to each major raid or roundup (the German term was *Aktion,* meaning an action or operation). The brutal October 1942 assault on the remaining structures of the organized Jewish community came to be known as the *Gemeindeaktion,* or community raid. It seriously depleted most of the nonmedical departments of the *Gemeinde* and the *Reichsvereinigung,* a process that continued in the succeeding weeks and months as individual employees received their notices for the transports. Although members of the hospital's staff continued to be included in the deportations, a higher percentage of them were spared, presumably because the Nazis still viewed the hospital as providing an essential service. Thus, as the months went by, the hospital's staff came to comprise an increasingly large percentage of the total remaining work force of the *Gemeinde/Reichsvereinigung.* The hospital was moving into the function it ultimately would have as the headquarters of what remained of Berlin's Jews, indeed of all German Jewry, and Lustig was entering into his role as the "one-man *Judenrat*" (Jewish leadership council) of all Germany.

Lustig's ascendancy to the directorship of both the hospital and the *Reichsvereinigung* brought into prominence two men who were to serve as his principal aides from then until the end of the war. One was Selmar Neumann, a nonphysician who acted as the hospital's administrative director. Little is known about Neumann's background. The other was Ehrich (also sometimes called "Erich," the latter being the more Germanic spelling of his forename) Zwilsky, who became Lustig's principal aide in running the *Reichsvereinigung.* Zwilsky was a pharmacist who was born in Landsberg in East Prussia. He was trained at the University of Königsberg in East Prussia, was employed there in a pharmacy, and then moved to Berlin in 1931. He worked for a non-Jewish pharmacy owner in Berlin until January 31, 1939, when his employer reluctantly fired him because he was Jewish, furnishing him with a glowing letter of recommendation. After many months of unemployment, Zwilsky obtained a job as an office worker for the Jewish *Gemeinde*. In January 1941, he transferred to the health department of the *Reichsvereinigung*.

The hospital that remained after the *Gemeindeaktion* was still a functioning medical institution, but its strength had been significantly sapped. Even before the October 1942 roundup, it had been deprived of some of its strongest doctors as the result of emigration and deportations.

Professor Martin Jacoby was formerly head of the Chemical Institute at the Moabit Hospital, one of Berlin's leading medical institutions, until he had to leave because he was Jewish. He served as head of the hospital's Institute for Physiological Chemistry from 1934 until he emigrated in 1939. Professor Paul Rosenstein was a longtime medical leader at the hospital and also a prominent figure in German medicine. He became director of the hospital's surgical outpatient clinic in 1919 and in 1923 was made director of the surgical department. He had had a distinguished career as a urologist, serving until 1933 as president of the Berlin Urological Association and as an editor of Germany's *Journal of Urological Surgery*. Dr. Rosenstein immigrated to Brazil in 1938. Professor Paul Schuster was fired in 1933 from his job as director of the neurology department of Berlin's Hufeland-Hospitals and became a doctor in the hospital's outpatient department and director of the neurology department. He emigrated in 1939.

The foregoing are only a few examples; the list was much longer. A 1938 photograph published in *Zerstörte Fortschritte* neatly sums up the situation. It shows a smiling Dr. Rosenstein with a group of happy-looking doctors and nurses. They are identified as Dr. Angress, about to immigrate to the United States; nurse Bella Baruth, about to immigrate to the United States; Dr. Herbert Jarwitz, immigrating to Palestine; nurse Lili Siedner-Cohn, headed for Palestine; male nurse Heinz Milwitzki, also about to immigrate to Palestine; nurse Edith Löwenberg, bound for South Africa; Dr. Werner Fliesser, departing for the United States; Dr. Fritz Landsberg, about to immigrate to England; and Dr. Kurt Hirsch, heading for the United States. Only three in the group have no place of immigration designated. About one of them no information seems to be known other than that she was Frau Dr. Broniakowsi. The other two, Georg Goldschmidt, a male nurse, and Dr. Erich Fischer, Professor Rosenstein's principal assistant, remained at the hospital. They were destined to be deported to Theresienstadt and from there to Auschwitz, where both met their deaths.

The pace of emigration slowed substantially after the German government banned Jewish emigration in October 1941, but even as late as 1942 and 1943 some of the hospital's doctors managed to leave Germany, while others stole away into underground existence.

Perhaps the most notable loss was the revered Professor Hermann Strauss, who had been chief of medicine at the hospital since 1910. Still active in his seventies, Dr. Strauss had long been one of the ornaments both of the hospital and of German medicine. He had been appointed "extraordinary" professor of internal medicine at Berlin University in 1902. His numerous scientific contributions covered a broad range of fields, including the study of kidney diseases, gastroenterology, proctology, diabetes, and dietetics. He was the inventor of the procedure for flexible sigmoidoscopy using insufflation (inflating the sigmoid colon with air) that still is practiced today. One of his interests was physiotherapy, especially spa therapy, which he recommended for rheumatic and similar diseases. When the new hospital was being built in the Wedding district, he was instrumental in ensuring that it included what was then a state-of-the-art physical therapy department.

In July 1942, Strauss was deported to Theresienstadt, where he died a few months before the end of the war. The circumstances of his deportation are unclear, except that it directly resulted from a confrontation either with the Nazi authorities or with a German soldier in the subway, depending on whose ac-

count one believes. The circumstances of his death also are con-
troverted. Many believed that he committed suicide upon being
selected for transport to Auschwitz, but Bruno Blau states that
this report was false and that Strauss died of natural causes. An
unpublished biographical essay that appears to be by a relative attributes his death to a heart attack.

Dr. Strauss was probably the most illustrious physician on the
hospital's staff. His character and fortitude served as an example
to others even after he himself had been removed physically from
the scene. Like Leo Baeck, he declined numerous opportunities
to emigrate. In an obituary erroneously written in 1942 on the
basis of a false newspaper report that Dr. Strauss had killed himself, his former assistant chief of internal medicine at the hospital,
Dr. Conrad Gossels, then in America, described Strauss in the
period after 1938 as providing an inspiration to his colleagues
through the resolute way he rose above the increasing difficulties
imposed by the Nazi regime and devoted himself to his medical
practice. Strauss's deportation left the hospital's internal medicine department bereft of its two leading doctors, since Dr.
Gossels had himself departed Berlin for the United States in the
early months of 1941.

The effect these departures had on the hospital is bleakly described by *Schwester* Carry, who left her job at the hospital in July
1942 when she learned that she had been assigned to "accompany" a transport to the East. She had noticed that no one ever
had returned from such an assignment and sensibly declined to
obey orders. Instead, she quit her job, went to the Nazis' Jewish
Labor Bureau, and asked for a forced labor assignment in a factory. In February 1943 she was warned by her boss about an
impending SS roundup of Jewish forced laborers (discussed in
Chapter 8). She and her husband then went underground. They
survived in hiding for more than two years until the war ended.

In *Schwester* Carry's eyes, although the hospital once had been
a preeminent medical institution, emigration had left it no longer

on a par with other Berlin hospitals "because they didn't have the right doctors anymore."

"A lot of the very able doctors with money," she continues, "had already left the country — for somewhere. And the doctors that were left were not the cream of the crop. We had a surgeon; he was chief surgeon. Whenever we admitted a gall bladder . . . we were sad and worried for the poor patient because she was a goner — or he."

The hospital's chief neuropsychologist, Dr. Hermann Pineas, also believed that the quality of the hospital and other communal services was deteriorating, but he put the blame on the Gestapo: "At the end, it was the tactic of the Gestapo to arrest and deport the most capable employees from the departments of the community administration, and thus the level of performance inevitably had to sink."

Regardless of the reasons (and the causes undoubtedly were multiple), the fact is clear that the hospital's staff was dwindling over time. At earlier points during the Nazi period, losses through emigration had been easily compensated by drawing on the large pool of unemployed and highly qualified Jewish doctors in Berlin. By 1942 this was no longer the case. The supply of skilled Jewish physicians in the city working outside the hospital had substantially dried up as a result of emigration, deportation, and, of course, suicides. As time went on and legal emigration became impossible, the staff also suffered diminution as key doctors and nurses decided that their chances of survival would be better underground. The risks and privations of illegal existence seemed preferable to relying, where applicable, on the fact that one's spouse was Aryan or on the hope that one's services would continue to be viewed as essential enough to keep one's name off the next deportation list. They all knew that after the next list there would be another, and yet another after that.

Schwester Carry, as we have seen, saw the light when she was assigned in July 1942 to a transport, ostensibly as a medical aide, not a deportee. Dr. Pineas's epiphany came when Leo Baeck, who had been his religious teacher, was deported in January 1943. A few weeks before he left, Dr. Else Levy, who had been in charge of the ear-nose-throat department, went into hiding. She never was heard from again and presumably died while living underground. Dr. Hans Knopp, as a half-Jew, might have escaped deportation, but he decided to take no chances. In 1942 he slipped away and returned to his hometown of Mainz, where he managed to hide until the end of the war. Bruno Blau describes how the radiologist who successfully treated him for cancer disappeared one day along with his assistant. They made it all the way to the Swiss border, where they prepared to sneak across into Switzerland with a group of Jews who were escaping Germany. After successfully getting across the border, the radiologist turned back to help another member of the group who had lagged behind. The result of this act of kindness was that both the radiologist and his assistant were arrested by the border police and taken back to Berlin. At police headquarters in Berlin both swallowed poison. The doctor died immediately; his assistant lingered for a while at the hospital before she died. Another of the radiological assistants who treated Blau also committed suicide, in particularly anguishing circumstances. Her father had been a famous Berlin doctor. She and her brother both worked at the hospital, he as a male nursing assistant. One day the brother disappeared. The young woman feared that she would be arrested as a hostage for his return and eventually deported in retaliation for her brother's disappearance. So, without waiting to see what would happen, she killed herself. The brother survived the war living underground.

There were numerous other suicides among the hospital staff. Writing to Conrad Gossels shortly after the end of the war, Meta Cohen, the wife of Dr. Helmuth Cohen, listed fourteen staff members who had killed themselves in the 1942–43 period, including at least two doctors and many nurses. Some had committed suicide together with their spouses, in one case together with the entire family. Although the percentage of suicides among the hospital staff seems to have been somewhat lower than the epidemic level among Berlin Jews in general, it was sufficient to exacerbate the personnel shortages.

One apparent suicide case turned out not to be real. The putative victim was one of the nurses, a close friend of *Schwester* Carry's and for a time her roommate in the *Schwesternheim*. The nurse had been carrying on an affair with Dr. Schönfeld, the hospital's director, who was a married man. The young woman mounted an elaborate and convincing charade. She disappeared, but she left behind a suicide note and drug paraphernalia, including a syringe. The note indicated that she had taken a fatal dose of drugs in despair over her frustrated love affair with Dr. Schönfeld and had then gone off to die somewhere else. Those who read the note assumed that she had hidden herself after the fatal injection so that she would not be found in time to be revived. In fact, however, she had run away to take up an underground existence, profiting from the notoriety of her relationship with Dr. Schönfeld to put on a show that might convince the Gestapo not to bother looking for her. The drama was enough to convince her friend Carry, who was grief stricken. It also appears to have persuaded the Gestapo. In any event, the young woman managed to survive in hiding. Ironically, not too long after the nurse disappeared, the *Gemeindeaktion* took place, and it was Dr. Schönfeld and his wife who really committed suicide.

By the end of 1942, in addition to the loss of Dr. Strauss, deportations had deprived the hospital of several of its principal remaining doctors. Among them were the famous dermatologist, Dr. Abraham Buschke; Dr. Oskar Rosenberg, the head of pediatrics; and Dr. Erich Fischer, who had become the head of surgery after Professor Rosenstein departed. At the beginning of 1942, the hospital also lost its last remaining handful of non-Jewish employees, among them the midwife Margarete Müller, when the authorities forced them to resign. They had remained loyal to the hospital despite all the Nazi anti-Semitic measures. Now, however, the Nazis would no longer tolerate the presence of non-Jews in the hospital. The sole exception was the chief pharmacist, Erwin Kantelberg, who remained until the end of the war, presumably because the Nazis did not want to have a Jew in control of the hospital's supplies of drugs.

Though weakened by the loss of medical staff, the hospital continued to carry out its traditional medical mission and even added new functions as time went on. For, as the Nazis implacably proceeded during the years 1942 and 1943 to destroy everything else that existed of Jewish medical and social services in Germany, the hospital, as we have seen, became the last repository of the remnants of the patient population these other institutions had served. Similarly, because the Nazis would not allow Jews to be treated in any Aryan hospital, the hospital had to provide new kinds of medical services that it had not traditionally offered.

One new area of activity was psychiatry. As Jewish patients were expelled from non-Jewish mental institutions and Jewish facilities were closed in various parts of Germany, Jewish mental patients were concentrated in a limited number of facilities — those, that is, who had not already been deported or included in the Nazis' secret program of murdering the mentally ill (Jewish and non-Jewish) within Germany. One of the repositories for Jewish mental patients was a Jewish psychiatric asylum in Benndorf-Seyn near Koblenz that the *Reichsvereinigung* had bought from the heirs of its founder, Dr. Jacoby. In June 1942 the Gestapo compelled Lustig to close the Benndorf-Seyn facility and transferred all the patients with foreign nationalities to the hospital. Most of the asylum's staff members were sent straight to a concentration camp, along with the asylum's remaining patients. The director of the asylum, Frau Shiff, and her aged parents accompanied the mental patients who were transferred to

Berlin. Frau Shiff claimed that Lustig had promised that her parents could stay with her at the hospital; however, a few days later the elderly couple were taken to Theresienstadt.

There were about thirty patients who arrived at the hospital from Benndorf-Seyn, mentally ill Jews who held the nationality of some neutral country. At that point, the Gestapo took the position that it would not kill such individuals or deport them to a death camp. As time wore on, these inhibitions disappeared and eventually all the psychiatric patients were deported, but for the moment the hospital was called upon to take them in. Jewish patients from other mental institutions in Germany arrived in July. This influx of psychiatric cases necessitated the opening of a psychiatric ward. With 120 beds, for a time it was the hospital's largest ward.

A similar need arose with respect to children. The hospital already had a pediatric ward for the treatment of sick children. As with mental institutions, however, the Nazis closed orphanages all over Germany. Many of the inhabitants were deported, but some were transferred to the hospital. Notably, in October 1942 the Baruch Auerbach Orphanage in Berlin was closed and all the children were moved to the hospital, which now had to open a *Kinderunterkunft*, or children's shelter, to house them. In December 1942, another sixty-two children and four infants were transferred to the hospital when the asylum in which they had lived was closed.

A quarantine facility was another requirement. Although the hospital had an infectious disease pavilion, it was not equipped to handle quarantine cases. *Schwester* Carry remembers that in 1940 or 1941 she contracted scarlet fever from a patient in one of the open wards. Because the hospital had no quarantine facility, she had to be sent to the *Urban Krankenhaus*, a Catholic institution. A day later another Jewish nurse who had worked on the same floor at the hospital arrived in the bed next to hers, also with scarlet fever.

"They were so nasty to us, so mean. Except for the food, they threw everything at us. . . . We received some mail, they threw it from the distance over onto the bed."

The two women were there during the entire forty-two-day quarantine period for scarlet fever. They were given little or no nursing attention, not because they were in quarantine but because they were Jews. *Schwester* Carry, as was typical with scarlet fever, developed agonizing joint pains. Her roommate was running a high fever. The *Urban Krankenhaus* nurses tossed some ointment and bandages in *Schwester* Carry's direction and left the two women without care. Carry had to crawl out of her bed and sit on the other nurse's bed so that her companion, virtually prostrated by her fever, could rub the ointment on Carry's joints and apply the bandages.

"And after that we made room at the hospital. . . . They must have been told 'don't send us any more Jews; you open your own [quarantine ward].' That's when we opened our own."

In addition to the mass deportations of communal officials and numerous doctors, a second significant event in 1942 was that the authorities compelled the *Reichsvereinigung* to transfer title to the hospital's real estate to the German *Akademie für Jungdmedizin*, or Academy of Youth Medicine. At the time, this legal move must have appeared a disaster to the hospital staff, but in reality it did not result in the hospital's ouster. The spacious grounds and attractive, well-constructed buildings were far too desirable for anyone to allow them actually to fall into the hands of the *Akademie*, an obscure and not particularly influential unit of the Reich's medical bureaucracy. Much more powerful organizations within the Nazi state coveted the property, namely, the RSHA and the Gestapo. As long as the hospital served the interests of either of these organizations, there were strong reasons to allow it to continue to occupy its premises. Indeed, allowing the hospital to remain open for as long as possible clearly served to stave off any claim the *Akademie* might have made that it was entitled to take possession of the hospital complex.

Soon after this transfer of title to the *Akademie*, a portion of the hospital was confiscated and occupied by the Wehrmacht. The buildings housing the gynecology department, the operating room, the nurses' residence, and the infectious disease ward were seized and turned into the Wehrmacht Reserve Field Hospital (*Lazarett*) No. 147. The Wehrmacht obviously had a great deal more clout than the *Akademie*.

The Wehrmacht seizure caused considerable disruption and came at a time when, as we have seen, demands on the hospital's facilities and staff were growing rather than diminishing. The nurses had to be rehoused, and a new operating theater had to be established and new quarters found for the departments that had been uprooted. The confiscation may have seemed like a harsh blow at the time, but it too proved to be unexpectedly beneficial. The hospital's complex of buildings were an integrated whole that was served by a single heating and lighting system. This meant that the occupants of the premises that remained as the Jewish hospital became the incidental beneficiaries of the privileged treatment the government reserved for the wounded soldiers in the *Lazarett*. The hospital's Jews had heat and light even when many Aryans in Berlin were shivering in their apartments as the war situation grew more desperate and the shortage of fuel more acute. They were certainly far better off than other Jews in the city, who were suffering miserably from the cold because the Nazis had confiscated their winter clothing, to be used by Aryans.

Moreover, relations between the hospital and the *Lazarett* in the years that remained before the end of the war proved to be surprisingly good. "As the officers in charge apparently were not anti-Semites," Hilde Kahan remembers, "and they also received all necessary supplies from our administration, there was a not unpleasant neighborly relationship. Our workmen liked to work for the Field Hospital, since there they usually got something to eat."

On occasion, the *Lazarett* furnished supplies and equipment to the hospital. Its presence must have helped sustain morale among the Jewish doctors and nurses. Vilified and humiliated by the German government and most of German society outside the hospital walls, repeatedly harassed by the Gestapo even within those walls, at least in the *Lazarett* they found a body of German medical personnel who on occasion were prepared to treat them as professional colleagues.

7

MAKING A LIFE FOR ONESELF
IN THE HOSPITAL

THE TWO YOUNG WOMEN in the dining room of the elegant Adlon Hotel, in the very heart of official Berlin on the fashionable Unter den Linden boulevard near the Brandenburg Gate, looked faintly out of place among the high Nazi functionaries, diplomats, and wealthy businessmen who frequented Hitler's favorite restaurant. An observer might have guessed that the dress each wore, not quite in the latest fashion, was her best garment, possibly her only "dress-up" frock. Their impeccable coiffures bespoke a recent trip to the beauty parlor, but the condition of their hands might have led an astute observer to conclude that these young women were more familiar with the typewriter or the slop pail than the refinements of an elegant dining room. Although they carried themselves with self-assurance, a keen eye might have noted a slight air of nervousness.

Anyone idly speculating on the identities of the pair easily could have concluded that these were two working girls who had saved their money over a long time to splurge on a night out in Berlin's premier restaurant — a once-in-a-blue-moon escape from the dull inadequacies of rationed food. Even the keenest observer might have been excused, however, for failing to guess that these were two Jewish nurses from the hospital. Who would have imagined that anyone in such a position would have the suicidal effrontery to take off her yellow star and illegally pretend to be an Aryan in a place not only where Jews were prohibited, but where the highest Nazis in the land congregated? The young women's crimes were multiple. The preparatory trip to the hairdresser, also without yellow star or identity papers, had been as much of an infraction as their presence in the Adlon's dining room. So, too, was use of the public transportation they had taken to get to the Unter den Linden.

For Ruth Lebram and her bosom friend Lotte Schüfftan, discovery would have meant immediate arrest and almost certain deportation to Auschwitz. And this particular excursion came perilously close to having such a tragic end. First, the two Jewish girls made the mistake of trying to order meat on a Friday (at that time, a meatless day for many Christians). The waiter looked at them askance, but fortunately did no more than point out to them that they must have forgotten what day it was. Then, a group of prominent Nazi officials came in and were seated at the next table. As time went by, Lotte became slightly tipsy. Ruth began to fear that Lotte, her tongue loosened by the unaccustomed bottle of wine, would say something indiscreet that could expose their real identities. Struggling to act normal, to suppress her fear, and to avoid provoking her friend into blurting out an objection that might give them away, Ruth managed to bring the meal to a hasty conclusion and get Lotte out of the restaurant before anything disastrous occurred.

Yet, the night out at the Adlon Hotel was only the latest — and despite Ruth's moment of fear, not the last — in a series of life-threatening escapades through which these two young women, living in a situation so bizarre as to be almost unimaginable and facing the daily threat of death, sought to bring some pleasure and normality into their young lives. Although the regulations required the yellow star to be firmly sewn onto their clothing, they had contrived ways of pinning it on so that it could easily be removed. Again and again, they would leave the hospital, removing their stars and hiding their identity papers, and go

off as if they were living normal lives: taking trips to the hairdresser and the cinema, riding the forbidden streetcars and sub-
ways, visiting restaurants and cafés.

Dangerous escapades by the younger staff members were only
one aspect of a more general effort by the hospital's population to
cling to a life that had some semblance of normality. It was a constant struggle to overcome the inherent abnormality of their situation, which sometimes lay concealed behind a bizarre but spurious appearance that life was going on as always. Indeed, it might
have appeared to a casual observer that life in the hospital was
proceeding very much the way it had before the war. Doctors and
nurses in their starched white uniforms circulated throughout the
buildings, ministering to the sick. Patients were admitted and discharged. Operations were performed; medications were adminis-
tered. Meals were prepared and served. Clerks and typists kept
registers and prepared documents. The details of the institution's
daily life were documented with bureaucratic thoroughness.

Looking a little closer, however, one would have seen signs of
important changes from prewar days. The staff's freshly laun-
dered and pressed uniforms bore yellow stars. Some of the patients were behind bars in the prison ward, and when they were
discharged, it was into the hands of the Gestapo, to be taken to
the *Sammellager*. The hospital was overcrowded, not merely because it was full of patients, but because its premises had become
smaller through the confiscation of buildings and because every
spare portion of what remained had been turned into living quarters for staff members and the population of Jews who had been
billeted at the hospital. Police and SS uniforms were often in evidence, as was the menacing presence of men in plain clothes
whose attire and bearing left no doubt that they were Gestapo
officers.

Even with these differences, the hospital as it existed from the
beginning of the deportations until the final months of the war
could have appeared to a superficial observer to be essentially the
same institution that had existed a decade earlier. The most im-

portant change was in the perilous situation of the hospital population, both staff and patients, and in the state of mind that their
situation engendered. Every Jew in the hospital was living on
borrowed time, and (with the exception of those who were too
young, too old, or too ill to understand what was going on) they
all knew it. Psychologically, then, the hospital existed in a world
profoundly different from the one in which it had been situated
before the mass deportations began late in 1941.

"It was like a small island unto itself," one survivor remembers, "cut off from the outside world." For the patients and some
of the staff, the hospital was their entire world. They lived there,
and rarely left. Even those patients who were not prisoners could
not go outside without exposing themselves to the risk of being
pronounced well enough to be deported. For the staff who resided on the premises, the restrictions on Jews' movements and
activities outside the hospital walls were so rigorous as to make it
pointless to leave unless there was a compelling need to do so. In
addition, although in the hospital one ran the constant risk of
being pinpointed for deportation during an inspection by Eichmann, Wöhrn, or another RSHA or Gestapo officer, it was no
less dangerous outside on the streets. There, one could be picked
up at any time by SS or Gestapo agents looking for Jews to fill
empty seats in a transport that was about to leave. And possessing
a certificate attesting that one was supposed to be exempt from
deportation was no guarantee of safety.

Most of the Jews who worked at the hospital after 1943 did not
live on the premises, but toward the end of the war an increasing
number took up residence there as the Allied bombing destroyed
homes all over the city. The unmarried nurses continued to sleep
at the hospital, although it had been necessary to improvise new
quarters for them after the Wehrmacht confiscated the *Schwesternheim*. But most of the young *Geltungsjuden* and Jewish men
living in mixed marriages who were sent in 1943 to work at the
hospital after the factory raids (discussed in Chapter 8) resided

outside with their families. So, too, did some of the intermarried full Jews on the medical staff.

For most of those medical staff and employees who lived off the premises, however, the hospital became the center of their existence. Forbidden from participating in any way in a normal life outside, they were as cloistered as those who lived on the grounds except for the fact that daily they had to undergo the painful and potentially dangerous journey to and from work. Those who lived closer than seven kilometers were forbidden to use public transportation; regardless of the weather, they had to walk to and from the hospital. Employees who lived farther away were entitled to special permits to use public transportation for their commute. That eased the burden of fatigue, but, wearing the yellow star, they were exposed to insults and mistreatment. *Schwester* Carry, who had married while working at the hospital and had moved out to live with her husband's family, obtained a permit allowing her to use public transit. She remembers that often the conductors, seeing the star she wore, would not allow her onto the streetcar, permit or not. To avoid such incidents, many of the hospital's female employees who were allowed to travel by public transportation would clutch their handbags to their chest, trying to hide their stars. Sometimes this worked; when it failed, the Jews were at risk of being ferociously insulted by fellow passengers and the streetcar conductors.

Increasingly over time, a hospital community developed. It was composed of the families who did live on the hospital grounds, some longtime patients or other residents, and those nonresident employees for whom the hospital increasingly became a focal point. This community displayed the characteristics of any village. There were strong friendships and love affairs. There were antipathies and even hatreds, all exacerbated by living and working together in overcrowded conditions and by the claustrophobic atmosphere that the Nazis' anti-Semitic measures had created. Not surprisingly, Lustig and at least one of his prin-

cipal assistants became targets of animosity. Although all the survivors interviewed for this book spoke warmly of Ehrich Zwilsky
and his family, many had harsh things to say about both Selmar
Neumann and his wife.

One story involving the Neumanns is told by Inge London.
The young woman worked in the kitchen under the supervision
of Selmar Neumann's wife. Relations between the two women
were so acrimonious that one day they got into fisticuffs. Mrs.
Neumann complained to her husband and asked him to call the
Gestapo, with the intention of having Inge deported. Luckily,
someone else telephoned Inge's mother, who rushed down to
the hospital and went with her daughter to the director's office.
They persuaded Lustig to intervene. He managed to save Inge
from being sent to the *Sammellager* and instead transferred her
from the kitchen to other duties. This case is quite remarkable.
Inge had committed an infraction for which deportation would
not have been an unusual punishment, and she had managed to
get on the wrong side of Lustig's closest associate in the hospital
administration. One would have thought that the chances of persuading Lustig to help in these circumstances were minimal, yet
he proved himself both approachable and sympathetic.

Despite these indications that Lustig had a human side, that
he even had a few friends among his hospital colleagues, there is
no doubt that the overall verdict on Lustig given by those who
worked with him is negative. Almost none of Lustig's contemporaries claim to have liked him or to have considered him a friend.
Generally he is described as cold and distant, unapproachable.
Schwester Carry says, "He had no contact with anybody except
those girls he had an affair with. He was completely out of reach
to everybody." Bruno Blau charges him with being "completely
inaccessible and not available either to the police prisoners or
their families." From the lowly perspective of the laundry and
sewing rooms (they were in the basement), Margot Neumann,
one of the half-Jewish forced laborers, complains that he did not
treat the workers well. She cannot cite any specifics, however.

Rather, it appears it was Lustig's haughtiness that gave offense. Even though the hospital community may have viewed him, at least to some extent, as a defender against the Nazis, whatever gratitude people felt was tinged with both suspicion and fear that Lustig was misusing his position to the detriment of the Jews for whom he was responsible.

This accusation seems to be inextricably bound up with the unlikable aspects of Lustig's personality, especially his temper and his authoritarianism, and with his sexual conduct, above all his having relations simultaneously with two of the Jewish nurses, *Schwester* Illa and *Schwester* Elli. Illa was Lustig's principal mistress. She appears to have been roundly disliked and feared by almost everyone else at the hospital, in part because it was perceived that she could influence whose names Lustig put on the deportation lists. Elli, in contrast, was well liked by some of her coworkers. When the *Sammellager* was moved to the former pathology building, Elli entered into a sexual relationship with the resident Gestapo commandant, Dobberke. Although this became the main focus of her sexual attentions, she also continued to sleep from time to time with Lustig.

The greatest risk to a pretty young woman, according to several accounts, was not being coerced into sexual relations with Lustig; rather, it was incurring the jealousy, warranted or not, of Lustig's mistress Illa. A hospital nurse, Gerda Haas, writes: "Our chief, the head of the hospital, Dr. Lustig, was advised by his girl friends with regard to the selection of persons for deportation. This meant that not only those doctors and nurses whose work was unsatisfactory were selected but also persons disliked by the girl friends. It also meant to become friendly with Lustig's current girl friend."

Hilde Fischer says that, while Illa was growing older, the young women arriving at the hospital were always younger and prettier. Whenever she could, Illa would see to it that the young attractive girls were on the next transport to the camps. Mrs. Fischer remembers that her husband, Dr. Fischer, was indignant at this behavior. One day, after a transport left, he reached the breaking point and reproached Illa for her actions. The Fischers were listed for the next transport to Theresienstadt. (In the end, while Mrs. Fischer was taken to the *Sammellager* within two or three days, her husband's deportation was delayed because of the shortage of surgeons at the hospital. Dr. Fischer was not taken away until he finished all the operations he had been scheduled to perform.)

Within the hospital community, fear of running afoul of Lustig or his mistresses was only one of many pressures. As the Gestapo continued to deport hospital personnel, the ever grow-ing imbalance between the heavy demand for the hospital's ser-vices and the reduced number of doctors and nurses meant that everyone had to work long hours. The staff members who still lived elsewhere in Berlin left their apartments early and got home late. They had little time for anything other than eating and sleeping before it was time to return to the hospital. Moreover, as the Allied bombing became more intense in 1943–45, many of the personnel spent one or more nights a week at the hospital, serving on air raid watch duty, acting as firefighters, and helping move patients to the basement corridors when the air raid sirens began to sound.

By 1943, with Germany's loss at Stalingrad and the intensifica-tion of Allied bombing of the city, it was reasonably clear to the Jews in the hospital that Germany was losing the war. By law, Jews were prohibited from possessing radios and from reading newspapers. Nonetheless, the staff found ways to gain an impres-sion of the war situation. No one, as far as is known, went so far as to risk keeping a clandestine short-wave radio and listening to the BBC's broadcasts to Germany. It does not even appear that any managed illegally to listen to the highly distorted war news re-ports that were broadcast on German radio. Still, what passed for news, as disseminated in the German radio and press, filtered through to the hospital staff from a variety of sources — the staff of the *Lazarett*, neighbors and tradesmen, things overheard on the streetcar or subway, surreptitious glances at discarded news-papers. By 1943, the hospital population, like many other Berlin-ers, had learned how to read between the lines of Nazi propa-ganda and discern the underlying truth: the war was going from bad to worse for Germany. The doctors, especially, followed the progress of the war with keen interest. In their rare moments of leisure or even over the operating table, they would engage in an-imated debates among themselves as to when Germany's defeat would take place. The question that aroused the greatest interest was whether the war's end would come soon enough to save the hospital and its population. No one had an answer. Conscious that they were in a race against time, that they risked dying in a final frenzy of Nazi fury even as liberation lay on the horizon, the hospital staff found the progress of the war a constant preoccu-pation.

In this heavy atmosphere of apprehension and mourning (for everyone had lost friends and relatives to the deportations), one might expect that life was unremittingly gloomy. Yet this was not the case. Certainly there was sadness; surely many of the patients must have been depressed; and an undercurrent of fear was an in-escapable feature of daily life. Yet most of the hospital population went about the activities of daily life with self-possession. People adapted to the circumstances that were forced upon them and met the challenges that life presented. And, as much as they could, they contrived to find such pleasure in life as the situation allowed.

Younger staff members, searching for diversion, took extraor-dinary risks, as typified by Ruth and Lotte's dinner at the Adlon Hotel. Wearing the star, of course, meant that all participation in the normal life of the city was automatically foreclosed. So the star had to come off. Nazi regulations, however, were very strict: the yellow star had to be securely sewn onto the Jews' garments. Failing to have it tightly stitched was an offense that could lead to deportation and likely death. Just such a death sentence in fact befell one of the hospital's nurses (described in Chapter 10).

Stitching and unstitching the star was not only impractical, but it also created too great a risk of detection. On a dress or coat, a star-shaped section less faded than the rest of the fabric or a line of stitch holes tracing the outline of a star could give the game away. Consequently, it became a practice among younger staff members to mount the star on a metal backing that was attached to a pin by which the device could easily be attached to the clothing and just as easily detached. Two young half-Jewish laborers, the Rischowsky boys, were masters at fabricating these pins and did so for many of the young women at the hospital.

Armed with the removable yellow stars, the risk takers among the hospital staff were ready to go out on the town. They were often aided in these ventures by the rigidity of the Nazis' racial stereotypes. Many Jews, especially among the *Mischlinge*, did not "look Jewish" in the terms of the racial theories that were taught in German educational institutions and promulgated through Germany's propaganda organs. (Indeed, this is why the yellow star was necessary in the first place, making it an implicit admission that the Nazis' racial theories were nonsense.) For them, once abroad in the city without the star, there was a good chance that nothing in their appearance would arouse suspicion in passersby. Those among the hospital staff who did fit the Nazis' stereotypical view of Jewish physiognomy and coloring were out of luck.

Having dinner in the restaurant most favored by the Nazi leadership may have been the boldest or most foolhardy exploit, but it was far from unique. And becoming inebriated while sitting next to high Nazis at the Adlon Hotel was not even the closest call Ruth and her friend experienced. Ruth and Lotte came even closer to detection on a trip to the hairdresser. This was an expedition the two young women made regularly, without yellow stars or identity papers and usually without incident. On this particular occasion, however, they found themselves trapped by an unexpected occurrence. Someone in the shop, either an employee or a customer, complained that she was missing a sum of money that she had brought in with her. A hullabaloo ensued, in the course of which the proprietor decided to hold everyone on the premises and send for the police. The two young Jewish women were panic-stricken, since a police inspection quickly would reveal that neither girl was carrying her identity papers, enough in Nazi Germany to ensure their arrest and eventual unmasking as Jews. Even worse, Lotte had inadvertently brought a photograph of herself in her purse, and the picture clearly showed her wearing the star. To further exacerbate the situation, Lotte was still trapped under the hair dryer. Ruth's coiffure, fortunately, had been finished; she was merely waiting for Lotte to be done. Ruth rose to the occasion. First, she managed surreptitiously to relieve Lotte of the incriminating photograph. She folded it into a tiny square and slipped it into her own bra. Next she set to work to talk herself and Lotte out of having to wait for the police. Happily, since they were being worked on when the money allegedly disappeared, they were not under direct suspicion. Ruth spun an inventive story as to why she and Lotte would find themselves in trouble with their employer if they did not return on time to wherever they were pretending to have come from, and the proprietor agreed that they could leave.

An even more dramatic and literal close shave occurred to a nurse named *Schwester* Ada. Hurrying home one night from an illegal sortie to a movie or café, she arrived on the S-Bahn platform just as her train was about to leave. She ran to jump aboard the train through the closing doors but lost her balance on the platform. To her horror, her leg slipped into the gap between the train and the platform's edge. The motorman apparently was unaware of her predicament, and her cries for help went unheeded. The train moved out of the station.

Fortunately, Ada's foot was neither crushed nor severed and her leg was unbroken. But her ankle and calf were badly bruised and a deep cut on her calf was bleeding profusely. Her fear of detection was even more intense, however, than the pain and shock. The stationmaster had come running to her aid, as had several

concerned passengers, but their offers of help were more dangerous than the wound she had suffered. If anyone summoned aid, if
she were taken to a hospital, if the police came to investigate the
incident, she would be unmasked.

It took every reserve of strength she could summon, but somehow Ada extricated herself from the situation, resolutely refusing
the offers of help from the stationmaster and the passengers.
Covering the wound with her handkerchief and trying to staunch
the flow of blood by pressing hard, she told the concerned on-
lookers that her injury was not serious. She turned aside their
urgings that she nonetheless wait for an ambulance to arrive,
proffering the story that she worked on a night shift and was late
for work. She would go home, she said, quickly clean up, and
hurry to her job. Like Ruth and Lotte's escape from the hairdresser's salon, the claim that duty called proved effective with
the stationmaster and passengers. The needs of the Fatherland
took priority over personal concerns. The German bystanders
could only admire the courage of this young woman whose sense
of duty led her to hurry off to her undoubtedly essential night
work even though she was so obviously in pain.

Only one person was not convinced, the crone whose job it
was to sweep the S-Bahn station. "There's something fishy about
this woman," she muttered, pulling at the stationmaster's sleeve.
"You should call the police." The stationmaster demurred. "Ask
to see her papers," the old woman persisted. "Maybe she's a spy
— or a Jew."

"I have to go home," Ada insisted. "Right now. I'll be late otherwise."

Somehow she pushed her way past the stationmaster, the bale-
ful old woman, and the helpful passengers and hobbled down
the stairs to the street. Hours later she arrived at the hospital after
a nightmarish journey. Limping, she had managed to make her
way slowly and painfully through the nighttime streets, in constant apprehension that her condition would draw the attention

of the Gestapo or police, who were abroad at all hours and always on the alert for anything suspicious.

Ada's mishap had no permanent repercussions. The same, unfortunately, was not so in the case of another hospital nurse who was traveling one day on the streetcar without her star and identity card. The fare system on the Berlin streetcars then was the same as it is today, a quasi–honor system in which the passenger buys a ticket for the correct fare, calculated by the number of stops to the chosen destination, but there is no ticket barrier or collection point. Instead, random inspections are made aboard the trams and as passengers alight; passengers who cannot produce a ticket for the correct fare are subject to penalties. The unfortunate hospital nurse paid for a five-stop ticket and, for some reason, traveled one additional stop. An inspector accosted her and asked her to produce her ticket. Because it was ten pfennig short of the correct fare, she was arrested. Her true identity soon was discovered, and she was sent to a death camp in the East.

The rest of the hospital staff were aware of the tragic cases of people who had been sent to concentration camps for violating the rules on wearing the star or the prohibitions on using public transportation. Some were persuaded that the risks were too great; others went blithely on their way, continuing to run enormous risks for a few moments of illegal pleasure or to rest their aching legs by riding the streetcar instead of walking the many miles between the hospital and their apartments. Even the two Beleski sisters, Ruth and Eva, behaved in very different ways. Eva describes Ruth as the strong one, the sister with the greater courage. Yet Ruth's risk taking was limited to covering her star with her handbag while she was aboard the streetcar. Because she and Eva lived in the distant suburb of Karlshorst, they had permits to use public transportation, so discovery was likely to cause embarrassment at most. Ruth says that Eva was more daring. She sometimes took the star off and went to the movies.

Ruth may not have known how daring Eva really was. Eva's ac-

count of her own exploits goes far beyond an occasional trip to
the movies:

> My poor mother nearly died. I used to go skiing. . . . All by myself,
> early in the morning. I left when it was pitch dark so that the neigh-
> bors shouldn't see me and came back when it was pitch dark. Most of
> them were very good; they wouldn't have done anything. But there
> was one, he was a so-and-so; he would have. . . . We did a lot. We had
> boyfriends. . . . I used to go swimming at the Olympic Stadium. I al-
> ways had [the star] on me in case we — although you weren't allowed
> to pin it on; it had to be sewn on. I thought I'd better keep it on me
> just in case. And I always was afraid when we were in the swimming
> bath that someone might look through my clothes and find it. But
> still we did it. . . . One did take some awful chances. We didn't think
> of it at the time.

The "we" to whom Eva refers were herself and her friend
Ruth Graetz. The boyfriends were both young Aryan men who
were serving in the German air force. They knew that the two
girls were *Geltungsjuden*, Eva says, but they were indifferent to
that. It was agreed that if anything happened, the young men
would claim that they never knew the girls were Jewish, a plausible claim since neither of them "looked Jewish." "For me that was
the main thing," Eva says, "to be careful that I didn't drag anybody else down with me." She admits, though, that on occasion
she broke even this rule. For example, once she wanted to ride the
train with Inge, an Aryan girlfriend. Because the two girls looked
slightly alike, Inge handed Eva her own identity card to hold in
case there was an inspection of papers. Happily there was none.
Although sometimes the police and Gestapo glanced only quickly
at passengers' identity cards, in which case the deception might
have worked, any more than a superficial glance would have given
the game away: Inge's eyes were blue; Eva's are brown.

One of the boldest forays without a star was brought off by
Rosemarie H., whose brother had been sent to the Sachsenhausen concentration camp. Rosemarie and her friend Marga-

rete, also a *Geltungsjude*, decided to take him a food package. They took off their stars, left their identity papers with the incriminating *Jude* stamp at home, and went by S-Bahn to Oranienburg. From the station they went on foot to the Sachsenhausen camp and walked boldly up to the front gate, where they went into the guardhouse and thrust the package at the guards on duty.

"Here's a package, a food package, for Hans H.," Rosemarie said, "and I want you to see that he gets it." The two young women left and began walking back down the road toward the town. "And here we hear some steps behind, somebody running. And I say, 'Margarete, they got us.' So she said, 'Just keep calm, just keep calm.' What does he say to us? 'You have my pen.' I had to sign for it — I signed a different name, by the way. I had that pen still in my hand. Needless to say we laughed afterwards, but it was not funny."

Going out in Berlin without one's star was dangerous. The police and the Gestapo were continually searching for Jews who had gone underground. Generally, one never knew when they would suddenly raid a public establishment and check everyone's identity papers, although sometimes there was a warning. In the last year of the war, when the *Sammellager* had been moved to the hospital grounds, the Gestapo commandant Dobberke proved to be surprisingly well disposed toward the staff, possibly because he had taken *Schwester* Elli as his mistress. From time to time, he would pass along a friendly tip: "Don't go to such and such a movie house today; there's going to be a raid."

Although Dobberke might have helped from time to time, the installation of the *Sammellager* at the hospital in 1944 introduced a new source of danger for staff members who might have been tempted to circulate illegally in the city: the *Spitzel* and *Greifer*, or informers and catchers. The most famous of these was the Jewish Gestapo spy Stella Kübler, whose story is told by Peter Wyden in his book *Stella*. Kübler and her fellow Gestapo informers spent the last year of the war living in the *Sammellager* on the hospital grounds, cheek by jowl with the victims they had sent to the *Sammellager* and the police ward.

Earlier, the risk of being recognized by Stella Kübler or one of her fellow renegades had not been so great. Many of the *Spitzel* were Jews born and raised in the Berlin Jewish community. In catching Jews who had gone underground, they relied on their wide acquaintance with former Berlin schoolmates, friends, neighbors, and fellow congregants. A substantial number of the young nurses who took off their stars and went out on the town, however, were girls from the provinces who had come to Berlin only as nursing students and had been living at the hospital ever since. There was little chance that they had met Stella Kübler or her ilk. So, too, many of the young *Geltungsjuden* who were assigned to work at the hospital had not been active in the Jewish community or had not moved in the same social circles as the *Spitzel.* Now that the *Spitzel* were living right there on the hospital grounds, however, things were different. There was every chance that a hospital employee who was abroad in the city without the star and Jewish identity card might run across a *Spitzel* on the street or in a café or movie theater and be recognized. No one knew for sure what Stella or her companions would do in those circumstances. Their job was to ferret out Jews who were evading deportation, not those who were not supposed to be deported and were merely breaking the anti-Semitic regulations. On the other hand, the *Spitzel* depended for their survival on achieving results. If they were running short of underground Jews to unmask, who could be sure that they would not try to gain favor with their Gestapo masters by throwing them a hospital employee who had committed the serious criminal offense of seeing a movie or visiting the hairdresser?

Many of the hospital staff chose not to run the risk of taking off the star to entertain themselves. Instead, some went as often as they could to the performances of the *Jüdische Kulturbund,* until that organization finally was disbanded in 1943. There they could hear some of Germany's finest actors, singers, musicians, and thinkers, all of them Jews who had been banned from practicing their art in any other forum, perform or give lectures before an entirely Jewish audience. Otherwise, the staff entertained itself on the hospital premises.

Schwester Carry looks back with pleasure at this aspect of the years from 1938 to 1942 when she was a nursing student, and then a nurse, at the hospital.

> And then there came the time when we were not permitted to go to a movie, to a theater or a concert or anything. We formed our own theater group — in the hospital. You know there came people from all sorts of life, from everywhere. There were people who wanted to be musicians; they never could get out and had no chances. And they played the piano beautifully. And there were people who had nice voices. So we formed our own theater group, and we sang duets and somebody played the piano, and we had great shows. I remember myself in a tuxedo with a high-topped hat in a play, singing songs in English and in German. And it was mobbed; the place was full. . . . We had a good time. That's why I say I have nice memories too.

Carry remembers that the performances took place in a large room in the main building and were attended by doctors, nurses, and staff. The patients were not invited. For Carry, music and rehearsing and putting on shows were a great solace in a life otherwise characterized by hard work and darkened by constant worry about what would happen to her parents and extended family.

Other survivors also remember participating in impromptu evenings of music and dancing at the hospital. Margot Neumann, one of the hospital's half-Jewish forced laborers, recalls lighthearted social gatherings among the support staff. She worked in a menial capacity, first in the laundry room and later in the sewing room, where repairs were made to the uniforms of the medical staff and to the hospital linens. The young people who did that kind of work generally did not fraternize with the nurses, even less with the physicians. But, she says, "We made it as pleasant as possible for ourselves, that's natural." At night, those on the night shift would gather in a room in the administration building where there was a piano. Someone played, and there was dancing.

There was a 10:00 P.M. curfew in the *Schwesternheim*, but it was no impediment to late-night gatherings. *Schwester* Carry remembers that when she was a nursing student one of the other student nurses was engaged to be married to one of the cooks. He had a key to an outer door leading to the kitchen, which was located in the basement. The student nurses would leave their rooms in the *Schwesternheim* for postcurfew get-togethers or romantic rendezvous in the hospital grounds and then, at a prearranged time, often midnight, they all would meet at the kitchen door, where the cook would see to it that they all got back in, enabling them to reach the *Schwesternheim* through the basement corridors.

In addition to lighter entertainment, there were religious services. A group of doctors and nurses led by Dr. Knopp formed a small choir to sing in the hospital's own synagogue. Although Carry remembers that at least one synagogue still was in operation in Berlin, the prohibition on using public transportation made it difficult for people from the hospital to attend Jewish services. Increasingly their religious needs had to be satisfied on the hospital premises.

However, these open Jewish services were not destined to last long. At some point, probably in 1942, the Gestapo prohibited all Jewish religious observances at the hospital. Some inhabitants then carried out clandestine services. In doing so they were keeping alive a tradition that ran back to the institution's founding. Prior to Nazi times, the hospital had always been a component of the Jewish *Gemeinde* and, as such, had maintained a Jewish religious character. The small but handsome synagogue had been an integral part of the hospital's main administration building from the time it was built. At the same time, the hospital had prided itself on welcoming patients of every faith, or of no faith. Indeed, as we have seen, Nazi pressure to limit the hospital's services to Jewish patients led to a financial crisis in the early years of the Nazi regime, so dependent had the hospital become on serving the general population. Thus the religious character of the hospital, at least from the time it moved to Iranischestrasse, had become more liberal and pluralistic than Orthodox. In fact, until it was eliminated by the Nazis during the period of the deportations, there had been another Jewish hospital in Berlin, maintained by, and primarily serving, the Orthodox Jewish community.

Having lived on the hospital premises at different times between 1930 or 1931, when she entered nursing school there, until the late 1940s, when she immigrated to the United States, Hilde Fischer was in a good position to observe the extent of Jewish religiosity at the hospital. She had resided there as a nursing student and then as a resident nurse, but she then left to work in a private clinic. She returned in 1938 when she married the surgeon Dr. Erich Fischer. Hilde remembers that the hospital's kitchen was kosher and was kept that way even after the Nazis made it difficult for Jews to practice the dietary laws. However, those laws were applied in a relaxed manner, and most of the people with whom she worked were not Orthodox.

Hilde came "from a completely *treyf* [nonkosher] place, from Westphalen, where they have the good *Schinken* [ham]," and the food she found in Berlin was not to her taste. So, in the 1930s, her mother would send her packages of home-cooked food, including pork sausage and salami. Living in the hospital, she didn't know what to do with this nonkosher food, so she asked the head nurse, the *Oberin*, for advice. The *Oberin* told her that she could eat the salami, even though it was made from pork, as long as she used her own utensils and not the hospital's. "That's how kosher we were." On the other hand, Hilde remembers that some people checked to make sure that there was no mixing of dairy and meat products. She herself, although she did not observe the dietary laws, would never have thought, while at the hospital, of mixing meat and milk and even went so far as to chastise another nurse for doing so.

Another longtime hospital nurse, Lisa Meyersohn, remembers her years as a nursing student starting in 1936. "On Friday nights we had religious meetings; we had to change to clean uniforms, and the services were led by young rabbis or candidates to be rabbis."

The Gestapo's prohibition of Jewish religious services at the hospital probably did not trouble many residents. Many patients and internees were either highly assimilated Jews, for whom religious observance was not a major concern, or were not Jews by religion at all. Defined as Jews only by the Nazi racial laws, they were compelled to be at the hospital either because it was the only medical facility at which they could be treated or, as in the case of Jewish husbands living in mixed marriages who had been sent there from western Germany, they had been housed there involuntarily. For others, however, religious observance was central to their lives, and they were not about to shirk their religious duties just because the Gestapo said so. Bruno Blau recalls:

> From time to time on holidays, on special Sabbaths and after the fortunate conclusion of a heavy bombing raid, in complete secrecy *minyanim* gathered in the hospital, in director Neumann's apartment, to which ten occupants of the hospital were invited through special trustworthy people. I, too, had the opportunity to participate in them. We had to go there as inconspicuously as possible, and after the end of the *minyan* return to our rooms separately, in part using the cellar corridors.

While Sabbath services seem to have been the province of the men, women were also involved in secret religious observances. One of the young women who worked in the hospital during the last two years of the war remembers attending clandestine ceremonies at which Hanukkah candles were lit.

Lustig was zealous in enforcing the Gestapo's strictures against Jewish observance. One of the many ironies of life in the hospital was that Selmar Neumann, Lustig's number two man, was the leader of the clandestine services. On this topic, at least, Lustig's trusted adjutant felt no compunctions about keeping him in the dark.

Klaus Zwilsky was a boy during the years he and his parents lived at the hospital. His Bar Mitzvah, which took place in the hospital's synagogue in August 1945 only a few months after the liberation, was the first Bar Mitzvah to be celebrated in Berlin after the war. Klaus remembers that he trained for the ceremony on a crash basis with the help of a Polish Jew who had survived the death camps and who ended up at the hospital as a refugee shortly after the war ended. But Klaus did not have to start from zero; he already knew how to read Hebrew and was familiar with the Sabbath liturgy because he had attended secret services in the hospital during the Nazi period.

Klaus's mother was a devout Orthodox Jew. One of the very few fully Jewish women who was living openly and legally in Berlin and yet was not employed at the hospital, Ruth Zwilsky was assigned to do forced labor at a Siemens factory. She left the Zwilskys' room in the hospital for work every morning at 6:00 A.M. and returned some twelve hours later. Despite this punishing schedule, she managed to maintain an observant Jewish household. Klaus says:

> One of my vivid memories is of her baking Matzo at Passover. She would roll out the dough and used the top of a saltshaker to make holes. (To understand this, imagine a shaker that dispensed salt via a small wheel at the top. This little wheel had teeth on it and by rotating it a little bit of salt was dispensed as each tooth passed the opening. The top of the shaker containing the wheel could be removed and was rolled on the dough to make the holes.) In any case my job was to stand guard outside the apartment to let her know whether anyone was coming, especially someone looking like Gestapo. To this day I marvel at her courage.

Thus, for a segment of the hospital's population, religion was something to hold on to in the midst of chaos and destruction. For others, love and sex also were sources of consolation, or at least diversion. As we have seen, the attempts of some in the hospital community to seek this kind of solace turned the hospital for one observer into a "vestibule of hell," a sinkhole of depravity where "everyone slept with everyone, all the medicine cabinets were quickly emptied, the last supply of narcotics dwindled away, there was a flourishing trade in black market cigarettes." This picture is at odds, however, with what seems to have been the real situation. No other survivor has any recollection that narcotics were diverted for personal use or that the medicine cabinets were quickly emptied. The chief pharmacist, Kantelberg, had control over medications, especially narcotics, and he appears to have been a model of rectitude as well as a friend to the hospital's Jews. Though the hospital was subject to the shortages that affected all of Germany as the war progressed, medical supplies were present until the very end. As for cigarettes, they were so scarce that Dr. Heinz Elkan, an addicted smoker, was forced to smoke tea and rose leaves. And as for sexual liaisons, they certainly occurred, but not, by all accounts, to an unusual degree.

The most conspicuous Lothario on the premises was the director himself. His name seems particularly appropriate in the circumstances. *Lustig* in German means "merry" or "jolly," but the root *Lust*, in addition to meaning "joy" or "desire," can also denote "lust," as in English. So notorious was Lustig's sexual appetite that it gave rise to a wordplay that circulated throughout the hospital behind his back. Before October 1933, when the Nazis forced Jewish functionaries to retire, Lustig, as a high official of the Berlin Police Presidium, had held the title of *Oberregierungsrat* Lustig, or Chief Administrative Counselor Lustig. Cleverly transposing these syllables, out of his hearing his contemporaries at the hospital referred to him as *"Oberlustratgierig,"* or "Chief Greedy Lust Counselor."

Beyond Lustig's well-known activities, the extent to which lust and extramarital sex prevailed at the hospital is unclear. The fevered picture given by Cordelia Edvardson has been accepted unquestioningly by some. Yet other witnesses fail to corroborate Edvardson, and all the survivors alive today who were interviewed for this book — almost all of whom were adolescents or young adults during the war years and thus at the right age to have been involved — deny that the hospital was a hotbed of fornication.

The truth probably lies somewhere in between, and a fairly accurate measure probably is given by Bruno Blau. Having nothing else to do with his time, Blau made it his business to know everything that was going on, and, given the mass of detail his postwar memoir contains, appears to tell everything he knows. In a passage on "love" in the hospital, he provides a list of every sexual peccadillo of which he is aware — not for the sake of gossip, he hastens to assure us, but as examples of the psychologically interesting behavior of people in a situation of danger.

Several nurses, Blau says, had casual liaisons with *Reichsvereinigung* officials and with married patients, some of whom, after they had been sent home, came back to the hospital to visit their paramours. One doctor, whose priapric performance seems to have rivaled Lustig's, had an affair with a senior nurse and later lived openly with her, but not before getting a younger nurse pregnant. After the war, this same doctor took yet a third nurse into his apartment and lived with her there until he was arrested by the Russians. (Blau does not indicate why he was arrested; presumably it was for reasons other than his promiscuity.) Another nurse carried on simultaneous affairs with a married doctor and a married *Reichsvereinigung* official. Finally, there was a doctor who seduced a young nurse trainee and impregnated her. When her parents found out what had happened, they forced the doctor to marry her. The marriage was not a happy one, however: the reluctant bridegroom ignored his wife and then abandoned her. He was able to make his way to Switzerland, thus escaping both the Nazis and domesticity. The pregnant young woman was deported soon thereafter.

One cannot be sure that Blau's extraordinary talents for collecting information penetrated between every pair of sheets at the hospital, but it seems likely that he became aware of most of the sexual relationships that occurred. If so, the list of illicit liaisons seems rather modest, especially in light of the intense pressure under which everyone was living and the fact that the hospital's staff and patients were thrown together in a crowded environment and deprived by the Nazis of almost every form of entertainment or recreation that the rest of the population was able to enjoy.

Whether lust was rampant or restrained, survivors' accounts leave no doubt that romantic love flourished — with or without physical expression. For many of the young women on the hospital staff the object of their yearnings, at least until he went underground in 1942, was the dashing young Dr. Hans Knopp. Photographs show him as a tall, blond, good-looking man, and what the camera also reflects is the extent to which he was a magnet for young women. A number of snapshots of Knopp have been published elsewhere or were located in the course of research for this book. Almost all of them show him surrounded by a group of women whose adoring expressions eloquently reveal the young doctor's role as the hospital's resident matinee idol.

One photograph of Dr. Knopp shows him in the operating theater, clearly having just scrubbed. His surgical apron is being tied by a young nurse named *Schwester* Eleonora, who appears to relish her proximity to him. On the back of this snapshot, which forms part of a collection donated after the war to the Leo Baeck Institute Archives at Berlin's Jewish Museum, is the nurse's handwritten notation: "Hans and I were as thick as thieves." Was this boasting or wishful thinking? All we know is that Hans Knopp and another nurse, the young, newly qualified *Schwester* Reyna (Ruth Lebram), fell in love with each other and that this was the love that ultimately prevailed.

Another Ruth, Ruth Beleski, also was romantically linked to a doctor. In 1943, when she was sent to work at the hospital, Ruth soon fell in love with Dr. Heinz Elkan, so much so that she vowed to stay with him even if he were deported.

"When he has to go, I'll go too," she told her mother, to

Frau Beleski's consternation. The need to follow through on that promise (or, as her mother saw it, threat) never arose, however. Possibly because Lustig liked him, Elkan was one of the small complement of fully Jewish doctors not living in a mixed marriage who survived the war while still working at the hospital. There was no formal engagement, nor did Dr. Elkan give Ruth a ring, but they made clear to each other that they intended to remain together and to get married as soon as the war ended.

Like all the doctors, Elkan labored unremittingly to care for the patients in the face of shortages of supplies and a significantly reduced medical staff. He had a habitual cough that everyone attributed to the effects of overwork and to his being an inveterate smoker. As the Soviets approached, the cough got worse. Liberation came, and he and Ruth began to make plans for their future. In May 1945, they talked about the pleasure they would have in going to the first theatrical performances when Berlin's theaters reopened. But Elkan already was sick in bed when these conversations took place, stricken with a previously undiagnosed case of tuberculosis that shortly would kill him. He died in October 1945.

Love and lust were not the only strong emotions that people experienced in the hospital. Life crammed together in close quarters understandably led to friction and enmities. Nor were stolen moments of pleasure, obviously, the daily stuff of life. Overall, conditions were difficult. Food was in short supply, and people were hungry much of the time. The rations available to Jews included no milk, butter, meat, eggs, or fruit. Vegetables were not rationed, but, by the time the Jews were allowed into the stores at 4:00 P.M., what was available ran from scanty to nil. Potatoes and coarse bread were the staple of everyone's diet, and no special provisions were available for those with gastric disorders — which were not uncommon in light of the tension under which both staff and patients lived. Hilde Kahan, for example, suffered from an ulcer and could not tolerate the bread. Her mother ate their entire bread ration, and Hilde confined herself to their potato ration. Only after the war ended, when milk became available, was she able to recover.

Grim and desperate circumstances did not keep laughter from being heard in the hospital, although often the humor was dark. Inge London remembers one example. Every week the patients in the *Extrastation*, reserved for first-class patients, received a supplemental ration of a chunk of salami. She and her friend Margot, who hardly ever saw meat on the table, used to observe this with envy. One day, a patient on the *Extrastation* died just after the salami had been distributed. Margot said, "I'm not going to give that back" and promptly took the salami and hid it for the girls to eat later. Shortly thereafter the body was carried out of the room. As it passed in the corridor, Margot walked over to the stretcher and addressed it: "Thank you for the salami."

Gallows humor persisted even in the most trying of circumstances. The nurses used to like to tease young Günther Rischowsky about his hair, which was abundant, unruly, and very curly. They made a habit of asking him why he didn't comb it. On the day that the Gestapo came to take Ruth Lebram to the *Sammellager*, Günther was watching as she was herded aboard the truck. Ruth turned and spoke to him.

"Günther," she said, "don't forget to comb your hair."

8

THE FACTORY RAID AND THE
FRAUENPROTEST

SWAYING WITH FATIGUE, Inge London stood in the barren garage at the Hermann Göring Kaserne, an army barracks on the outskirts of Berlin. The unheated structure was painfully cold, and there was nowhere to sit down. Although the space was large, it was full to overflowing with panicked Jews. The fortunate ones had been able to grab their coats before the SS herded them onto the trucks. The others shivered. They had been there for hours without food or water. The garage reeked of urine and feces. Lacking bathroom facilities, even buckets, people had been forced to evacuate on the floor. Over the long hours of the afternoon and evening, the number of corpses had increased. Some people, already weakened by years of grueling forced labor and inadequate rations, now pushed over the edge by the shock and brutality of the arrests, had died of natural causes. Others had killed themselves by slitting their wrists or by ingesting the supply of poison that many Berlin Jews carried with them at all times against just this eventuality.

Inge had found a friend in the crowd, a former schoolmate who worked in a different factory. The two girls were at the point of collapse; they had been standing for hours. To sit on the cold concrete floor, awash with human excreta, was unthinkable. Suddenly Inge's friend took off her coat and threw it over the corpse of a woman lying on the floor nearby. She gestured to Inge, and the two young women sat down on the body, huddling together under Inge's coat.

Only hours before, early that morning of Saturday, February 27, 1943, anyone unfortunate enough to be out in the early morning chill would have seen Inge, yellow star on the breast of her coat, trudging as usual to her forced labor job at a Siemens munitions factory. Although half-Jewish, she was classed as a *Geltungsjude* and was not saved from the misery and indignity of having to wear the star or of having to do forced labor and to walk rather than ride the streetcar.

All across Berlin anyone astir in the predawn dark could have observed other tired workers wearing yellow stars as they made their way to munitions factories, street-cleaning squads, and other hard and undignified work. For even as the transports continued to set out almost weekly for the East with their human cargo, there still remained some forty thousand Jews in Berlin. All but the young children and the infirm worked at forced labor for a pittance and subsisted on the scantiest of rations. Many were half-Jews, like Inge, or Jews living in mixed marriages, like her father. The remainder were full Jews whose deportation notices had not yet arrived. Virtually the only full Jews left in the city who held normal jobs were those on the staff of the hospital and the few employees in what little remained of the Jewish communal organizations.

Inge was already well into her workday at 9:00 A.M. when the SS stormed into the factory. Shouting and swearing at the Jewish workers, they quickly and brutally herded the workers out into the cold and onto trucks that were waiting in the yard.

"You are being taken to the Lustgarten," the SS commander announced. (The Lustgarten was a public park, a place in which Hitler was fond of giving speeches.)

"When you get there you all will be shot."

As the truck rumbled through the Berlin streets, riding in fear, pressed tightly in among the shivering bodies of her fellow Jewish workers, all Inge could think of was the tragedy of her life. She was only seventeen years old and was on her way to be killed, without even having a chance to see her parents or brother again.

After a while, however, she began to realize that the truck had been moving for too long. Their destination could not be the Lustgarten; they already would have been there. She was not surprised, when the trucks stopped and the SS men hustled the Jews out onto the ground, to find that she was in a military installation on the city's fringe.

The massive raids that started on February 27, 1943, came to be known as the *Fabrikaktion*, or factory raid, because they began with simultaneous roundups of Jewish workers in all of Berlin's large factories. In addition to the pain, hunger, fatigue, and fear that the arrested Jews suffered, many were in shock, taken by surprise. For, even after the deportation of more than a third of Berlin's 1941 Jewish population, they had dared to hope, because of their contribution as workers in war-related industries, that those who remained would be left alone in the misery and degradation to which the Germans already had reduced them. Everyone knew that the war was going badly and that able-bodied workers were in short supply. Despite the privations they were enduring, the Jews in Berlin's munitions industries were among the most skilled and hard-working laborers available. To eliminate them would be a serious blow to the war effort.

Albert Speer, minister of war production, was of precisely that view, and for months he had managed to prevail in the intense debate that raged within Hitler's cabinet between himself and the Nazi true believers led by Göring, Himmler, and Goebbels — not to speak of Hitler himself. For Speer, winning the war was the most important issue. He needed the skilled labor of these Jews. However much they might have prayed in secret for the English and Americans to win, in the factories most Jews worked with skill and dedication, knowing that their lives depended on it. The Berlin Jews already had been reduced to the status of virtual slaves. Speer knew that, deprived of every right and almost every material possession, they were powerless to harm the Third Reich. But, for the died-in-the-wool Nazi ideologues, winning the war against the Allies was never as important as winning the war against the Jews. It was, in particular, an embarrassment to have declared that the Reich's "Jewish problem" had been solved and still to have forty thousand Jews circulating in the streets. Ironically, the growing ferocity of the anti-Semitic measures made the embarrassment all the worse. Conspicuously branded with the yellow star, obliged to walk everywhere and to queue up at grocery stores during the single afternoon hour when Jews were allowed to shop, Berlin's remaining Jews had become much more noticeable to other Berliners in 1943 than a much larger number had been in 1938.

Hitler had allowed the argument to continue for months, in cabinet meeting after cabinet meeting. He seemed to be ambivalent. Then, one day, he announced his decision. Speer had lost. The Berlin Jewish workers were to be eliminated, and not by gradual attrition through continued deportations. Instead, they all were to be sent to the East in one giant operation that, as events transpired, was to play a significant role in the hospital's struggle to survive in ever more precarious circumstances. The plans for the raids were kept as secret as possible so as not to alert the victims and give them time to slip away into underground existence. The same reason lay behind the decision to carry out the raids in the factories where the Jews were concentrated; these raids were to be followed by a roundup of those Jews who, for one reason or another, were at home.

Hilde Kahan witnessed the *Fabrikaktion* from the vantage point of the hospital. To her the lightning raids of February 27 were no surprise. On February 26, 1943, the day preceding the raids, the leadership of the *Reichsvereinigung* transmitted orders by telephone to the hospital to make available a number of stenographers for the next morning. At 9:00 A.M. on February 27 telephone reports began to arrive at the hospital that arrests were taking place all over Berlin. At the same time there were instructions to supply clerks, *Ordner*, doctors, and nurses to serve at the hastily established collection camps. The hospital also was ordered to prepare food for ten thousand people.

Hilde Kahan's first reaction was concern for her widowed mother, who was at her forced labor assignment. She called the factory where Elsa Kahan worked and was assured that her mother was there. Twenty minutes later she called again and learned that the Gestapo had just taken away all the Jewish women. She frantically thought about what to do. Around her, other hospital and *Reichsvereinigung* employees were in the same predicament. Everyone had family members, and no one knew where they were. While their first instinct was to minister to their families, they had their work to do. There was much confusion and unceasing activity. Hilde remembers that all the telephones were ringing. Orders from the Gestapo had to be transmitted, as did those from Lustig. Some callers wanted information; others needed to be calmed. Meanwhile, a large number of hospital employees had been required to report for duty at the collection camps, increasing the burden on those left behind.

Many employees wanted to go look after their families, but no one was allowed to leave the building. In any event, to be out on the street would have been a mistake, since every Jew found in a public place was arrested. Some hospital employees who were off the premises were detained, and the police held them for hours despite their identification cards indicating that they were hospital employees who should not be deported.

When the doctors who had been sent to the collection points returned to the hospital, to be replaced by others, they were able to give some of the employees information about their families. Hilde Kahan was informed that her mother was being held in the former entertainment center known as the Clou. There was great uncertainty about how to help those who had been taken. "We had no idea whether our chief, Lustig, would support us and we were dependent on his moods." Some time before, those who resided outside the hospital had been given certificates attesting that they worked for the Jewish community and listing the family members living with them. These certificates were posted on the doors of the rooms in which they lived so that the Gestapo would not seal the apartment when other Jews living there were transported. Someone thought of trying to use these papers to obtain the family members' release. Apparently with Lustig's approval, some hospital employees were able to use friends who were exempt from wearing the star to retrieve the papers from their apartment doors. The next morning, when a new set of doctors went from the hospital to relieve those in the collection camps, they took the certificates with them for presentation to the Gestapo. The Gestapo released the family members.

Among them was Hilde's mother, whom she had not seen for five days. The elder Mrs. Kahan returned to their apartment, where a friend who was not required to wear the star took food to her. As the days passed, other Jewish occupants of the Kahans' apartment were arrested and taken away. Finally, Hilde was given a few hours' leave during which she was able to visit her mother, but the ordeal was not over.

Unlike the rest of the population, Jews did not receive their ration cards in the mail but had to collect them in person. This gave the Gestapo another opportunity to make arrests. When Hilde went to fetch ration cards for herself and her mother, she was told that, despite being an employee of the hospital, a status that had obtained her mother's release from the Clou, she was to be deported. She was placed on a truck and driven to one of the collection camps. There a friendly *Ordner* managed to obtain her release on the basis of the certificate she carried attesting that she was exempt from deportation. She returned to her post at the hospital.

Most of the arrested Jews ended up in four principal locations. The Hermann Göring barracks were one; another was a former riding stable on Rathenowerstrasse. A third was the former Jewish home for the elderly on Grosse Hamburgerstrasse. The fourth main holding camp, perhaps the strangest of all, was installed in the plush Art Deco premises of the Clou, where Hilde Kahan's mother was confined. The Clou was a large restaurant and nightclub at Mauerstrasse 82. It had recently been closed because the existence of such places of entertainment was deemed incompatible with the total and increasingly desperate state of war in which Germany now found itself.

All of the roundups on February 27 were carried out by SS men from the elite *Leibstandarte* division, Hitler's corps of personal bodyguards. These were the hardest of all Germany's troops, men chosen for their strength and heartlessness, especially toward Jews. Armed with bayonets and whips when they arrived at the factories, they brutally herded the Jews onto trucks, shouting at them to move faster, beating people indiscriminately.

While the SS raided the factories, the Berlin police and the Gestapo fanned out across the city, arresting wearers of the yellow star on the streets and raiding Jewish apartments to pick up the elderly and the children who were too young to work. Although the raids on the factories all took place on February 27, the arrests on the streets, in apartments, and at Jewish institutions continued for twelve days. Gerda Haas, then a twenty-year-old nurse at the hospital, remembers how heart-rending she found it when the Gestapo assigned her and other hospital nurses to collect Jewish orphans who had been lodged with various Jewish families throughout the city. Each was given four or five addresses and told to go with a team of Gestapo and police officers, pick up the children, and have them at the collection point by 4:00 A.M. the next morning.

Unlike in previous deportations, the affected Jews were given no opportunity to prepare for travel. They were taken at their workplaces in the work clothes they had on, without luggage and, in many cases, as already noted, without even their outer garments. This time, because the Nazis were not seeking to beguile the victims into coming along docilely, there was no need to keep up the pretext that the Jews were being resettled. In carrying out earlier deportations, the SS and Gestapo had made some attempt to minimize overt brutality, at least in public venues. But in the *Fabrikaktion* the Jews were mistreated from the moment the SS arrived at the factories, so much so that one of the SS men involved, *Hauptsturmführer* Rudolf aus den Ruthen, was moved to write a letter of protest to a superior officer, Dr. Brandt. In it he described witnessing repeated scenes at the Clou in which crowds of Jews, many of them women, were beaten with whips as the *Ordner* loaded them onto the trucks that would carry them away for transport to the East. The beatings took place systematically, even though the Jews were moving as quickly as was possible. He wrote:

> I report this event to you in such detail . . . because I believe it would be well to remind all responsible offices to order all official actions regardless of particular circumstances to be carried out in strict compliance with regulations. This, in these particular cases, is not for principles of humaneness nor out of feelings for the prisoners. I believe that you also believe, dear Comrade Dr. Brandt, that anything else would not be compatible with true Germanic behavior. We certainly don't want to give the impression of being unfeeling sadists.

On February 27, 1943, Rosemarie H. was on a truck that carried workers from the battery factory where she worked. Only seventeen, Rosemarie was spunky and defiant. The indignities and privations that had been heaped upon her as a *Geltungsjude* had not broken her spirit. The workers from her factory were taken to the former stable located on Rathenowerstrasse. The scene that Rosemarie encountered there was no less hellish than what Inge London was facing in the Hermann Göring Kaserne. In the stables some two thousand people were crammed into a barren and inadequate space. They shivered in the bitter winter cold. Many among the crowd of prisoners were badly bruised, others bloody from their wounds. Laughing SS men stood around watching the prisoners and taking photographs.

Ruth and Eva Beleski also were in the crowd of prisoners on

Rathenowerstrasse. The sisters both worked at the I.G. Farben factory. Eva recalls that day:

> It's funny; people always know. When we left home that day we knew something was going to happen. My mother cried her eyes out when we left. And we knew and we went there like a lamb to the slaughter. And on our way there . . . (on that particular day we walked) . . . we met these two SS blokes. . . . And they asked us the way . . . and looked at us and smiled, very nice. And we looked at each other, and off we went. And when we got to the gates . . . we were welcomed with violence and onto the lorries right away. We knew but we could not do anything about it. What can you do? We had nowhere to go to.

The thought of going underground had passed through their minds, but they had rejected it.

> Who with? Who to? We didn't know anybody. . . . And the funny part was, on the lorry we sat on . . . there were a couple of SS blokes in charge and I looked at one, I stared at him, I was really near tears. And my sister wasn't frightened; [she said] "don't show them." And he had tears in his eyes that SS bloke. He didn't like what he was doing. But, it happens.

Back at the hospital, through all the confusion and despite the overwhelming fear they felt for themselves and their loved ones, most of the staff worked on. Preparing food for so many prisoners was a formidable task. Eventually, provisions were delivered to the collection camps and distributed, but only after as much as a night and a day had passed without the prisoners' having been given food or water. Nurses and orderlies from the hospital visited the collection camps to inquire about children or elderly people who might have been left at home without care and then spread out through the city to look after them. Others labored to bring whatever succor they could to the imprisoned Jews. Meanwhile, some of the full Jews among the hospital staff were being arrested and themselves thrown into collection camps. A few managed to negotiate their release, but not all of the hospital's employees or their families were as lucky as Hilde Kahan and her mother.

The depredations on the hospital staff left the institution seriously short-handed. A source of new blood would soon appear, however, as the result of one of the most extraordinary events of the Nazi period, the *Frauenprotest*, a public demonstration by Aryan wives and mothers, accompanied in some cases by their Aryan relatives, for the release of their Jewish husbands and *Geltungsjuden* children.

Rosemarie H. saw the entire *Frauenprotest* firsthand. At the Rathenowerstrasse stable where she was confined, the prisoners were made to line up and, one by one, appear before SS officers seated at a table. Ever meticulous in bureaucratic formalities, the SS men collected name, address, and date of birth from each prisoner, checking the information against their own records. Then each prisoner was given a tag bearing a number and destination for transport to the East.

After Rosemarie's information had been registered and checked, an SS officer took a placard on a string bearing a number and destination, Theresienstadt, and hung it around her neck. Rosemarie promptly took it off and handed it back. Then she drew from her pocket a copy of her mother's birth certificate, which showed that her mother was Aryan. Her mother had told her to carry it on her person at all times in case something like this ever happened. Rosemarie remembers, "They were very confused. They didn't know what to do with me." Finally the officer told her to "stand over there," in the corner. "I stayed there all day, but I sat on the floor. And some people I recognized I told them, 'Tell them that your mother is a Christian.'"

It appeared to the prisoners that actions like Rosemarie's had unnerved the SS and Gestapo. After a while, Rosemarie, the Beleski sisters, and the other young *Geltungsjuden* confined in the Rathenowerstrasse stables, as well as the Jewish husbands of

Aryan wives, were segregated from the other prisoners and then loaded again onto trucks and taken to a building on Rosenstrasse that had been confiscated from the Berlin *Gemeinde*. There they were joined by other Jewish spouses and children of Aryan women from other collection camps around the city, including Inge London from the Göring barracks. Men were confined on one floor, women on another. The toilet facilities were inadequate; there were long lines at all times in front of the few lavatories. There were no comforts; the rations were meager. But to the Jews who had been at places like the Hermann Göring Kaserne and the Rathenowerstrasse stables, the Rosenstrasse camp was a great improvement.

The stay on Rosenstrasse left indelible memories on everyone. Some two to three hundred women were confined together in an empty room. Ruth Beleski recalls: "Nothing to eat. They served, if I remember that correctly, one meal a day. I remember the sauerkraut. No spoon, nothing. And we still had an old ticket from the streetcar. It was made from cardboard. My sister and I had it and we used that for a spoon." The meager meals were supplied by the hospital. The hospital employees who delivered them asked for volunteers from among the prisoners to help in their distribution. Both Rosemarie and Inge stepped forward. They were permitted to carry food upstairs to the men's quarters. In this way both were able to locate their fathers and determine, to their relief, that they were still on Rosenstrasse and had not been badly injured.

Meanwhile, as the news of the raids spread through the metropolis and its suburbs, as husbands and children failed to return from work, their Aryan mothers and wives began to panic. Many went to the nearest police station or Gestapo post and demanded to know where their loved ones had been taken. Some mothers protested to the authorities that the arrests were illegal; Jewish spouses and half-Jewish children of Aryan women were supposed to be exempt from deportation. The wives and mothers quickly discovered where their husbands and children were being held.

Some, on making inquiries at the local police station, had been advised to go to Rosenstrasse for more information. Once a few knew what was going on, word spread quickly. Soon women began to appear in the street in front of the Rosenstrasse building. Some went home as evening fell, but others came, and many stayed through the night. They began to shout:

"Release our husbands." "Give back our children."

The chanting could be heard inside the building. Although the Gestapo and SS guards warned them to stay away from the windows, the inmates of the improvised Rosenstrasse collection camp could see the crowd that had gathered in the street. As the succeeding days went by, the number of demonstrators mounted. Some of the wives were joined by non-Jewish relatives; women came with their sisters and brothers. There even were men in military uniform in the crowd. The number waxed and waned throughout the day and night (the crowd was thickest in the evenings after working hours), but even through the night there were always people in the street in front of the building. It is not known how large the demonstration really was. Estimates vary from several hundred to several thousand. In light of the impact it had on the Nazis, however, it is hard to believe that the numbers were not substantial.

The days passed while the authorities, wracked with indecision, considered what to do. While they cogitated, on the night of March 1–2, 1943, Berlin was pounded with a major air raid. British bombers numbering around 250 dropped both explosive and incendiary bombs on the city. The Rosenstrasse building was spared, but St. Hedwig's Cathedral, only a few hundred meters away, received a direct hit. When the air raid sirens began to wail, the women in front of the building took shelter in nearby public shelters or in the Alexander Platz subway station. When the all-clear sounded, they emerged and resumed their vigil.

Inside the building, their husbands and children waited, wondering what was going on. Rumors repeatedly swept through the crowd of prisoners, some hopeful, others pessimistic. The naked brutality of the factory raids and the earlier confinements had been replaced with only a normal level of SS and Gestapo cruelty. That was better, but bad enough.

Rosemarie remembers that one of the women in the room where she was confined, seeing her mother in the street below, wrote a note and dropped it through the window. The Gestapo officers in their office on the ground floor saw the piece of paper flutter to the ground. A group of Gestapo men burst into the room and announced that because a paper had been thrown out of the window, a group of women would be taken downstairs to be punished.

"Twenty of you have to volunteer," they said. "If there aren't twenty who come voluntarily, then we'll come back and choose forty ourselves."

No one knew what the punishment would be. The Gestapo were perfectly capable of taking the twenty women outside and shooting them. A likely alternative was immediate deportation, probably to Auschwitz. The women argued and speculated, giving voice to their fears, but no one volunteered. Finally one woman, a former schoolteacher, spoke up.

"This is probably just a threat," she said. "I don't think they're going to kill or deport anyone over this. But, whatever they're going to do, it's better that only twenty suffer instead of forty. I'll go and I hope there are nineteen more of you who, for the greater good, will find the strength in themselves to withstand whatever the Gestapo has in mind."

Eventually nineteen other women also volunteered. The Gestapo men came back and escorted them downstairs. After a while they returned. No one had been killed or deported, but all had been beaten.

Day after day the protest continued. As the arrests of inter-married Jews and *Mischlinge* continued across the city and word of the Rosenstrasse protest spread, groups of Aryan relatives of arrested Jews appeared in front of other collection sites, demanding their release. But the largest protest remained that on Rosenstrasse.

The protesters held on tenaciously. On Thursday, March 4, there was a disturbance in front of the former *Gemeinde* building. Gestapo officers forcibly escorted ten of the demonstrating women away. One of them later reported that they had been taken to the Labor Bureau, where they were set to peeling potatoes all day until they were released. Others in the crowd noted what had happened and worried about the fate of the women who had been taken away. Some hung back a bit, but the demonstration went on, as it had since the day after the *Fabrikaktion*. Soon an open vehicle appeared carrying four SS men, two in front and two in back. The ones in back had machine guns. One of the SS officers ordered the crowd to disperse or be shot; then the vehicle drove straight into the crowd. The protesters were scattered momentarily as they ran and tried to find shelter. But, when the vehicle had passed, the crowd reappeared.

An even more dramatic scene occurred the next day. The street was full of protesters. Suddenly there was screaming, and people began to run away. SS men had appeared and posted two machine guns, training them on the crowd. There was no reason for the protesters to believe that the SS would not use those machine guns, that they would not ruthlessly shoot down as many women as it took to end the demonstration. Yet, despite the virtual certainty that deadly force would be used against them, some of the women stood their ground. Soon others who had fled began to return. Shouts could be heard, accusing the SS of being murderers and cowards.

A non-Jewish woman, protesting for the release of her Jewish husband, recalls the street as "dark with a sea of heads, a thousand people. I went there every day, and each day there were more and more." She remembers that the crowd grew to include even people who did not have any relatives imprisoned on Rosenstrasse.

"Murderers, murderers, murderers," the crowd shouted. The protesters saw an SS officer open his mouth and speak, but the noise was too great to hear what he said. Some feared that the command to fire had been given, but the crowd stood its ground. Instead of firing on the protesters, the SS officers dismounted their machine guns and went away.

On March 6, Goebbels, in his capacity as the *Gauleiter* of Berlin, gave the order for the release of the Jewish spouses and *Mischlinge* children imprisoned as a result of the roundups. Numbering some five to six thousand, they returned to their homes, where most survived to the end of the war. Thirty-six Jewish men who were married to Aryan women (twenty-five from the Rosenstrasse camp and eleven from the Grosse Hamburgerstrasse camp) had already been deported to Auschwitz, where fortunately they had been spared the usual "selection" and immediate gassing of those deemed unfit for work. Instead all had been sent to outlying work camps. They were brought hastily back to Berlin in a normal passenger train, with the exception of one who was too ill to travel. Because these men had witnessed conditions at Auschwitz, however, the Berlin Gestapo felt that they could not be allowed to mingle with the population at large. On their return to Berlin they were interrogated by the Gestapo and forced to sign false confessions to crimes punishable by death. Then, charged with capital crimes, they were interned in a labor camp in nearby Grossbeeren.

There is no doubt that the Rosenstrasse protest, coming as it did shortly after the Germans' disastrous defeat at Stalingrad and in the wake of the March 2, 1943, air raid, which brought massive death and destruction to Berlin, was the cause of Goebbels's decision. The spirit in which it was made is amply revealed by an entry in Goebbels's diary:

> Schacht gave me a long lecture about the current situation in Berlin after the last air raid. It is extremely serious. The damage done to the capital is very great and we judge that it will take six to eight months

before things are half way restored. Just at that moment the SD [security service] thought it was the right time to continue the evacuation of the Jews. Some rather unpleasant scenes took place before the Jewish old age home where the population had assembled in large numbers and even sided with the Jews. I shall give an order to the SD not to continue the evacuation of the Jews at such a critical time. We should wait a few more weeks and then carry out the operation more thoroughly.

(Goebbels appears to have confused the former Jewish old age home on Grosse Hamburgerstrasse with the former *Gemeinde* building on Rosenstrasse. The Grosse Hamburgerstrasse building was used as a *Sammellager* and a small demonstration occurred there as well, but the principal demonstration was on Rosenstrasse.)

On March 9, Goebbels visited Hitler, who assured him that he had responded correctly to the protests. But Hitler made it clear that eventually Goebbels would have to rid Berlin of its Jews — who, in the wake of the final wave of roundups, consisted almost entirely of *Mischlinge* and Jews living in mixed marriages. What the Rosenstrasse *Frauenprotest* had accomplished, in short, was a reprieve for some five or six thousand intermarried Jews and their offspring. As it turned out, the reprieve outlasted the war. The other Berlin Jews who were rounded up in the *Fabrikaktion*, some thirty-five thousand, were deported to Theresienstadt or Auschwitz. The majority of those who went to Theresienstadt were later shipped to Auschwitz or another death camp. Most of the thirty-five thousand perished.

For Berlin Jewry, the *Fabrikaktion* and the roundups that followed in the succeeding weeks meant the end of the road. When the operation was completed, all full Jews had been eliminated from the city, except for those who were living in hiding or with false identities, a small number who were protected by Nazi officials for various reasons, and the handful who remained on the staff of the hospital and the *Reichsvereinigung*. What remained of Berlin's Jews was a scattered and demoralized remnant.

For the hospital, the removal of the bulk of the remaining Berlin Jewish community posed two immediate threats. First, the sudden reduction of the potential patient population removed much of the rationale for the hospital's continued existence. The successful outcome of the *Frauenprotest*, however, ensured that a number of Berliners whom the Nazis classified as Jews, and thus automatically excluded from hospital services anywhere else, would remain in the city, at least for a while. The question was whether they would prove a sufficient basis for keeping the hospital open. Thus the hospital's future, already doubtful before the *Fabrikaktion*, was even more threatened. (Indeed, within days the Berlin Gestapo would make its move to liquidate the hospital entirely.) Second, the arrests and deportations of full Jews on the hospital staff had left the hospital short of workers, especially nurses and nonmedical personnel. This, too, could provide an excuse for the Gestapo to close it.

Just as the population provisionally rescued by the *Frauenprotest* gave the hospital a continued reason for being, so too did this population provide the answer to the shortage of staff: the young *Geltungsjuden*. We have seen how Ruth Beleski and her sister Eva, both working at an I.G. Farben factory, were picked up by the SS as they entered the factory gates, taken to the stables on Rathenowerstrasse, and from there transferred to Rosenstrasse. There, as the mopping-up phase of the *Fabrikaktion* continued and the demonstrations began in the street outside, a Gestapo officer came to the door of the room one day and announced that he needed somebody who could type. Although Ruth had secretarial training, she decided to keep silent. It seemed safer to remain in the room with her sister and the other women than to put herself, all alone, into the Gestapo's hands. But Eva spoke up.

"Here — my sister, my sister," she said, pointing to Ruth.

The Gestapo officer took Ruth out of the room and told her to stand in the corridor and wait. She stood in the hallway for hours. No one gave her any work to do; no one gave her any explanation. As the hours passed, her fear grew. She thought that the Gestapo were going to shoot her. The one meal the prisoners were given that day was distributed to the women inside the room, but she was given nothing to eat. Late in the day, with no explanation, the Gestapo officer came and pushed her back into the room.

The next day another Gestapo officer came. Just as before, he announced that a typist was needed. Upon returning to the room the preceding evening, Ruth had begged Eva not to repeat her impulsive action of the previous day. But her plea was to no avail. Eva believed that it could only help Ruth to have a skill that the Gestapo needed. So, when the Gestapo officer made his announcement, Eva once again spoke up and told him that Ruth was a good typist.

The officer escorted Ruth downstairs to the office in which the SS and Gestapo were recording the vital statistics of the prisoners. Ruth was put to work typing lists of the people who were being held in the building. The work was unrelenting. She typed for thirty-six hours straight, until finally she was so exhausted that she fell asleep at her typewriter. Throughout the day and night, as she worked, a Berlin policeman had sat behind her. Now, as she slumped into unconsciousness over the typewriter, the policeman leaned over and gently shook her awake.

"If I were you I wouldn't sleep here," he quietly said. His action may have saved her life.

When Ruth had completed her work, the Gestapo officer in charge — she remembers his name as Krell — asked her a series of questions about her secretarial skills and experience. Her answers must have been satisfactory, for, in her presence, he went to the telephone and made a call.

"Lustig," he said, "I have a secretary for you." Then he turned to Ruth. "I'm sending you to work at the Jewish hospital."

"I was in no position to make any demands," Ruth remembers, "but I did anyhow. I told Krell, 'I won't go anywhere without my sister.' To my surprise, he said, 'Your sister can go with you.'"

The two girls were released to return to their mother in Karlshorst and ordered to report to the Jewish hospital for work on

The hospital's main administration building in the 1930s, as seen from the corner of Iranischestrasse and Schulstrasse. *Jewish Museum Berlin. Photograph: Herbert Sonnenfeld*

One of the operating rooms in the 1930s. *Jewish Museum Berlin. Photograph: Herbert Sonnenfeld*

A hospital ward in the 1930s. *Jewish Museum Berlin. Photograph: Herbert Sonnenfeld*

The pharmacy shortly after the end of World War II. The man and woman on the right are Ehrich Zwilsky and his wife, Ruth. *Collection of Klaus Zwilsky*

Dr. Heinz Elkan.
Collection of Ruth Winterfeld

RIGHT: *Schwester* Ada (*left*)
and *Schwester* Carry. Ada's
right leg is bandaged as
a result of the injury she
suffered while illegally
riding the S-Bahn without
her yellow star. *Collection
of Carry Friedlander*

Patients and nurses in the 1930s. *Jewish Museum Berlin. Photograph: Herbert Sonnenfeld*

Dr. Hans Knopp surrounded by his admirers. *Collection of Carry Fried-lander*

Doctors and nurses taking a tea break at the hospital. The stars on their uniforms indicate that the picture was taken after September 1941. *Collection of Ruth Winterfeld*

RIGHT: The inscription KRANKENHAUS DER JÜDISCHEN GEMEINDE as it appears today, unchanged since before the advent of the Nazis, on the pediment of the original main administration building on Iranischestrasse. *Photograph: Daniel B. Silver*

LEFT: The principal medical building in the 1930s, seen through the main entrance gate on Iranischestrasse. *Jewish Museum Berlin. Photograph: Herbert Sonnenfeld*

RIGHT: Dr. Sally Herzberg (*right*) with Dr. Mendelsohn (first name unknown). *Collection of Klaus Zwilsky*

ABOVE: Dr. Herzberg lecturing in the nursing school, probably in the late 1930s. *Collection of Golly Dowinsky*

RIGHT: Golly Grünberg as a pediatric nurse in the late 1930s or early 1940s. *Collection of Golly Dowinsky*

BELOW: A snapshot taken in the hospital garden in March 1939 by *Schwester* Eleonora (Elfrieda Jeanette Bloch) before she emigrated to Britain. From left to right: Dr. Joachim Levy, Dr. Hans Knopp, Dr. Siegfried Ostrowski, Dr. Erich Fischer, and Dr. Gerald Glaser. *Jewish Museum Berlin. Jeanette Barth collection*

Schwester Eleonora (*left*) in March 1939 with colleagues in the urology department. Dr. Goldschmidt is in the background. The man holding the alarming apparatus in the foreground is Asch, a male nurse. *Jewish Museum Berlin. Jeanette Barth collection*

Schwester Eleonora tying Dr. Knopp's surgical gown, July 1939. Penciled on the back of the original snapshot is the note "Hans and I were thick as thieves." *Jewish Museum Berlin. Jeanette Barth collection*

The rededication of the hospital's synagogue after the end of the war.
Collection of Klaus Zwilsky

A demonstration by Jewish survivors after the war. The banner reflects
the tragic decline of the Berlin Jewish *Gemeinde* from 186,000 members
in 1933 to 5,100 in 1945. *Collection of Ruth Winterfeld*

March 9, 1943. Ruth remembers that when they arrived they were made to feel unwelcome because they and other half-Jews like them had been sent to replace full Jews who were slated for deportation. In her case it was Hilde Kahan whom Ruth was meant to replace. In the end, because of Lustig's intervention, Kahan kept both her job and her freedom, "but she always felt threatened. It was awful for us, it was awful for them, the situation."

Like the Beleski sisters, Inge London and Rosemarie H. also found themselves assigned to the hospital. The prisoners who were about to be released were told that they would not return to their previous jobs in munitions factories. Instead they were to be assigned to even more backbreaking and degrading tasks.

Ever feisty, Rosemarie H. remembers, "I wasn't going to clean latrines. They were looking for people to wash trains and clean streets and whatever they had to do. And I thought, 'I'm not going to wash their trains.'" She was spared by the appearance of a nurse named *Schwester* Maya who had been sent to Rosenstrasse from the hospital to choose twenty women as general laborers. Before working in a factory, Rosemarie had been assigned for a year to the Jewish old age home, the *Altersheim*, across Iranischestrasse from the hospital. She had met *Schwester* Maya while escorting residents to the hospital for medical attention. "She picked me as the first one, because she knew me. And then we got a paper and we were discharged."

Inge London was among the nineteen others whom *Schwester* Maya selected. As time went on, other young *Geltungsjuden* were also released from Rosenstrasse to work at the hospital, in some cases chosen by Dr. Lustig in person. This was the way in which the brothers Günther and Felix Rischowsky found themselves in forced labor at the hospital. Günther recalls:

On April 3, 1943, Dr. Lustig and Selmar Neumann (the administrator) appeared at the collection camp on Rosenstrasse with an SS staff sergeant to collect laborers for the Jewish Hospital among the young

Geltungsjuden. When a grounds-keeper was requested I volunteered and was accepted because of my training at Gross-Breesen. My brother Felix was not accepted. I told them that I would not go without my brother. Dr. Lustig did not want to cause trouble and declared that he would employ the two of us. Felix was to assist with autopsies. We reported on April 10, 1943 at Iranischestrasse. Hilde Kahan, Lustig's secretary, informed us that "Dr. Dr." was to be used in addressing Lustig. Dr. Heinz Elkan . . . took Felix into the pathology building. I was turned over to Inspector Chaskel who led me to the garden maintenance cellar. We worked as best as we could, more than was expected of us. We were aware that the hospital represented a fortress for life. We worked wherever we were assigned, whether at the child care center, in the garden, as roofers, for nailing in windows, as ward helpers, or as elevator operators.

The brothers' Jewish father also was assigned to the hospital, where he did clerical work. The energy and ingenuity of the Rischowsky brothers contributed greatly to the hospital's ability to muddle through as life in Berlin became increasingly difficult in the last years of the war. And, as two of only a handful of young men in an institution increasingly staffed by young women, they left a lasting impression on their female coworkers.

One cannot look back on the *Frauenprotest* on Rosenstrasse without wonderment and a painful sense of what might have been had Germans chosen to manifest opposition to Hitler's anti-Semitic measures earlier and in other circumstances. For the *Frauenprotest* demonstrated the extent to which, despite the totalitarian nature of the Nazi regime, Hitler feared social protest and depended on the cooperation of the German people to sustain the Nazi government. The persecution, torment, and eventual deportation of full Jews had passed with no significant adverse reaction from Aryan Germans, but when the Nazis' measures to annihilate Jews in mixed marriages and their *Mischlinge* children came into irreconcilable conflict with another key value of German culture, the maintenance of family life, at least some of the Aryan members of Berlin's intermarried families finally reached the limits of what they were willing to accept. Their reaction — the only public demonstration that ever occurred in Germany against the Nazi persecution of Jews — gave Hitler pause.

For Hitler and the Nazi leadership, the release of the husbands and children in response to the *Frauenprotest* was at most a tactical retreat. There was no lessening of zeal for their ultimate objective: to destroy the Jews. The deportation of most of the Jewish forced laborers left one conspicuous Jewish target in the Nazis' sights, the hospital — the last significant Jewish institution functioning in Germany and a place that harbored numerous Jews who were not protected by intermarriage or mixed parentage. It was only a matter of days until the Gestapo made its move.

9

THE CONTINUED ASSAULT
ON THE HOSPITAL

IN MARCH 1943 the *Fabrikaktion* was in its final days. The hospital was still reeling from the turmoil that the roundup of the Jewish workers, including many members of its own staff, had engendered. Hilde Kahan comments, "For us there was no more time to rest." On March 10 she was sitting at her desk in Dr. Lustig's outer office when two people, a Gestapo man and a criminal policeman, appeared asking for Lustig. They were soon joined by successive groups of officers from the Berlin Gestapo headquarters and the criminal police, until a total of ten officials were with Lustig in his office. Kahan received a note from the doorman informing her that Gestapo trucks were waiting in the street in front of the administrative building.

Kahan had no doubt as to what was going on. She was aware that, not long before, the Gestapo had arrived with trucks at the Jewish hospital in Munich in just the same fashion and had deported the entire establishment — patients, doctors, nurses, and all other employees. The arrival of so large a contingent of Gestapo and police officers, with trucks waiting in the street, could only mean that the hospital was about to be closed and everyone deported.

But Lustig was not ready to capitulate. He knew that, as a Jew, he could not argue against what was planned. What he could do was announce that he could not comply with the orders he was being given because they had not been approved by the hospital's direct bureaucratic overseer, the Jewish affairs department in the RSHA, whose head was the infamous Adolf Eichmann. He called Eichmann's office and explained what was going on. Then he handed the telephone to one of the Gestapo men. The officers who had been ordered to arrest the entire hospital population were told to stand down. The trucks drove away empty.

Drawing on both his reserves of courage and his intimate understanding of the German bureaucratic mentality, gained in his many pre-Nazi years as a senior official of the Berlin Police Presidium, Lustig had stared down the Gestapo. Although technically the RSHA and the Gestapo were part of the same organization and under the ultimate authority of the same leader, SS Führer Heinrich Himmler, in reality the huge German apparatus for exterminating Jews was rife with internal bureaucratic rivalries and tensions. Clearly, the Berlin Gestapo headquarters and the RSHA had conflicting aspirations for the hospital and for the prime piece of real estate it represented.

Within the hospital, there was no way to keep secret the news that the Gestapo had come to take away the entire hospital population. The trucks had stood in Iranischestrasse, where everyone could see them. For the staff and patients, a group of people whose nerves were already stretched to the breaking point, this must have been almost unbearable.

For some two weeks, the hospital had been at the center of the action as the *Fabrikaktion* proceeded implacably onward. Numerous doctors, nurses, and patients had been taken for transport to the East, even as the protest continued on Rosenstrasse. Doctors and nurses had been forced to go to the collection points and to witness the fear and suffering of the Jews who were awaiting deportation. Some had been pressed into service to act as *Ordner*. In that role, they were compelled to go to the apartments of doomed Jews, alone or in the company of the Gestapo or police, to bring people to the collection points. These included forced laborers who, for one reason or another, had not been at their workplaces on February 27, or family members of detainees who had been at home at the time of the raids — parents too frail to work, children too young for forced labor.

Back at the hospital itself, the repercussions of the *Fabrikaktion* were pervasive. Almost everyone had friends or relatives who had been taken. And for those with near ones who had not yet been arrested there was the constant fear that an arrest might happen at any time. As always, suicide cases poured into the hospital, an inescapable reminder of the disaster that was consuming Berlin Jewry.

Yet there is no indication that on March 10 the arrival of the Gestapo and the police caused panic at the hospital. Whatever sense of despair people may have felt, they maintained their self-control. Such outbursts as may have occurred must have been muted or few in number; no one who was there mentions them in recollections of the day. The same continued to be true over the next several days even as the drama continued to unfold.

The disappearance of the Gestapo and its trucks provided only a temporary respite; it was very brief indeed, according to Hilde Kahan. As she remembers it, half an hour after the trucks departed, three new visitors appeared in Lustig's office. They were the head of the Berlin Gestapo headquarters office, the director of the Berlin *Sammellager*, and Fritz Wöhrn, a specialist in the RSHA Jewish affairs department. The subject of their meeting with Dr. Lustig was the deportation of a significant proportion of the doctors, nurses, and administrative staff of the *Reichsvereinigung* health department, the hospital, and the remaining Jewish nursing homes. The outcome of the meeting was a decision that a full 50 percent of the personnel would be deported, together with their families. The officials ordered Lustig to prepare a list with the names of those selected and to hand it over to the Gestapo at 7:00 A.M. the following day.

No record has been found of this meeting, and the sharp-eared Hilde Kahan was on the wrong side of the door to hear what transpired. No one knows, therefore, what kind of bargaining went on, if any. Nor can it be known whether the decision to deport half of the health personnel in the remaining Berlin Jewish communal organizations was made then or earlier in the day.

Given the sequence of events, the decision to deport so many people looks like a bureaucratic compromise. One cannot be sure whether the policy of Eichmann's section of the RSHA was specifically to keep the hospital open or whether Eichmann preserved the hospital's existence to maintain bureaucratic primacy over the Berlin Gestapo, to assert the principle that no other office had the right to interfere with the Jewish institutions that had been placed under RSHA control. The decision at least partially satisfied the Berlin Gestapo's lust for Jewish bodies to fill the transports. Moreover, the Gestapo could have viewed such a large-scale deportation as validating its claim to have at least some jurisdiction over the hospital and its inhabitants.

Did Lustig originate this Faustian bargain, offering up fully half of the total number of his professional colleagues and employees as the price of saving the hospital, and thereby himself and his job? Or was this decision imposed on him in circumstances over which he had no control whatsoever? It is unlikely that anyone ever will know.

There ensued a terrible night. Hilde Kahan and another secretary in Lustig's outer office were kept at their desks all night. Lustig remained behind closed doors in his office, drawing up the lists. According to Kahan, he was assisted in this task by his two principal adjuncts, Selmar Neumann and Ehrich Zwilsky. From time to time, the secretaries were called in and names were dictated to them to be added to the typed list that was growing longer by the hour. In the end, counting both the employees and the members of their immediate families, there were three hundred names on the list.

Little is known about how the list was drawn up. In particular, it is unclear whether Neumann or Zwilsky made any independent contribution to the process. Among those who were selected for deportation, both then and later, a small number survived the camps. Most of them, not surprisingly, heaped bitter reproaches on Lustig for his role in choosing them to be deported; some included Lustig's assistants in their criticisms, based solely on their presence in the room with Lustig that night.

In fact, it seems unlikely that Lustig made his choices on a corrupt basis or based his decisions on improper suggestions from Neumann or Zwilsky. Five months earlier, when called upon by Günther to choose the communal officials who were to be deported in the *Gemeindeaktion,* Lustig had not turned to others for advice. Why, then, when faced with a similar task on the night of March 10, 1943, would he let the decisions be made by his assistants?

More plausible is the idea that Lustig was trying desperately to deal with this halving of his staff in a way that would permit the hospital to continue to function as a viable medical institution. Hilde Kahan reports that in the course of dictating names to her he explained that he was acting only to keep the hospital alive. "I have to run a hospital," he said, adding that he could not send away all the doctors or all the nurses or leave any other category of necessary personnel entirely stripped of staff, "because, after all, I still have sick people here." Similarly, he wanted the *Reichsvereinigung* to play an effective bureaucratic role in administering the affairs of whatever number of Jews might be left in Germany. If too many people or the most effective people in any department were deported, leaving that department incapable of functioning, the future of the whole entity would be at risk. It is believable that, in trying to plan how these entities could function at half their former staffing, he sought the advice of his two principal lieutenants, Selmar Neumann for the hospital and Ehrich Zwilsky for the *Reichsvereinigung.* But, even had he wished to choose the deportees based on his personal feelings about members of the staff, even had he no moral scruples against allowing his subordinates to make choices based on their likes and dislikes,

Lustig was intelligent enough to realize that giving in to this temptation could put his entire future in jeopardy.

If we will never know more about what was going on behind the closed doors of Lustig's office that night, what transpired outside those doors has been vividly described. Although Lustig enjoined Neumann, Zwilsky, and the two secretaries to maintain strict secrecy, there was no way to hide what was happening. The visit of the Gestapo with its trucks had put the entire hospital staff on alert. The appearance shortly thereafter of three high Nazi officials, all of them centrally involved in deporting Jews, heightened the speculation and tension. The disappearance of Lustig and his two principal assistants behind closed doors in the middle of the night, coupled with the noise of the typewriter in the outer office, told the story well enough to a population that already had been through fifteen months of deportations, repeated losses of loved ones, and constant wondering about when one's own name would be on the list for the next transport.

Throughout the evening and night, members of the staff hovered as close as they could to Lustig's office. Whenever the assistants or secretaries emerged for a moment, they encountered colleagues who were waiting in the corridor, hoping to find out what was going on and to determine whether they had been chosen. Hilde Kahan remembers that one colleague, who half a year earlier had been selected for a transport and at the last moment had been held back because of a sickness, and who had since then spoken often of suicide, looked at her with a sly expression and said, "I know that I am not on the list as long as you still look me in the eye." Kahan did look her in the eye, knowing full well that she had just typed her name on the list. (Once the deportation notices had been delivered, the unfortunate woman was closely watched to ensure that she did not kill herself.) Experiences like this made Kahan feel numb as she did her work. "The consciousness of our helplessness pushed me nearly to the ground."

The deportation of half of the staff and their families was a brutal blow to the hospital, in terms of both its ability to function and its morale. It was not, however, a fatal one. The medical staff, although materially diminished, still managed to cover the departments and medical services the hospital provided. The expertise of the deported doctors and nurses was irreplaceable, but the influx of young *Mischlinge* and Jewish men living in mixed marriages who had been released as the result of the Rosenstrasse protest provided at least some replenishment to the nursing and support functions.

For the dwindling number of full Jews on the hospital staff who either were unmarried or were married to other Jews and thus were not protected from deportation, the events of February and March 1943 created an atmosphere of impending doom. From one day to the next, there could be no assurance that any one of them was safe. The magnitude of their concern was increased by the arrival of new employees designated to take over their jobs. Hilde Kahan remembers being profoundly disturbed by the arrival of Ruth Beleski as her designated replacement. It confirmed her view that the Gestapo's aim was to eliminate all the "full Jews" and to replace them with Jews who had "Aryan relatives" and thus were not slated to be deported. Even though she escaped deportation and Lustig assured her that she would remain as his secretary, from then on she and her unprotected colleagues constantly feared that they were being allowed to continue working for only as long as it took to train their replacements.

In Hilde Kahan's case, the apprehension only too soon proved to be a reality. Not long after the *Fabrikaktion* and the mass deportation of hospital employees, she and her mother had been expelled from their apartment, since they were the only Jews remaining there. Always concerned about her mother's fate, Kahan had managed to secure a small room for the two of them in the hospital's maintenance building. The elder Mrs. Kahan was in that room when the Gestapo raided the hospital one day in May 1943.

Hilde Kahan was visiting one of the nurses when another nurse came running in, crying that Gestapo men were on the premises and had just arrested the hospital's social worker. Hilde hurried to the administration building, where she learned that a large number of Gestapo officers were there, picking up people for deportation. Among them, she was told, were the pharmacist and his wife. (The actual pharmacist, Kantelberg, was not Jewish, so this could only have meant the Zwilskys, since Ehrich Zwilsky had been a pharmacist before going to work for the *Reichsvereinigung.*)

Lustig was not in the hospital at the time. Because the Gestapo monitored the hospital's telephone lines, Hilde Kahan did not want to call him. Instead, she asked Kantelberg to go outside and call Lustig from a public telephone. Then she ran to fetch her mother, and the two women went to the kitchen for the all too familiar ritual of preparing sandwiches for the people about to be transported. It was not long before a Gestapo man and a criminal police officer arrived in the kitchen to arrest them. They were forced to return to their room and dress for their trip in the presence of the two men. Taking the knapsacks they kept already packed for such an eventuality, they were herded onto a truck and driven to the *Sammellager.* There they encountered many other employees of the *Gemeinde* and *Reichsvereinigung* whom they knew.

For Hilde Kahan and her mother this saga had a happy ending. Kahan claims that she was resolved not to lower herself by pleading for Lustig's intervention. She had reason to mistrust Lustig's attitude toward her; he had threatened her with deportation on several occasions. Once, warning her to maintain the strictest secrecy about the lists she was typing, he told her, "If you talk about the transports, you'll be the first on the list." Another time, when she asked if a typing job could wait until the next day, he replied, "If you would like to go to [the concentration camp at] Lublin, you can leave the work until tomorrow." This time, however, she received Lustig's help unasked. He apparently valued her secretarial services enough to pull whatever strings were necessary: in the morning he showed up at the *Sammellager*, and soon thereafter the *Ordner* told Kahan that she was free to return to her job. When she asked about her mother, however, she was told that the release order applied only to her.

"In that case, I'm not going," she replied.

Lustig and the *Ordner* in the *Sammellager* tried to persuade her to take the release that was being offered and leave the mother to her fate. They argued that the women's vow to stay together would prove unavailing, since everyone knew that as soon as they reached a concentration camp they would be separated. Hilde Kahan remained adamant, however, refusing to quit the *Sammellager* without her mother. To her surprise, after many hours had passed, she was told curtly to take her mother with her and leave.

The Zwilskys also were beneficiaries of Lustig's ability to influence the choice of deportees. Although word was out on the evening of the May 1943 raid that they were on the Gestapo's list, in the end they were not taken. Klaus Zwilsky, then an eleven-year-old boy, has no idea how the selection of people was made. He does recall, however, that his father once told him that at some point Lustig made a choice between the Zwilsky family and another family, that of the pediatrician Rosenberg, and that the Zwilskys had been spared at the expense of the others. Since accounts of the May raid suggest that on this occasion the Gestapo came already armed with a list, it appears that Lustig, in order to retain his trusted assistant, managed to persuade the Gestapo to substitute another family in their place.

Far less fortunate were two hospital staff members, nurse Golly Grünberg and her lover, Dr. Sally Herzberg, who was on the list of those who were rounded up in the same May raid. Their story demonstrates how successfully, even as late as the spring of 1943, the German authorities were able to deceive Berlin's Jews concerning the true nature of Theresienstadt and to dissimulate the Nazis' plan to kill most of the people they sent there.

Like many other *Geltungsjuden,* seventeen-year-old Golly Grünberg, returning after *Kristallnacht* to her high school in Bremen, had found the doors closed to her. Her ambitions to graduate high school and study at Bremen's Institute of Arts were shattered. Soon she learned that the only place remaining where Jewish girls could earn a state diploma was the hospital's nursing school. Although this would not have been her first choice of profession, she enrolled and spent the years 1940–43 there.

Working on the pediatric ward, she became aware of the handsome young internist, Dr. Sally Herzberg, Ruth Zwilsky's brother. Born in Breslau, he studied medicine there and came to work at the hospital in 1937. Fond of drinking milk, the young physician showed up in the pediatric ward every day to partake of the supplies made available to the children. His good looks and great sense of humor made him a favorite among the nurses, not the least Golly. Early on, he told Golly, "I'll never fall in love with — or marry — a nurse or a woman who smokes." Although she was both, the statement gave her no concern. She knew that he already was smitten, and the feeling was mutual. The atmosphere of fear in which they lived only intensified their relationship.

When Sally was taken during the Gestapo raid on the hospital, Golly and his family felt reassured by the fact that the transport on which he was scheduled to go was destined for Theresienstadt. Sally was held in the Grosse Hamburgerstrasse *Sammellager* for several weeks. During this time, Golly agonized over whether she should volunteer to follow her beloved to Theresienstadt. She wanted to be with him. Moreover, the thought that her half-Jewish status might be of help to him there weighed on her conscience. Word of her dilemma spread around the hospital, and many friends and colleagues offered their opinions, both for and against volunteering. In retrospect, she recognizes that the best advice she received was from *Schwester* Elli: "Golly, for something like this one does not volunteer!" Both Golly and Sally, however, believed the story the Nazis sedulously disseminated, that Theresienstadt was a self-governing Jewish community where deportees from Germany were allowed to live in some degree of comfort and dignity, an impression fostered by carefully censored letters that those remaining in Berlin received from earlier deportees in Theresienstadt. Golly decided to volunteer and joined Sally in the *Sammellager.*

> Sally was sitting on the floor among some of his friends and colleagues when he saw me walk through the door and felt me fall into his outstretched arms. His elation upon seeing and holding me hardly knew any bounds, neither did our belief that we *were* doing the *right* thing; that we *would* survive what it was that's in store for us; we were young; we were strong; we were healthy and, most importantly, we were *together!*

Sometime later, to their surprise, Lustig appeared at the *Sammellager* and read out a list of some ten to fifteen names of detainees who were to be released and allowed to return to the hospital. When he called out Sally's name, the young doctor, without hesitation, shook his head and announced that he wished to stay on the transport. He explained that this way he could be sure of going to Theresienstadt and of being with his sister Gisela Kozower and her husband and children, who already had been sent there. If he missed this transport, he said, who knew how long it would be — maybe only weeks — before he would find his name on the list for another transport, perhaps this time to Poland. Lustig made no effort to change Sally's mind.

Golly stayed by Sally's side, and the same year, the couple married in Theresienstadt. Rabbi Leo Baeck performed the ceremony. In the fall of 1944, only months before the end of the war, Sally Herzberg was sent to Auschwitz. Once again, the Nazis offered Golly the chance of following him. Believing the Nazis' promise that wives would be reunited with the husbands they chose to join in Auschwitz, she accepted, but she never saw Sally again. He had been gassed on his arrival.

The May 1943 roundup was atypical in that the Gestapo arrived with a list of deportees apparently drawn up without Lustig's participation. In most cases, although specific individuals were taken for deportation for specific reasons, such as punishment for an infraction of the Nazis' rules, the Gestapo levied a numerical quota and left it to Lustig to make the selections. The aim was to make efficient use of the trains that Adolf Eichmann and his henchmen were scheduling to carry Jews to the East. Each transport had to have the requisite number of Jews to fill the train. Thus saving one person almost always meant sacrificing another. Hilde Kahan takes pride in the fact that she and her mother were released from the *Sammellager* without anyone else's having been arrested in their place, but whether this really was the case is open to question. In all likelihood, somewhere in Berlin two more Jews were rounded up to fill the Kahans' places on the transport; at least Hilde Kahan (unlike Ehrich Zwilsky) did not have to bear the burden of knowing who they were.

As time passed and the number of Berlin Jews who were left to fill the transports grew smaller and smaller, the hospital and the remaining nursing and old age homes, with their concentrated population of Jews who could be seized with minimal effort, became more and more inviting targets for the Gestapo. Over a short period, the Gestapo eliminated the *Siechenheim*, the nursing home attached to the hospital, and the other two remaining Jewish nursing homes in Berlin, located at 15–16 Auguststrasse and Elsässerstrasse 54. The raids on the Auguststrasse and Elsässerstrasse nursing homes came within days after the June 1943 dissolution of the Berlin *Gemeinde* and the deportation of its last president, Moritz Henschel, together with the formal dissolution of the *Reichsvereinigung*. The list of patients was provided to Lustig eight days in advance with the statement that the deportees were to be transferred to a hospital in Theresienstadt. The Gestapo's list contained the patients' names and details of the medical treatment each had been receiving. The total number of patients deported on this occasion ran to some three hundred, plus a number of medical personnel. According to Kahan, the victims bore their fate stoically. There was no whimpering or crying in response to commands issued by the *Ordner*, even though most of the patients probably knew that theirs was a journey from which they would never return.

The announcement that Theresienstadt was the destination was greeted with relief and even pleasure by the doctors and nurses who had been listed to join the nursing home inmates in their deportation. Their hospital colleagues organized a party for them to celebrate their supposed good luck in being sent to Theresienstadt instead of to Poland.

The authorities moved in a similar fashion against the *Siechenheim*. Lustig's office received an order one afternoon to prepare for deportation bedridden patients in the *Siechenheim* whose names the Gestapo provided; the list also contained the patients' ages and medical particulars. The staff was given two hours to produce the deportees ready for transportation to the *Sammellager*, from which they were to be shipped to Theresienstadt. Kahan reports that, when the hospital staff protested that these patients were too sick to be transported, the Gestapo was unmoved, since it was prepared to have them carried away on stretchers if need be. Kahan's description of the incident shows the single-mindedness of the Nazis' anti-Jewish mania. They were completely indifferent to the fact that the people whom they were about to cart away were old, helpless, and on the verge of death, entirely incapable of performing any of the imaginary evils the Nazis attributed to the Jews.

In the two hours allotted by the Gestapo, the hospital's social worker and nurses rushed to ready the patients for their journey. They dressed them warmly and packed for each a small bundle containing underwear, shoes, and a warm blanket. Many of the patients, even if not normally incontinent, had to be diapered and then rediapered because they kept wetting themselves out of fear. Thus the process of getting the patients ready went slowly, as did the loading of the trucks. When the trucks failed to leave at the end of the two hours, the telephone began to ring every few minutes in Lustig's office; the Gestapo wanted to know why it was taking so long. Someone explained that the delay was due to the fact that most of the old people had trouble climbing up onto the trucks.

"Give them a kick in the ass," the voice on the other end of the line replied. "That'll speed things up."

In these actions, as in so many other deportations, the Gestapo's preferred victims were the most helpless segments of the patient population. After the elderly and chronically ill, the next target was the mental patients, who had arrived in 1942 when, as we have seen, the Gestapo had turned the hospital into a kind of ghetto for Germany's remaining Jewish mental patients. These patients usually held foreign passports, since the Jewish mental patients of German nationality already had been eliminated. Many had been "euthanized" right there in Germany, as had many Aryans who were mentally ill or mentally defective. Thus the secret killing of the mentally ill, which in some respects was the Germans' trial run for their genocide against the Jews and Gypsies, constituted an "equal opportunity" murder program, one of the rare instances in which the Nazis put Jews on an equal footing with Aryans.

For a brief period, the hospital provided a sheltering environment for the unfortunate surviving Jewish mental patients. As director of the psychiatric ward, Dr. Pineas was keenly aware of the hospital's shortcomings:

> The facilities of the ward were extremely primitive, the nursing care by totally untrained personnel was completely inadequate. What the situation was regarding nutrition one can easily judge for oneself, given the limitations on food supplies. Still, the most essential examinations, tests of cerebrospinal fluid and Cardiazol treatment were carried out in the case of schizophrenics. Besides that, I also had nu-

merous cases of nervous diseases in the private ward. To have to work
under such inadequate conditions was torture.

Notwithstanding its limitations, the psychiatric ward did provide
care for its patients. Although little treatment could be provided,
the patients' symptoms were kept more or less under control by
keeping busy at least those patients who could do some form of
work and by giving the inmates access to the fresh air in the hospital's spacious gardens.

Some of the mental patients were quite happy in their new
home and became familiar and useful members of the hospital population. Hilde Kahan remembers two in particular. One,
known popularly as Evchen, or "little Eve," was a transvestite
who formerly had been the chief engineer for a large electrical
utility. He became the institution's horologist, in charge of repairing all the clocks. Instead of jam sandwiches, to which he was
entitled as compensation for his efforts, he asked the nurses to
give him jewelry and articles of clothing. Another of the mental
patients, Fridolin, was a craftsman and liked to assist the hospital's maintenance staff. The tragic peculiarity of his case was that
he was not actually Jewish. He had fled from Aryan asylums ob-
stinately insisting that he preferred to be in a Jewish asylum. (In
Nazi Germany if anything was proof of insanity, that had to be it.)
His predilection for a Jewish environment ended up costing him
his life, but in all likelihood it would have been forfeit in any
event — he had been institutionalized for sex offenses and consequently would have been a prime candidate for either "euthanasia" or a death camp.

The brief idyll of the mental patients was not to last long. One
day a Gestapo official visited the hospital and was appalled that
mental patients were wandering freely around the gardens. Fearing that one might attack him on some future occasion, he issued
an order that the mental patients be confined to their wards. Under those conditions, the task of the doctors and nurses was significantly increased. Without adequate medication and deprived

of the occupational therapy and access to the outside that had helped keep the patients quiescent, the staff now had more difficulty trying to keep them under control.

This was a challenge that did not last long, however. Now, as 1943 drew to a close, a year and a half after the transfer of the mentally ill to the hospital, the protected status of the mental patients came to an end. The Gestapo issued an ultimatum requiring the foreign governments in question to take steps to protect their nationals by July 31, 1943. None of them took any action. Freed from whatever concern about foreign reaction had kept these patients from being deported or killed before then, the Gestapo acted. The patients' foreign passports, which the hospital had been holding for them, were confiscated, and on November 21, 1943, the hospital's entire psychiatric population was shipped to Theresienstadt, accompanied by several nurses.

Hilde Kahan tells of receiving one day, probably about a year or more later, a document from the office of Walter Dobberke, the Gestapo commandant of the *Sammellager* on the hospital's grounds. (This incident could have occurred no earlier than 1944, since the *Sammellager* was located elsewhere in Berlin before that.) On one side was a list of mental patients who had been at the hospital, along with their nationalities. On the other side was a secret order from the Berlin Gestapo headquarters. It read: "The mentally ill Jews are to be summarily shot in the forest of Sachsenhausen near Oranienburg."

To Hilde Kahan the piece of paper, clearly sent by mistake, was a hot potato. She immediately gave it to Lustig and asked that he return it to Dobberke without letting him know that others had seen it. She knew full well that if the Gestapo discovered that she had become privy to this incriminating information her own life would be in peril. Another telling piece of paper relating to the fate of Jewish mental patients also came into Kahan's hands. This was a bill sent to the *Reichsvereinigung* by an insane asylum in Chelm, a Polish town near Lublin. It demanded fifty marks per head for the expense of cremating several hundred Jewish mental patients who reportedly had died there. Their only "treatment" undoubtedly had been to be put to death.

With the deportation of so many hundreds of the elderly, bed-ridden, and mentally ill from the hospital, not to speak of half the staff in March 1943 and many more at intervals thereafter, one might wonder how there could have been anyone at all left at the war's end, let alone some 800 people. The answer lies in two factors. The first is that the hospital was a very large institution. In the 1942–43 period, when the Gestapo's depredations were at their height, the hospital had 600 beds. Of those, 120 had been added to house the mental patients who had been brought to the hospital from around Germany. Even not counting the psychiatric ward, at 480 beds the hospital was a large medical facility, and, in the 1942–43 period, all those beds were occupied. Before the medical staff began to evaporate through deportations, emigrations, and flight into illegal existence, the complement of doctors, nurses, and support staff for a hospital of that size had been very large.

The second factor, as mentioned earlier, is that the hospital's population was periodically replenished by the arrival of different groups — patients, including the mentally ill, and nonpatients, such as intermarried Jews and part-Jews who had been bombed out and orphans who had nowhere else to go when the Nazis closed Jewish orphanages. Late in the war, there was another influx of nonpatients, this time resulting from a Gestapo initiative in other parts of Germany to separate Jewish men living in mixed marriages from their Aryan spouses and to bring them to the hospital.

This was an example of the unremitting efforts of Nazi zealots at lower levels and in the provinces to undermine the high-level decisions that protected Jews living in mixed marriages. One tactic was to separate Jewish men from their Aryan spouses in the hope that this would be a first step toward persuading or forcing the parties to divorce, thus ending the Jewish husband's protected status. In 1943 a number of Jews living in mixed marriages in

Hamburg, Frankfurt am Main, and other places were brought to Berlin and lodged in the hospital. The Gestapo assigned these men to work on the reconstruction of a building at 116 Kurfürstenstrasse that formerly had been owned by a Jewish fraternal association. The building had been confiscated by the Security Service and the Gestapo, which were in the process of fortifying it and constructing underground bunkers and other defenses for use in a possible final battle with the Allies. (As it turned out, all these precautions were unnecessary, since Gestapo personnel were among the first to run away when it became clear that the city was going to fall.) Later, a second contingent of Jewish men married to Aryan women came to the hospital from Westphalia and the Rhineland. These people, part of a larger group of men forcibly separated from their wives and sent to various labor camps, had become too ill or weak to perform hard labor and so were shipped to the hospital.

To Bruno Blau, who had spent long months in the hospital's prison ward, the way these men were treated made them the equivalent of prisoners. They were confined to the hospital grounds and permitted to write only one letter a week. Although brought there because they were unfit to work, the Gestapo nonetheless assigned them various tasks. Shortly before the end of the war, in what was possibly the most bizarre episode in the hospital's history under the Nazis, the Gestapo set up a workshop for the manufacture of children's clothing in one of the large halls. The Jewish men from the Rhineland and Westphalia, together with prisoners in the *Sammellager* who were awaiting deportation, were set to work sewing the clothing in two shifts, day and night. This undertaking may well have been a personal enrichment scheme on the part of the Gestapo officers involved. No one was paid a salary, there was no rent to pay, and the heat and power came from the hospital's budget. The only manufacturing expense, therefore, was the cost of raw materials. It is not known who benefited from the profits.

Another reason the hospital remained populated until the end of the war is that it became the seat of the rump *Reichsvereinigung* (often called in German the *Rest-Reichsvereinigung*). As we shall see, this organization continued its activities, under Lustig's direction, without interruption even after the Nazis officially dissolved it. The organization's offices were located in the hospital's administration building. There, a small staff, including Ehrich Zwilsky, whose life Lustig bartered to save, carried out the work of the *Reichsvereinigung*. A number of those administrators lived in rooms at the hospital, sharing with others a precarious existence as the war entered its final phase.

10

PRISONERS AND SURVIVORS

ON A COOL BERLIN summer's day in July 1943, SS *Hauptsturm-führer* Fritz Wöhrn arrived at the hospital for one of his frequent unannounced inspections. As a special case officer in the hospital's bureaucratic master, the *Judenreferat* (Jewish affairs department), subsection B of Department IV of the RSHA, he had been assigned responsibility for the direct supervision of the hospital. On this occasion, he began, as was his custom, with a visit to Lustig.

From the window of Lustig's first-floor office, Wöhrn noticed, about ten meters away, an attractive young woman leaning out of one of the windows in a hospital corridor, watching children at play below in the garden. Wöhrn was moved neither by the young woman's healthy, attractive appearance nor by the innocent pleasure she was taking in watching the children. All he noticed was that she was not wearing a yellow star. He ordered Lustig to have her summoned at once. Lustig picked up the telephone and instructed Hilde Kahan to find the girl and bring her to his office. Thus began the nightmare that was to lead Ruth Ellen Wagner to her death in Auschwitz five months later.

The daughter of a Jewish father and an Aryan mother, Ruth Wagner was one of the Rosenstrasse *Mischlinge* who had come to work at the hospital in March 1943. She was employed as a stenotypist in the office of the *Reichsvereinigung*. Because she was classed as a *Geltungsjude*, she was subject to the regulations requiring Jews to wear the yellow star. By order of Eichmann's office, these regulations had been extended to apply even within the hospital's buildings and grounds, despite the fact that the institution, by Nazi law, was open only to Jews. Accordingly, all personnel were required to have the star tightly sewn on their office apparel, smocks, uniforms, or surgical gowns. Ruth Wagner, twenty-one years old at the time, was one of several young women who rebelled against this requirement. While she carried a star and a safety pin around with her at all times in case of need, she did not sew the star onto her clothing.

With Lustig and Wöhrn expecting her appearance within minutes, there was no time for Ruth to do anything about the absence of the star except to pin it onto her dress. The trembling young woman was ushered into Lustig's office, where the SS officer, notorious for his anti-Semitic brutality, coldly eyed her. He saw immediately that the star was not sewn on and took note of the fact that she was made up with lipstick and fingernail polish, which Jews were not supposed to wear. Wöhrn did not arrest Fräulein Wagner on the spot, however, but instead sent her to bring him her coat so that he could see whether, as she had claimed, the star was tightly sewn to it.

Hilde Kahan and other hospital employees did their best to avert the impending disaster. Wagner came out of Lustig's office in tears, saying that she was supposed to bring Wöhrn her overcoat with the star sewn onto it but that she couldn't because the coat had no star. Hilde Kahan told her to go to the corridor where the young woman's coat was hanging and that she would follow with a star and a sewing kit. Wagner left the outer office and Kahan quietly followed, carrying the spare star and sewing kit she kept in her desk for just such an emergency.

The ruse failed, however. No sooner had Kahan returned to her desk than Wöhrn and Lustig came into the anteroom, asking where Fräulein Wagner was. Kahan had no choice but to tell them where the girl was to be found, and there, in a corridor, they surprised her in the act of stitching the star to her coat. Wöhrn began to yell and curse. Attracted by the noise, the hospital's personnel officer, Kleemann, stepped out into the corridor to see what was going on. Wöhrn ordered Kleemann to slap Fräulein Wagner in the face. Kleemann took the young woman into his office, which was next door to Lustig's. There he shouted abusively and made a noisy pretense of slapping her, hoping that this would allay Wöhrn's anger and spare Ruth further punishment. Wöhrn was not fooled, however. He had the young woman locked up in a small room near the gatekeeper's lodge. Several hours later, she was picked up by another SS officer and taken to the *Sammellager.* Before the year ended she was dead.

Fräulein Wagner's fate was the daily nightmare that haunted every Jew at the hospital. More than half a century later, her case and others like it remain alive in the memories of survivors. The tenuous nature of the hospital population's existence was demonstrated over and over. There were the Gestapo's repeated demands that Dr. Lustig reduce the staff by designating quotas of employees for deportation. There were the visits of Eichmann and members of his staff in which patients were chosen to be sent to the East. There were arrests of staff members on the streets and on the hospital grounds for infractions — real or pretended — of the myriad oppressive rules to which Jews were subjected.

Yet, despite these assaults against the hospital population, when the war ended some eight hundred people had survived. The prisoners left in the *Sammellager* when the Gestapo fled survived only because time ran out on the Nazis before they could load these victims onto a transport to a death camp. The others survived for more complex reasons. In the race against death, the eight hundred or so people who were liberated in April 1945 were the winners. On the other side of the balance were the losers, the thousands — the number is not known with any degree of precision — who passed through the hospital as patients on their way to a terrible fate or who were taken from the hospital's staff to be deported.

Many of the losers fell prey, like Fräulein Wagner, to the Nazis' predilection for seizing on minor rule violations as a basis for deporting *Mischlinge* or Jews living in mixed marriages who otherwise would have been saved. Wöhrn was a past master at this maneuver. His position entitled him to drop in on the hospital unannounced whenever he felt like it. At these surprise intrusions, he reveled in entering a room and making the entire staff present stand at attention while he conducted his inspection. As illustrated by his persecution of Ruth Wagner, he was unrelenting in his search for faults that could justify punitive action and obsessed with the proper sewing on of the yellow star. The lucky among the staff suffered no more than Wöhrn's vitriolic verbal abuse, the reasons for which were entirely capricious. For example, in June 1943 he confronted young Günther Rischowsky in the hospital garden and showered him with insults for allegedly having planted the potatoes too far apart. His favorite response on uncovering any infraction by a staff member, however slight, was to tell Lustig or another hospital administrator that the guilty party was to have his head beaten to a pulp. Although they never carried out this instruction literally, just hearing it was sufficiently demeaning and frightening.

Another of Wöhrn's arrests that members of the hospital staff found unforgettable was that of Kurt Bukofzer, who died for a well-meaning slip of the tongue. Again, the occasion was one of Wöhrn's unannounced inspections. On an October day in 1943 the young *Mischling* was temporarily manning the doorman's booth. As Wöhrn strode through the main entrance, the SS man called out imperiously, "Is Lustig on the premises?"

"Herr *Obermedizinalrat* Dr. Dr. Lustig is in his room," the frightened young man replied. The new recruits who arrived after the *Fabrikaktion* had been briefed by their supervisors: Lustig insisted on being addressed by his multitudinous official titles, even though the Nazis long since had rendered them invalid. The sudden appearance of the hospital Jews' most persistent nemesis had unnerved Bukofzer, and he apparently had not had the wit to realize that this rule applied only out of the Nazis' hearing.

Bukofzer's reply sent Wöhrn into a paroxysm of rage. He berated the temporary doorman for having had the temerity to apply an honorific to Lustig.

"Jews no longer have titles," he shouted. He called for Lustig and Selmar Neumann. When they appeared, Wöhrn passed sentence.

"Lustig, he is going to Hamburgerstrasse," he said, referring to the *Sammellager* then located on Grosse Hamburgerstrasse. Wöhrn then issued his customary order to have the accused struck on the head. Hoping that corporal punishment would slake Wöhrn's blood lust and avert the threatened deportation, Neumann beat the young man vigorously on the head, but the befuddled and terrified Bukofzer only stood there and grinned. Later that day he was arrested and taken away, not to the *Sammellager* but to a labor camp near Berlin. The mistreatment he suffered there caused him to collapse, and he was brought back to the hospital, this time as a patient in the police ward. He died there on September 22, 1944.

On another occasion when Wöhrn was prowling around the hospital, he encountered someone in the garden who he thought did not look Jewish. He immediately accosted the man and asked to see his identity papers. On determining that the visitor indeed was an Aryan, Wöhrn demanded to know what he was doing there. The man explained that he was a former patient of Dr. Windmüller, a hospital doctor who lived with his wife on the premises. Although Nazi law now forbade his former physician from treating him, the man had remained friendly and had come to bring a small gift to the Windmüllers. Wöhrn sent the visitor away with a warning that he would be punished if he ever appeared again at the hospital. Dr. and Mrs. Windmüller were on the next transport and were never seen again.

The inspections conducted by Eichmann and Wöhrn were episodes of terror for the hospital staff. Employees tried to scurry into secluded parts of the buildings and stay out of sight, but many had to remain at their posts. Ruth Beleski felt particularly exposed on the occasions when she had to sit in for Hilde Kahan in Lustig's outer office. "I always tried to stay away, but you had a job to do too. If you weren't there, you were gone too." Harry Brod, whose late mother was a hospital nurse, remembers what she told him:

> When quotas were not being met, Eichmann personally went through the hospital picking those to be taken. He assembled a meeting of the hospital staff at which he went through the ranks pointing at people: "You, you, you," he said, as his assistant wrote names on a clipboard. My mother noticed that he was singling out those who were fat and wore glasses. She fit both categories. As his gaze was turning to her area of the group, she bent down behind a taller nurse standing in front of her. She was passed over.

That Adolf Eichmann personally visited the hospital to select patients and staff for deportation seems to be a little-known aspect of a career that has received enormous scrutiny, not least in the course of his trial in Jerusalem. The picture of Eichmann emerging from his trial was that of a bureaucratic enabler, a man who directed the logistics of the Final Solution and managed the paperwork, but who remained remote from the actual fate of individual victims. To find that in fact he looked some of those victims in the eye and selected them to be deported from their hospital beds challenges one's preconceptions, to the point of raising doubts as to whether the reports about Eichmann's personal intervention at the hospital are correct and whether the actions of his subordinate Wöhrn might have been projected onto him. Yet several survivors independently report that Eichmann visited the hospital in person, and, since the same individuals also vividly remember Wöhrn, it does not appear likely that they could have confused Eichmann with his henchman.

An interesting question is why Eichmann's personal role in persecuting hospital patients and staff was not discovered and adduced in evidence at his trial. It would have gone a long way, one might have thought, toward controverting the image that Eichmann sought to create of himself as a cog in the bureaucratic machinery, actuated only by the need to do his job and not by anti-Semitic animus or evil motive. In the absence of any answer to this question one can only speculate. It is probable that the prosecutors' research simply was not thorough enough to unearth this particular facet of Eichmann's career, that the Berlin Jewish Hospital was too minor a detail to attract anyone's attention, especially in preparing for a trial that was to serve as a showcase to educate young Israelis and the world about the devastating extent of the Nazis' genocide. Moreover, even had the hospital and the role Eichmann played been known to the prosecutors, it seems doubtful that the Israeli prosecutors would have wanted to draw attention to the fact that there were Jews under Eichmann's direct control who survived in Germany. In a trial that depicted the Holocaust in stark contrasts of black and white, the saga of the hospital would have introduced an unwelcome tint of gray.

It would be natural to assume that the occupants of the police ward were destined to end up in the loser column, but this was not always the case. Paradoxically, being under arrest for some specific infraction over and above simply being Jewish saved a small number from being sent to a death camp. Throughout the Nazi period but in greatly increased numbers from *Kristallnacht* through the period of the deportations, German Jews (mostly men) were arrested on a variety of charges and incarcerated — sometimes in jails, sometimes in one of the many harsh labor camps on German soil, most often in one of the concentration camps inside Germany. Many Jews were murdered in these camps, but not all were.

Conditions in the labor and concentration camps were not easy to survive, and, once the deportations were in full swing, Jewish inmates were at risk of being sent to Auschwitz or another of the death camps. For example, there was a mass deportation of hundreds of Jewish prisoners from the Sachsenhausen concentration camp. Yet, for reasons that defy explanation, some Jewish inmates were not deported. And, as we have seen, among those who remained in the concentration camps, as well as those in the *Sammellager* and even aboard the transports, on occasion an individual who fell ill was sent to the hospital's police ward to be treated. While this was intended to be a way station on the road back to a labor or concentration camp or onward to a death camp, sometimes a police ward patient remained under treatment long enough to be saved by liberation.

The number of prisoners in the police ward varied. Bruno Blau counted about twenty at the time he was first incarcerated there, but the number grew over time to some eighty. For the prisoners, the police ward represented a marked improvement over conditions in the jails, labor camps, and concentration camps from which they had been transferred. They received the same medical care and food as the regular patients; indeed, "frequently they received extras, which the patients did not get." They also were permitted to go outside twice a day. Those who were capable of working were assigned light tasks, such as working in the hospital kitchen or cleaning the hospital, the streets, or the Gestapo office in Französischestrasse.

Nonetheless, these patients existed in a climate of constant fear. In addition to having the omnipresent risk of being sent to a death camp, life in the police ward grew especially risky as the Allied bombing intensified. The police ward was located on the top floor of the main medical building, closest to whatever might fall from the skies. For the rest of the hospital's population the network of underground passageways served as bomb shelters where patients and staff could take shelter the moment the air raid alarm sounded. The patients in the police ward, however, initially were not permitted to use these shelters. Then, as the intensity of the raids in the immediate vicinity of the hospital increased, it was decided that the police prisoners also could be taken to the basement, but only with the Gestapo's prior approval. Obtaining Gestapo approval by telephone took so long that often the hospital was under active bombardment before the police prisoners could be moved.

Although the hospital itself was not a target, some industrial facilities in the Wedding district were, and the Allied bombing of the neighborhood was frequent and heavy. The hospital suffered considerable physical damage, very little of it from direct hits. Most resulted from the air pressure of nearby explosions and from flying shrapnel and debris. Eventually in the course of one raid, the bombing was so close and so heavy that the male nursing assistant who had been left in charge of the police ward took it upon himself to bring the prisoners down to the basement without Gestapo permission. This initiative did not lead to adverse consequences, and thereafter the inmates of the police ward regularly were taken to the basement when the raids began, without prior Gestapo authorization but under the guard of two *Reichsvereinigung* officials.

Bruno Blau was one of the winners who survived the war at the hospital. He identifies a number of others who passed through the ward, most of whom died but a few of whom survived. Some were notable figures, such as Theodor Wolff, who had been a well-known writer and the editor of the important newspaper *Berliner Tageblatt*. Wolff had left Germany in 1933 and settled in Nice. He was arrested there after the Germans conquered France and taken back to Germany, where he was successively held and interrogated in a large number of different Gestapo posts and civil prisons until he developed an inflammation on his arm and was sent to the hospital's police ward. There he was operated on, but he died of heart failure some ten days later at the age of seventy-six.

Another notable police ward inmate was the well-known economist Professor Dr. Franz Eulenberg, who had been the head of the Berlin School of Commerce. He had been baptized in his youth and was a practicing Christian with no ties to the Jewish community, but by Nazi lights he was still a Jew. His marriage to an Aryan should have protected him from deportation. However, he was arrested by the Gestapo because his secretary, who was Jewish, went into hiding from the Gestapo, although she continued to show up for work with Eulenberg. When she finally was arrested, her boss was accused of "aiding and abetting Jews" and was destined to be sent to a concentration camp as punishment. He fell ill while in Gestapo custody and was sent to the police ward, where he soon died.

A distinguished scientist who passed through the police ward was Dr. Ernst Eichengrün, a chemist at the Bayer works who had invented aspirin. Also protected from deportation because he lived in a mixed marriage, he had continued to work for Bayer, but his continued productivity on behalf of his employer led to his downfall. In applying for a patent on one of his inventions he omitted the obligatory middle name *Israel* from his signature. For this he was arrested and, having fallen ill in custody, was sent to the hospital as an inmate of the police ward. When he recovered he was sent to Theresienstadt, where Bayer had a laboratory set up for him so that he could continue his work for the firm's benefit.

One of the lucky ones was a police ward inmate named Fildermann, a young man in his thirties who was the son of a prominent Jewish leader in Romania. The younger Fildermann had been living in Cannes. The Germans arrested him there and took him to Paris and from there to Berlin. He was incarcerated and interrogated at the Gestapo headquarters on Prinz-Albrechtstrasse and then was transferred to the former Jewish old age home on Grosse Hamburgerstrasse, which served as a *Sammellager* until that activity was moved to the hospital grounds. The young man was suspected of being in prohibited contact with his father. Possibly because of the father's prominence in Romania, which was ostensibly a German ally rather than a conquered territory and which asserted the right to persecute its Jews on its own terms, he was not subjected to the brutal torture that other Gestapo prisoners had to endure. Instead the Gestapo had him held in solitary confinement in the hopes that he would crack. When he failed to confess, they decided to place him in the hospital police ward, even though he was not sick. There, he was again kept in solitary confinement and not permitted to talk to any other patient or to have any means of passing the time. As time wore on, however, and Fildermann continued not to give in, the Gestapo lost interest and allowed the conditions of his confinement to be loosened until he eventually was treated like all the other police ward patients.

Fildermann normally would have been sent on a transport to the East if the doctors had not taken the position that he was a diphtheria carrier who needed to be isolated, even though he had no apparent symptoms. Since the Gestapo had a horror of diphtheria, this was a well-calculated ploy; indeed, the diphtheria quarantine ward was the one place that no German official ever would enter. The German authorities, however, demanded a blood sample to verify this claim. Blau recounts that, fearing that such a sample would prove negative, Dr. Elkan, the supervising physician, substituted the blood of another patient who was known to test positive for diphtheria. The ruse was successful, and the young man spent the entire rest of the war as a police ward patient, although he was in perfectly good health.

Another survivor in the police ward was Ursula Finke, a young Jewish woman who had gone into hiding to avoid deportation. In August 1944 Finke had the bad luck to be recognized on the platform of the S-Bahn Gesundbrunnen station by Behrend, one of Stella Kübler's fellow informers. When he tried to arrest her, she jumped in front of an oncoming train. Finke came to her senses lying under the train to screams of "Turn off the juice." She recounts that railroad employees arrived and pulled her out from between the two train cars. She was carried to the station office and then taken by ambulance to the hospital. Although her foot had been mangled almost beyond recognition, she felt no pain and did not lose consciousness until she reached the gates of the hospital.

When she awoke in the middle of the night, she discovered that surgery had been performed and that her foot and leg were encased in an elaborate two-part cast to allow the foot to be rebandaged every day. Three doctors, Lustig, Helischkowski, and Cohen, treated her, but it was Lustig who personally bathed and rebandaged her foot every day, removing the bone splinters that kept coming to the surface. Ordinarily her foot would have been amputated and then she would have been deported to Auschwitz. However, for some reason Lustig wanted to save her. He managed to do that by exploiting the vanity of a senior Gestapo officer named Moeller who had studied medicine for a few semesters and who fancied himself something of a medical expert. Lustig presented Finke's situation as a chance for Moeller to participate in a medical experiment to see whether a foot so severely injured could be saved.

My life was not worth anything anyway; therefore, it would not have been so bad if my foot cost me my life. This way, however, I remained incarcerated in the interests of Mr. Moeller, behind barbed wire in the Iranischestr., chained to the bed, the foot for months in traction, with the most insane pain. At night the surveillance personnel came through the rooms, stuck flashlights into beds to see that everybody was there, and constantly people were transported away, even on stretchers, so that I ended up having screaming fits out of fear of being transported away in this condition. I was the only full-Jewish woman that remained in custody for that long.

For a small number of prisoners, confinement in the police ward was the ticket to freedom because it provided an opportunity for escape. On one occasion, the nurse on duty left the floor for some reason during her shift. While she was gone, two of the prisoners broke through the bars on the windows, hastily put sheets together, climbed down, and escaped from the hospital grounds. As punishment for her dereliction of duty, the nurse was deported to Theresienstadt. She survived the war there, but only after almost dying of an illness brought on by the brutal conditions in which she had to work.

Of course, it must be remembered that escaping from the police ward was no guarantee of freedom and may have decreased the chances of survival. The prisoner still was a Jew with little to no prospect of getting out of Germany, homeless on the streets of Berlin, without any papers and hunted by the Gestapo and the police. For most of the escapees there is no information as to whether they survived to the end of the war. One who did, however, was a prisoner named "Jim" (this is how he was known to the English-speaking individual who interviewed him in a displaced persons camp after the war).

The son of a Jewish father and an Aryan mother, Jim was arrested for some infraction and sent to the hospital, where it was discovered that he had tuberculosis. He spent some time in the police ward, but the treatment he received there made little progress. Somehow Jim became aware that the Germans intended to deport all the serious tuberculosis cases to a death camp in the East. He thereupon decided to escape. Fortunately, his mother was allowed to visit him in the hospital. Their visits were monitored by a Gestapo officer, but because the mother was a deaf-mute, they were allowed to converse in sign language, which the Gestapo man did not understand. Thus the mother and son were free to plan his escape under the Gestapo's nose.

The method he used is not recorded, but the escape was successful. One of the women who worked as a nurse in the police ward, Mrs. "A," told the same interviewer that "Jim" had asked her one day what time she normally came on duty. She replied that her official shift began at 8:00 P.M. but that she often arrived at 7:00 P.M. to help the other nurses. "Jim" became very insistent and suggested to her that the next day she not do any work outside her regularly scheduled hours. He gave no explanation other than to criticize another of the nurses and suggest that it was time that this woman did her fair share of the work. Mrs. A heeded the advice and arrived the next day at 8:00 P.M. to find the hospital in the midst of a commotion. "Jim" had escaped precisely between the hours of 7:00 P.M. and 8:00 P.M.

Not all attempted escapes were successful. Perhaps inspired by the escape of two other prisoners, one patient tried to get away by tying sheets together and lowering himself from the window. He slipped, fell to the ground, and broke his back. He was carried away on a stretcher to the next transport and shipped to Auschwitz, where incoming prisoners who were incapable of performing hard labor were gassed immediately.

A section of the hospital other than the police ward that housed many who fell in the winner category was the *Extrastation*, or extra ward. This, at its origin, was a ward for private patients or those who were able to supplement from their own funds the payments made by German public or private medical insurance so as to upgrade their level of care. (Documents from the 1930s indicate that the hospital had several classes of patients, of which the "patients of the third class" were those supported by the public welfare system.) By the time the hospital entered the climactic phase of its struggle under the Nazis, however, the extra ward had become a place of refuge for a small number of Jews who were protected from deportation for one reason or another. Most of these people figured on the so-called B-List (for *Behörden-Liste*, or list of authorities) and were under the protection of someone high in the Nazi hierarchy.

The "patients" in the *Extrastation* lived in rooms in the main building; they ate in their rooms and the meals were supplied by the hospital kitchen. One of the most notable was "Excellence" Schiffer, a former minister of justice in the pre-Nazi German government. Although baptized, he had to wear the yellow star, but he was protected from deportation, as was his unmarried daughter, who lived with him. How Schiffer escaped deportation is unknown — possibly it was because of his prominence and former high government position; possibly it was due to his political connections; perhaps he once had done a service to someone who now was high enough in the Nazi regime to protect him. The father and daughter had two rooms in the *Extrastation*, furnished with their own furniture. They survived there until the end of the war. Schiffer then became the head of legal affairs in the Soviet-occupied zone. Schiffer was a conspicuous presence at the hospital, since every morning he took his constitutional in the garden, in rainy weather wearing a black overcoat and galoshes.

Many of the remaining Jews in the extra ward were something of a mystery, and why any of them was allowed to remain there defies precise explanation. Reportedly, there were several members of the Rothschild family, and there was a Frau Oppenheimer, a member of another extremely wealthy family. She was apparently either ill or incapacitated, because she received nursing care from Meta Cohen, one of the hospital nurses and the wife of Dr. Helmuth Cohen. Perhaps she had managed to retain some of her wealth despite the Nazis' confiscation of Jewish assets and used it to buy herself a protected position. Yet many other wealthy German Jews tried to do the same and failed. Selmar Neumann's aunt also lived in the *Extrastation*. It is possible that her nephew's position as administrative director accounts for her presence there, but one can only wonder how she managed to avoid deportation while Lustig's father did not. Yet these anomalies occurred. Hilde Kahan's mother, for example, lived out the war in Hilde's room at the hospital, protected by nothing more than Lustig's desire not to lose a good secretary and the daughter's determination not to let her mother be deported without her.

Perhaps the most mysterious inhabitants of this section of the hospital were a family named Gordon, a husband, wife, and infant son. Gordon had a Russian passport, but survivors doubt that the family was Russian. They were under the protection of the Swedish embassy, and someone from the embassy came to visit them from time to time and brought extra food. Many survivors of the hospital remember the Gordons, but no one knows how they managed to secure refuge in the hospital and survive to the end of the Nazi period. Another intriguing patient was an elderly woman whom Dobberke often visited. She was the mother of a Jewish boy who had been Dobberke's childhood best friend. Another extra ward patient, a man named Ehrenhaft, was always in a wheelchair. The day the Soviet troops arrived, however, he discarded the wheelchair and began to walk.

Among the luckiest were the Jews who were interned in the hospital specifically for the purpose of hostage exchanges. Through neutral intermediaries, the Germans and British arranged occasional exchanges of German nationals who had been interned in Palestine, then under British control, for Jews from the hospital. These exchanges were carried out by assembling the people to be exchanged in camps, in both Germany and Palestine, that were under Swiss protection. Then the two groups were taken to Turkey, where a one-for-one exchange was effectuated at a railway station.

A final group of unexpected survivors were the orphans who had been swept into the hospital's care as Jewish orphanages were liquidated. Useless to the Nazis as laborers and with no one to claim protection for them, these children were in principle the most vulnerable to deportation. The fully Jewish children were in fact deported, but the staff of the hospital and the *Reichsvereinigung* attempted to save as many of the rest as they could by demonstrating that the children were *Mischlinge*. This was only possible because the some sixty orphans who remained, aged between six and eighteen years old, either were known to be *Misch-*

linge or had been born illegitimate, with no clear record of who the father was. With respect to the latter, the staff did laborious research to demonstrate that the father had been Aryan. The *Reichsvereinigung* social service department was charged with searching out the putative father and then unearthing birth certificates and marriage and baptism records of the father and even the grandparents in order to demonstrate that the child had the requisite level of Aryan blood to qualify as a *Mischling*. Some of the children were saved through these efforts, but the total number is not known.

It is easier to remember the winners than the losers — the winners survived to tell their tales. For those who cared for the patients, though, many of the strongest and most poignant memories are of the dead. One of the many affecting stories is that of a patient named Frau Rosenberg. She and her husband, both Jewish, had gone underground to avoid deportation. One day, the wife went out to search for food, was hit by a bus, and suffered a severe concussion. She was taken to a German hospital, where her false identity was unmasked and it was discovered that she was a Jew. She immediately was transferred to the hospital, where the doctors and nurses made her as comfortable as possible.

One day Eichmann and Wöhrn came into the ward where she was lying in bed and began to interrogate her about her husband's location. Frau Rosenberg said that she had no idea, pretending that the injury she had sustained to her head had made her lose her memory. At Eichmann's command, Wöhrn hit her in the face. Eichmann then told her that they would return in a week and give her one more chance to tell them the truth. A week later the same scene was replayed, but Frau Rosenberg remained adamant in claiming that she had lost her memory. Eichmann again ordered Wöhrn to beat her in the face and then told the poor woman that she had one more week, that the next time would be her last opportunity to save herself. One morning during the intervening week, Frau Rosenberg's dead body was discovered in her bed. A male nurse named Mayer had taken pity on her and supplied the pill that she used to kill herself. Unaware of what had happened to his wife, Herr Rosenberg managed to remain in hiding and survived the war. After the liberation, he turned up one day at the hospital looking for his wife, and someone on the staff had the task of telling him how she had died.

11

THE WORK OF THE
REICHSVEREINIGUNG AND THE
HOSPITAL, 1942–45

SOME ASSERT THAT the *Rest-Reichsvereinigung* was "fictitious, lacking any real activity." Others have claimed that the hospital effectively was out of business as a medical institution during the last two years of the war, so depleted of staff and supplies that it could not function. If these accounts were correct, the hospital from 1943 onward would have been nothing more than a combined ghetto and prison camp. This was not the case, however. The evidence clearly shows that the *Reichsvereinigung* office in the main administration building carried out real administrative activities, albeit primarily as an instrument of the Nazis' system for controlling and harassing Germany's remaining Jews. It is no less true that the hospital fulfilled its medical mission without interruption from the beginning of the war to its end, admitting, treating, and discharging Jewish patients. It maintained to the end a core staff of physicians able to cover the needs of the various medical departments and an overworked nursing staff that managed to hold its own with the help of the *Mischlinge* forced laborers who had been sent to work there. In the last weeks of the war, as we will see, these doctors and nurses performed heroically under the most appalling conditions.

It may seem strange that the German government dissolved the *Reichsvereinigung* only to immediately reconstitute it, albeit in a state of dubious legality. Yet both actions responded to needs of the Nazi authorities. The dissolution of the *Reichsvereinigung* in June 1943 at the same time as the Berlin *Gemeinde* had symbolic value as a response to a politically embarrassing situation. Although the Nazi propaganda machine had repeatedly boasted to the German public that the "Jewish problem" had been solved, the truth was that there still were identifiable Jews in Germany, especially in Berlin. Publicly abolishing the last Jewish organizations was a way of proclaiming that Jewish existence in Germany officially had come to an end — a way of clouding the reality that as of June 30, 1943, there still were 9,529 persons living legally and openly in Germany whom the Nazi racial laws labeled as Jews — mostly *Mischlinge* and Jews living in mixed marriages. Most of those, 6,790, were in Berlin.

However, as a practical matter the RSHA and the Gestapo still found it useful to have a captive Jewish body to administer the affairs of the remaining Jews. The Nazi modus operandi in dealing with Germany's Jews had always depended on exploiting the services of Jewish organizations. Such an organization could keep track of the remaining population, disseminate further restrictive laws and decrees, and, when the time came, serve as an instrument for the roundup and destruction of the last German Jews. Happily, that time never arrived, but it surely was the intention and expectation of most Nazi officials that it would.

Consequently, the authorities charged Walter Lustig and what remained of the now dissolved *Reichsvereinigung* with the responsibility of carrying on the same work the *Reichsvereinigung* had done before June 1943. Since Jewish schools had been abolished and other social welfare establishments soon would be, its remaining functions were to run the hospital and the Jewish cemetery at Weissensee. In addition, there still were other issues to be handled, such as providing financial aid for impoverished Jews and housing for Jews who had lost their homes in the bombings.

Those eligible for such aid primarily were Jews living in mixed marriages.

The question of what to call the rump *Reichsvereinigung* briefly vexed the authorities. It was suggested that it be renamed the *Vereinigung Jüdischer Mischehe-Partner,* or Association of Jewish Partners in Mixed Marriages, but the RSHA vetoed the idea. A name change would have required an official action by the Interior Ministry, and this information would have had to be published in the official journal, an action that risked drawing too much attention to the matter. (It is ironic but typical of Germany in the Nazi period that almost sixty thousand Berlin Jews could be murdered with no legal process, but the name of the *Reichsvereinigung* could only be changed in accordance with the full procedural requirements of German administrative law.)

Faced with this dilemma, the RSHA decided that the lesser evil was to allow the *Reichsvereinigung* to continue to function under the same name and in the same manner as if it had never been dissolved. The fact that it lacked legal status to do so apparently was not seen as an obstacle. This is somewhat difficult to reconcile with the punctilious adherence to legal formality that apparently stood in the way of changing the organization's name. However, strange inconsistencies were an important characteristic of German official life under the Nazis (how else can one explain sending deportees to the hospital for emergency operations to make them well enough to be put back on a train for Auschwitz?), and spasms of slavish adherence to bureaucratic procedure alternated with rampant illegality. One aspect of the compromise that the Gestapo reached was to prohibit the *Rest-Reichsvereinigung* from using printed letterhead. The correspondence still went out under the same letterhead as before, but the secretaries had to type it anew for each letter.

The inconsistencies occasionally provided a chink in the wall that surrounded the Jews and thus contributed to the survival of a few. In this case, the decision to continue the *Reichsvereinigung* in operation saved the lives of its handful of employees. They kept themselves alive by keeping busy. For the remaining almost two years of the war, the small group of Jewish bureaucrats in Room 25 of the hospital's administration building continued to churn out paper, correspond with government agencies, and issue highly official looking documents, all under the typed letterhead of the *Reichsvereinigung der Juden in Deutschland.* Looking at the surviving administrative files of the *Reichsvereinigung* from 1943 to 1945, which are filled with such documents, one constantly has to remind oneself that the fewer than ten thousand *Juden in Deutschland* whose affairs were being handled with such bureaucratic punctilio constituted less than 2 percent of the number who had been there in 1933.

The assertion that the *Reichsvereinigung* had no real activity after June 1943 is belied by the records that survive. Despite an air raid in February 1944 that destroyed many of the organization's files, substantial amounts of its correspondence and financial documents remain from the period 1943–45. These, together with interviews that K. J. Ball-Kaduri conducted with former *Reichsvereinigung* officials after the war, show that the *Reichsvereinigung* was handling business right up through 1945. One of its functions was to act as an intermediary between the authorities and those of Germany's remaining acknowledged Jews who were compelled to be members. The latter included all persons defined as Jews except Jews living in privileged mixed marriages, most of them Jewish women who were married to Aryan men. Although it was open to these people to become members of the *Reichsvereinigung* voluntarily, few did, no doubt fearing that the risks of being officially listed as members of a Jewish organization far outweighed whatever benefits might accrue. The main activity of the *Reichsvereinigung* was administering health and welfare issues for the German Jews.

At the time the *Reichsvereinigung* officially was dissolved in June 1943, it was responsible for health and social welfare matters for all its Jewish members who resided in the original Reich and the Sudetenland. Specifically, this meant administering clinics and hospitals, ambulance services, old age homes, orphan asylums, and nursing homes; operating cemeteries; and providing financial aid and clothing to the needy. The physical scope of these responsibilities shrank with great rapidity through the rest of the year as the Nazis eliminated one Jewish welfare institution after another. By the end of 1943, everything relating to health and welfare was concentrated on the hospital premises on Iranischestrasse, and the care of the dead was limited to the cemetery at Weissensee.

Nonetheless, the *Reichsvereinigung* had to see to the social welfare needs of the small population of intermarried Jews scattered throughout the Reich. The predissolution *Reichsvereinigung* had maintained a system of branches, including several in Berlin itself. The regional branches, in turn, had been represented by local branches in larger municipalities and, in smaller places, by individual representatives, known as "trustees." The mass deportations in early 1943 put an end to the *Reichsvereinigung*'s system of local offices. In its place, for the remaining Jews situated in places other than Berlin, Lustig relied on a network of individual trustees. At one time there were more than forty of these throughout Germany, although over time deportations reduced that number.

A good deal of the work of the *Reichsvereinigung* consisted of administering the tangled real estate affairs of the hospital and, to a lesser degree, the Weissensee cemetery, as well as running the financial affairs of these two institutions and administering the funds from which welfare payments were made to certain Jews in need. All of the assets of the *Reichsvereinigung* had been transferred to the Berlin Treasury Department. A portion of these resources in the amount of 5,000,000 reichsmark was put at the disposal of the RSHA and the Gestapo, from which amounts were made available to the *Reichsvereinigung* for the conduct of its activities. Of the 5,000,000 reichsmark, however, 3,500,000 reichsmark were frozen in a special account, from which funds could be withdrawn only with the Gestapo's special permission. This left

1,500,000 reichsmark for all the *Reichsvereinigung*'s activities, including running the hospital. As it turned out, these funds were sufficient, and at the time of liberation they had not all been expended. From the money the Gestapo had provided, as well as what it could collect from patients or their insurers, the *Reichsvereinigung* had to pay the costs of running the hospital, including the salaries of the doctors and nurses, supplies, and maintenance. Even though action had begun to transfer legal title to the property to the *Akademie* and three of the pavilions had been confiscated and occupied by the *Lazarett*, the *Reichsvereinigung* still was responsible for the upkeep of the entire complex. Thus one of the *Reichsvereinigung* officials, Dr. Radlauer, remembers, "I had constantly to negotiate with the management of the military hospital."

All of this generated a considerable flow of paper. Much of the correspondence involved seeking instructions or authorizations from the RSHA or responding to the frequent demands that Eichmann and his subordinates made for information. All communications with Eichmann's office had to be written using a special typewriter font. Accordingly, Hilde Kahan had two typewriters at her desk, one of which was reserved solely for letters to the RSHA.

Insurance claims were a major area of activity. The Jews who were in forced labor in many cases were covered by medical insurance through their employers. Thus the *Reichsvereinigung* had to file masses of insurance claims to recover reimbursement for treating them. In some cases, these claims were not paid. Lengthy correspondence and even legal proceedings ensued, dragging on well after many of the patients had been deported and probably killed. For example, in February 1943, Lustig wrote to the RSHA asking for its intervention in the attempts by the *Reichsvereinigung* to collect payments for Jews who had worked in labor camps building the Autobahn system. The *Reichsvereinigung* had reimbursement claims outstanding against the Autobahn administration, as well as against two commercial companies, the Kurmärkischen Wood Fiber and Cellulose Company and the German Explosive Chemicals GmbH. It had claimed almost nine thousand reichsmark from the companies for medical services it had rendered to their Jewish forced laborers, apparently in 1941 and 1942. (At seven reichsmark per day, the hospital's standard charge, this represents a substantial amount of hospital time.) Appealing to the main government insurance office after none of these claims had been paid, the *Reichsvereinigung* had been advised to sue. It had done so and won. The two companies then had paid, but the Autobahn administration had not heeded the tribunal's order. So Lustig sought the help of his bureaucratic masters at the RSHA in putting pressure on the Autobahn administration to pay the some ten thousand reichsmark that remained due. Unfortunately, there is no record of the outcome of Lustig's effort.

The takeover of the *Reichsvereinigung*'s assets by the Berlin Treasury Department led to a strange episode, one that proved a lifesaver for at least one of those involved. Among the last *Reichsvereinigung* officials to be deported from Berlin were two finance officers, Dr. H. Krebs and Dr. Hans-Erich Fabian. Both were sent to Theresienstadt. Six weeks later, however, the Gestapo brought them back to Berlin, where they were housed in Gestapo custody and set to work unraveling the *Reichsvereinigung*'s financial accounts so that all of the assets could be uncovered and the books balanced. Every day, the Gestapo brought the two men to the *Reichsvereinigung* offices at the hospital, where they pored over the files, helping their RSHA masters to identify the *Reichsvereinigung*'s property. Meanwhile, probably to encourage them to serve the RSHA diligently, their families in Theresienstadt were spared from joining the majority who were sent to the death camps.

Krebs was taken back to Theresienstadt in January 1944, and there appears to be no record of his subsequent fate. Fabian remained in Berlin until February 1944 and then was returned to Theresienstadt, where he and his family survived the war. After liberation, Fabian eventually served as head of the postwar Berlin Jewish *Gemeinde*. It is interesting that Fabian is the source of the untrue assertion, quoted at the beginning of this chapter, that the post–June 10, 1943, *Reichsvereinigung* was fictitious, since he was in the *Reichsvereinigung*'s office every day for at least six months after that date. It is apparent, however, that he developed an animosity to Lustig, which may explain why he felt called upon to disparage the role of the *Reichsvereinigung* under Lustig's leadership.

As the Allied bombings made more and more Jews homeless, the social welfare function of the *Reichsvereinigung* grew in importance. Jews who had been bombed out applied to the *Reichsvereinigung* for financial assistance or for help in relocating. It appears that the number of cases in which some form of help was extended was substantial, but the information that has survived does not permit any precise evaluation.

One of the tasks of the *Reichsvereinigung* was a procedure known as the *Heimeinverkaufsverträge*. This was a cynical deception that the Nazis practiced on elderly Jews who were slated for deportation to Theresienstadt. The victims were told that they were to be relocated to what in today's euphemistic jargon would be called a "continuing care community," where all their needs would be met. In return — in a transaction remarkably similar to the terms on which many old people today enter real lifetime care institutions — they were required to sign over title to all their assets. The job of identifying those assets and having the elderly Jews sign the necessary documentation to relinquish title was assigned to the *Reichsvereinigung*. Although the Nazis had no compunctions about simply seizing the assets of the Jews they deported, the *Heimeinverkaufsverträge* saved them considerable effort. In particular, it probably encouraged those victims who believed the falsehood to turn over everything they owned instead of trying to conceal some of their assets.

Bruno Blau, who was in a position to know, remarks that the hospital did not exist as a hospital in name only, but that the patients were treated and cared for there in an orderly way. Despite the recurrent deportations of medical personnel, he writes, enough of the staff were allowed to remain that the hospital could continue to function medically, "even if the manner of care left something to be desired and, above all, insufficient attention was paid to the cleanliness of the institution, which in the past had been exemplary."

How extensively the medical staff was reduced by deportations, suicides, and escapes to underground life is impossible to tell with any precision, since the surviving records are too fragmentary to reveal the names of all the doctors who were at work at any particular time between 1938 and 1945. The records do, however, portray the dimensions of what occurred. The hospital's surgical register shows twenty-eight doctors, including an oral surgeon, as having performed surgery in 1941. Five of these apparently served only as anesthetists. The number is at best only an approximation of the size of the hospital's full-time medical staff in that year. Not every doctor on staff necessarily performed surgery, although it appears that a large percentage did. Moreover, some of the names appear only once or twice in the course of the year. This suggests that the doctors in question may have been among the small number of Jewish *Krankenbehandler*, almost certainly living in mixed marriages, who remained in Berlin and treated patients outside the hospital with occasional surgical privileges there. By way of confirmation, the Israeli historian Rivka Elkin identifies a similar number, some thirty doctors, who appear to have been working at the hospital during 1942.

What is unclear is how many doctors there were at times after 1942. In some cases Elkin is able to specify when physicians on the 1942 list left the hospital, either through deportation or by going underground. In some cases, she identifies those who were still there in 1945. For many, however, the person's fate is unknown after 1942.

A rough guide to the size of the hospital's professional staff after the deportation of fully one-half of its employees in March 1943 is found in a surviving document that lists staff members living at the hospital and those residing elsewhere. The document shows gross salaries, the amounts deducted for rent if they lived at the hospital and for food if they took their meals there, and a list of employees who lived at home but were charged for the midday meal they ate at the hospital. The document is undated, but internal evidence puts it at sometime in late 1943 or 1944, since it contains the names of people who are known to have joined the hospital staff only after the *Fabrikaktion* and omits names of people known to have been deported in March 1943.

The document is curiously incomplete. It does not contain the names of some individuals who have been unmistakably identified from other sources as living at the hospital at the time. Among them are Hilde Kahan's mother and at least two families, the Neumanns and the Zwilskys. In some cases it lists spouses and children, but it omits to do so in others, notably in the case of Dr. Helmuth Cohen. Taking these limitations into account, as well as the uncertainty about the exact date, the document is useful. It shows approximately sixty doctors, nurses, and support personnel living on the hospital premises, together with a handful of family members. It shows some twenty-four other people who worked at the hospital but did not reside there, including many of the *Mischlinge* who arrived after the Rosenstrasse protest.

Putting Elkin's information together with the document just described and the accounts provided by survivors, one can estimate that at least ten physicians still were working at the hospital on the day of liberation. Possibly there were one or two more. This represents a dramatic reduction in the size of the professional staff as compared with 1941, but the number is still large enough to demonstrate that the institution remained capable of performing a true medical role. The nursing staff, which probably numbered around seventy before the large deportations of hospital personnel began, seems to have been reduced to somewhere around twenty at liberation. This figure, however, is even less solid than the estimated number of physicians and is confused further by the fact that some of the forced laborers who had arrived in 1943 and had been pressed into duty as nursing assistants had become trained for nursing duties by 1945, whether or not they actually had a license.

Another indication of the hospital's level of medical activity can be derived from records that survive of admissions and mortality. These statistics almost all show the same pattern: a sharp spike in almost all causes of mortality during the years 1941–42, the years of the most intensive deportations and the violence and suicides that surrounded them. This is hardly surprising given the adverse health effects inevitably produced by the enormous tension and fear under which Berlin's remaining Jews were living, as well as the violence and deprivation to which they were exposed. In terms of the medical use of the hospital, the mortality figures are only an indirect reflection of the number of patients who were treated, but nonetheless they are revealing.

How did the hospital fare as a medical institution after the *Fabrikaktion* in early 1943 had eliminated most of Berlin's remaining Jews? Surviving patient registers show that 1,468 patients were admitted to the hospital in 1943. In 1944, there were only 719 admissions. In 1945, 245 patients were recorded as admitted during the first four months of the year, the period that included the final days of the war and the arrival of the Soviet troops. It is unclear, however, whether these figures include all the wounded who were treated during the chaotic last weeks of the war. Although the staff had been zealous in maintaining orderly and meticulous records, one must wonder how carefully "admissions" were registered while the hospital was under constant bombardment. After liberation, the number of admissions for the remainder of 1945, May through December, amounted to 2,319, producing a yearly total of 2,564. This compares to an annual average of 3,243 in 1932–37, before the hospital reached a high of 4,585 in 1938, the year of *Kristallnacht.*

If overall admissions were low, the death toll, as a percentage of admissions, rose sharply during the 1943–45 period. In 1943, the 425 deaths that were recorded represented almost 29 percent of the number of admissions. In 1944, the 124 deaths were more than 17 percent of the number of admissions, and in 1945 the 567 deaths constituted more than 22 percent. In contrast, from 1922 to 1938 the hospital's ratio of deaths to admissions varied from 8.55 to 15.8 percent.

Clearly 1944 was the low point of the hospital's medical activities. Admissions during the first four months of 1945 fell to an even lower level on an annualized basis, but as soon as the Soviet troops gained control of the neighborhood and the staff was able to begin reestablishing normal activities, the number of patients admitted to the hospital rose substantially. In May 1945, there were 217 admissions, almost as many as during the four preceding months put together, and the monthly numbers ranged from 225 to 389 for the rest of the year. This increased level of activity partly reflects the fact that almost immediately after the liberation the hospital was faced with the medical care of the returnees from Theresienstadt, the death camps, and the concentration camps in Germany.

Even in the last desperate days of the war, the hospital worked as a fully functional medical institution and remained in surprisingly good condition, considering the deteriorating state of affairs in Germany. Although all of Germany was suffering from a paucity of medical supplies in the last year of the war, the hospital was not badly situated; indeed, it kept up an exchange of medications and equipment with the *Lazarett* right up to the very end. The pharmacy was well staffed and well furnished with medications. In this regard, the Nazis' decision to place the pharmacy in the hands of an Aryan, Kantelberg, who probably was able to obtain substantial supplies to which a Jew would not have had access, was highly beneficial. Not only was the hospital relatively well equipped for its own needs, but it was able to send a supply of medications along with every transport, although these probably were diverted and never used for the benefit of the Jewish deportees.

With the fall of the Nazi regime, the hospital's services became available to non-Jews. Its birth register for the last weeks of the war and the first weeks of peace provides an interesting confirmation of the hospital's rapid return to its prewar role. A double line ruled across the page marks the date of liberation, April 24, 1945. The last entry above the line records the birth, on April 14, 1945, at 11:20 P.M., of a daughter, Claudia, to a Jewish woman. The father is not identified. The next entry below the line shows the birth, at 1:25 A.M. on May 11, 1945, of a daughter, Marion, to a Protestant mother. Again, the father's identity is not noted. The register called for that information only if the mother was married. Even after all that the hospital and its inhabitants had suffered under the Nazis, the hospital's registrar apparently did not think in May 1945 of simply not filling in the column that required the religion of the mother and, if the child were legitimate, of the father.

12

THE TWILIGHT OF THE NAZIS

EDITH, WELL KNOWN AS a tomboy, was in her favorite position, perched on the roof of one of the hospital buildings with a stone in her hand, repairing bomb damage. As she looked down she saw that the hated *Spitzel* Eugen Kahn was passing in the courtyard below. The opportunity was irresistible. She dropped the stone on his head. To her dismay, it missed.

Kahn hurried back to the *Pathologie* and complained to his Gestapo master, Dobberke, who summoned the young woman to his office. He asked her if she had dropped the stone on purpose.

"No. It fell out of my hand," she lied. "I'm always doing this work, and accidents happen." Although Dobberke was skeptical, Edith escaped serious punishment. Even then, in the last phase of the war, the threat of deportation was very real, and when deportation was not possible there were always the dreaded concentration camps on German soil to which a *Geltungsjude* like Edith could be sent for punishment. Instead, Dobberke ordered her to be confined for two weeks, but she was released in a few days when her Aryan mother came from Halle and pleaded with him.

Edith's experience encapsulates the three dominant aspects of life in the hospital from 1944 to the end of the war — incessant bombing raids, endless repairs, and an undesired proximity to the Gestapo and the Jewish renegades living in the *Sammellager* at the back of the garden. In the face of constant damage inflicted as the result of Allied bombings, it was of paramount importance to keep the hospital intact and functioning.

"We had to protect our hospital as far as we could," Ruth Beleski remembers. "If the hospital hadn't been there, we wouldn't have been there. They wouldn't have put us up in a hotel or anything."

Despite the proximity of the *Lazarett* and the presence of the Gestapo post in the *Sammellager*, the hospital was entirely on its own in confronting the Allied bombings. The Berlin fire department would have nothing to do with a Jewish facility. So the hospital's chief electrician organized the hospital's own air raid watch and firefighting brigades. A Jewish former fireman who was married to an Aryan woman had been sent to live at the hospital as part of the Gestapo's attempt to break up mixed marriages. He was put in charge of training the staff in how to fight fires. Most of the able-bodied young people, including those who lived at home and only came to work at the hospital during the day, took turns staffing the *Nachtwache*, or "night watch." So too did many of the medical staff.

During air raids the job of the *Nachtwache* was to watch for damage to the hospital premises and to extinguish any fires. The most perilous aspect of this work was looking out for incendiary bombs. It was imperative to locate any incendiary device that might fall on the hospital and deal with it immediately, lest the entire set of buildings go up in flames. To do this, several watchers stationed themselves on a wooden observation platform located on the roof of the main medical building so that they could spot any incendiary bomb falling within the hospital's boundaries and communicate its location to the fire brigade below. This was harrowing work. The watchers were forced to stand, unprotected, in the open, at the highest point in the hospital, while shrapnel and debris flew through the air around them. Miraculously, no one was killed or seriously injured in the process. A less dangerous part of the fire watch was circulating throughout the hospital buildings checking that blackout precautions were being observed. Eva Beleski remembers that the fire watch teams stayed on duty for an entire week, sleeping together in one room, "like in a real fire station." Although ostensibly there were no alcoholic beverages at the hospital, the doctors and pharmacists somehow managed to manufacture a small supply. When the young men came down from the fire watch platform after an air raid, their hair sometimes literally standing on end, each was given a single swig.

Following the raids and the firefighting came the job of cleanup and repair. Once again, the hospital had to rely entirely on its own resources. Staff members taught themselves how to do carpentry and masonry work. As windows were blown out or broken, there were no supplies of glass to replace them, so the broken panes had to be covered up with scraps of wood or even cardboard.

The roof was the most vulnerable part of the structure. The hospital had started the war with a solid roof composed of three layers of ceramic tiles. Successive bombings blew tiles off, layer by layer, until at the war's end there was hardly a single layer. Repairing damage to the roof was a continual necessity. Young women learned to become roofers. Eva Beleski remembers that "the roof needed replacing all the time" and that she reveled in doing that work. Her official job was as a secretary in the admitting office, but she did everything. "I was young; I was strong. I repaired roofs." The work was dangerous. Because no one would supply replacement building materials to Jews, there was no choice other than to scrounge them from bombed-out sites, which necessitated climbing out onto the ruined roofs of half-destroyed houses. These expeditions occurred only a few times. Transportation was virtually impossible to obtain, but somehow the electrician managed to procure the use of a truck so that half a dozen hospital employees could visit bombing sites and liberate roofing tiles.

Food was another item in short supply. The hospital gardens

had been torn up and converted into vegetable plots. These were tended primarily by Günther Rischowsky, who had had some agricultural experience prior to his arrest in the *Fabrikaktion* (and who had received the abusive dressing-down from SS officer Wöhrn over his potatoes). Young Klaus Zwilsky, twelve years old in 1944, often served as Rischowsky's helper in the vegetable gardens. Deprived of any opportunity to go to school, unable to leave the hospital grounds, and with only a handful of other children his own age in the hospital, Klaus was delighted to have something to do with his time. Rischowsky's agricultural experience became especially handy when a portion of the garden became a cow pasture. The owner of a dairy not far from the hospital, like many other people in the neighborhood, observed that the hospital had been spared direct hits in the bombings and that no one had been killed there. He came to share the belief, current in the vicinity, that God was protecting the Jews in the hospital and, deciding to put his cows under divine protection, moved them onto the hospital grounds. Rischowsky, who had learned to milk a cow, turned his talents to taking some of the milk for the benefit of the hospital.

Conditions grew increasingly chaotic and crowded. Despite the heroic efforts of the self-taught carpenters, masons, and roofers, some of the bomb damage was too extensive to repair adequately, and parts of the hospital buildings had to be abandoned. At the same time, an increasing number of families from Berlin and even other places in Germany whom the Nazis classed as "Jewish households" were finding themselves homeless because of air raids. The *Reichsvereinigung* was responsible for the rehousing of these people, and the hospital was often the only place that could be found.

The final drama began in January 1945. As the Red Army began to close in on Berlin, the Allied bombing became even more intense. Hilde Kahan remembers that the Germans began to talk about the retaliation that might be visited on them for their crimes against the Jews. At the same time, however, no one did anything to help the few Jews who remained in Germany. Even as late as March 27, 1945, less than a month before the liberation, transports left from the *Sammellager* on the hospital grounds, including some of the last Jews the Gestapo had managed to uncover in hiding. One transport went to Theresienstadt. The advance of the Soviet forces had cut off access to Auschwitz and the other death camps in Poland, so the remaining Jews who would have been deported there instead were sent to concentration camps in Germany, primarily Sachsenhausen and Ravensbrück.

Beginning in mid-February 1945, Hilde Kahan and the other staff members rarely had the chance to take off their clothes. They caught such sleep as they could, fully clothed, so as to be ready to run to the next emergency. Every night there were three or more air raids. Each time, the patients who were bedridden had to be carried to the basement. Because of the frequent interruptions of electrical power, it was not safe to use the elevator. Eventually, the frequency of the air raids made it impractical to keep moving the patients. Their beds were permanently relocated to the basement corridors, where they spent the remaining months of the war.

In one particularly heavy air raid, the hospital was left with forty bomb craters in the garden, but not a single casualty was suffered. The Aryans living nearby took note of this phenomenon and concluded that the hospital was under the Lord's direct protection. The next time the air raid sirens sounded, a mob stormed the hospital's back gate, and the gatekeeper was unable to keep them from getting in or from taking refuge in the basement. The Gestapo promptly requisitioned a section of the basement corridors and created a segregated bomb shelter for Aryans, increasing the crowded conditions.

As the weeks passed, the situation became more and more desperate. The Gestapo men and the Jewish renegades in their service showed increasing signs of nervousness. In mid-April, several of the *Greifer* and *Spitzel* disappeared. They had run away, hoping to escape the retribution they knew would follow an Allied victory. The Gestapo began burning the records that were kept in their office in the *Sammellager*. The files were loaded into large wash baskets and carried into the hospital's utility area, where they were burned in the incinerator. For two weeks, from morning to night, Gestapo men threw papers into the flames.

For the hospital's Jews it was a period of the highest psychological stress. On the one hand, it was evident that the end was near, and they could not help but derive satisfaction from the fact that those who had persecuted them were showing abject fear. Dobberke himself was drunk much of the time. On the other hand, no one could escape the fear that death would intervene before that day arrived. The hospital was under almost continual assault from the air as the result of bomb attacks on nearby targets. The Soviet forces were advancing on the city, and it was clear that the hospital soon would be in the middle of a dangerous battle zone.

Every Jew who worked or lived at the hospital also understood the very real possibility that the Nazis would complete their work of Jew killing in a final massacre just before going down to defeat themselves. As Blau notes, "The more critical for the Nazis the military situation became, the more dangerous did the situation become for the Jews." The rules that had protected those living in mixed marriages and the *Mischlinge* could be reversed at any time. In addition, there was the omnipresent danger of arbitrary action by the SS or the Gestapo, who felt themselves less and less trammeled by directives from above as conditions in Germany became increasingly chaotic. Even with the Red Army already fighting against fierce German resistance street by street, hospital employees who lived off the premises were picked up by SS men and summarily shot. And of all Berlin's Jews, those living in the hospital were the most exposed. Living day and night under the surveillance of the Gestapo, they had nowhere to run or hide.

For days the hospital's occupants had been able to hear the sound of artillery barrages from Frankfurt/Oder, not far from the city. Finally, in the early hours of April 21, there was a brief period of quiet. Hilde Kahan remembers being beside herself for fear that the Wehrmacht actually had beaten back the Red Army, as the German radio had been proclaiming. The doctors who had served in World War I laughed at her for being so credulous and told her not to lose her nerve at the very final moment of the war. Sure enough, within hours the Red Army began artillery bombardment of Berlin.

Thus began the hospital's final days under Nazi rule. Shells began to fall on the surrounding streets. The two Rischowsky brothers, making their way home from work, were hit by shrapnel and brought back to the hospital as casualties. Günther lost his arm, putting an end to his career as a gardener, but happily not to his life. The police issued instructions that all civilians take to the bomb shelters and cellars. The entire hospital population, healthy as well as sick, moved into the basements to await the end of the battle. Supplies of food and water were brought down and stored in the basements, and makeshift clinic and operating room facilities were set up. Someone had had the foresight to install a large kettle donated by the *Lazarett* in one of the basements. This became the kitchen for such meals as the inhabitants were able to cook. The some eight hundred surviving Jews in the hospital were destined to endure this troglodytic existence for nearly two weeks, as outside Red Army units manned barricades at one place, SS men at another, and Nazi snipers roamed the rooftops, shooting at anything that moved.

Soon the wounded began to arrive. The spaces that had been set aside to receive emergency cases and for use as operating rooms were filled. Patients had to be placed wherever there was room; the dying lay next to the less sick or in the corridors assigned to the healthy members of the nonpatient population. The electricity had gone out, with no prospect of restoration until the battle was over, since the main power cable passed over a bridge that had been blown up. A meager amount of light was supplied by lighting wicks that floated in containers of oil. The public water system had been cut, and water was in very short supply. The only available source was a well on the hospital grounds, from which water could be drawn only at great risk, as snipers could be hidden anywhere in the buildings and in the ruins beyond the walls, and shrapnel, bomb debris, grenades, and machine gun bullets were passing over the buildings and through the gardens. There was no source of heat.

Throughout all this wounded people were being brought in continuously, most of them non-Jews, although at least one was a Jewish soldier in the Red Army, who shortly died of his wounds. By the light of the oil lamps, the doctors and nurses worked without respite in the makeshift medical facilities, trying to treat the wounded as best they could. Eventually the space in which to lay the sick or wounded grew so reduced that many of the healthy people had to pass their days and nights in a sitting position. A number of the elderly and ill hospital patients died, having succumbed to the unsanitary conditions, the cold, and the lack of light.

Klaus Zwilsky remembers that his father and others volunteered to bury the dead in the hospital garden during pauses in the artillery barrage. Often their work was interrupted by the beginning of the next artillery assault, and they had to drop their task and return to it later. "I can still see my father putting on his helmet to go outside and my mother begging him to be careful. As a veteran of World War I, I am sure my father felt it his duty to go." Albeit hastily, the Jewish dead were given Jewish funeral rites, even under the omnipresent risk of artillery shells and bullets. Later, a few months after the fighting ended, the Jewish dead were disinterred from their graves near the chestnut trees and reburied in the Jewish cemetery at Weissensee.

Only the telephone still worked. Bombings, artillery shells, the destruction that occurred all around — none of this interrupted telephone service. Employees living outside the hospital called to report what was going on. The Red Army was approaching from all sides; clearly the city would shortly fall. Yet the German radio continued to broadcast defiant promises that, even though Berlin was surrounded, the German troops would fight their way through and free it. Finally, the Red Army occupied the broadcasting stations and the Nazi propaganda came to an end.

Morale continued to plummet among the Gestapo officers and they began to disappear. Dobberke remained until close to the very end. In the early hours of the morning of April 24, Hilde Kahan, still unsure how long it would be before the hospital would be free of risk from the Nazi authorities, responded reflexively to the circumstances in which she had been living for years — the disposition of human lives through lists, official documents, and signatures. She drew up release papers for the prisoners in the *Sammellager* and the police ward and persuaded Dobberke to sign them. Dobberke then made his escape, taking with him his Jewish mistress, *Schwester* Elli. For the first time in years, the hospital was out from under the control of the RSHA and Gestapo. There are no records of what fate, if any, the Nazi authorities had in store for the hospital's occupants. Many survivors are convinced that Dobberke was under orders to shoot them all before the Red Army could rescue them and that weapons for that purpose had been brought into the hospital. According to these reports, *Schwester* Elli persuaded her Gestapo lover that he should ignore these orders and instead should make his escape as quickly as possible, lest, after the inevitable Allied victory, he be punished for carrying them out.

Later that same day, in the afternoon, the Red Army arrived. All the staff and patients in the *Lazarett* were arrested and held as prisoners of war. As we have seen, the Jews in the hospital had a hard time convincing the incredulous Soviet troops that they should not also be treated as enemies, but in the end they prevailed. The initial contact with the hospital's liberators was not entirely a happy one, however. Klaus Zwilsky remembers that the first troops to reach the hospital were shock troops, mostly from Mongolia; the soldiers were fierce fighters but undisciplined. They set to work relieving the hospital's inhabitants of their jewelry, including Klaus's parents' wedding bands. A few days later, more disciplined soldiers arrived and tried to restore as much of the plundered property as possible. The Zwilskys got their wedding rings back.

The war was still not over. The Soviet troops set up a field artillery unit in the hospital garden and bivouacked on the grounds for several weeks. Their small Caucasian horses gnawed on the rosebushes. The Soviets fired on the German forces, but the Germans had run out of ammunition for their artillery, thus saving the hospital from being bombarded in return. Although, as far as the survivors can recollect, no woman was raped in the hospital, outside the liberating Soviet troops were unrestrained in their behavior.

In fact, so terrible were conditions in Berlin under the first wave of Soviet troops that some of the hospital's employees who lived elsewhere sought refuge in the hospital. Rape was the principal danger. In Weissensee, Ruth Graetz was unemployed and living at home, since she had recently been barred from continuing with her job at the hospital because of the Nazi racial laws. Years before, her resourceful mother, fearing that, as a *Geltungsjude*, Ruth might still be deported, had started a legal proceeding in which she fraudulently claimed that her late Jewish husband had not been Ruth's real father, that Ruth was the illegitimate product of a liaison with another Aryan and therefore was fully Aryan herself. After years of litigation, including an examination of Ruth by a Nazi institute of racial studies, the tribunal, some three months before the end of the war, had declared the young Jewish woman to be fully Aryan. Now, ironically, that decision had put Ruth directly in harm's way by keeping her at home. A Russian soldier was billeted in the apartment where the two women lived. Ever resourceful, Frau Graetz found a Czech girl (presumably one who had been brought to Berlin to do forced labor) and bribed her to come every night to sleep with the soldier so that he would leave Ruth alone.

In the suburb of Karlshorst, the Beleski sisters found conditions under occupation by the Soviet troops so unbearable that they took their mother and fled, leaving everything they owned behind them. Two others who wanted to leave Karlshorst went with them, and the group of five walked all the way to the hospital. On the way, they met some Jewish soldiers from the Red Army, to whom the girls recounted all the evils that had befallen them. The Russian soldiers broke into tears and, using silver spoons that they had just confiscated and were carrying in their boots, tried to feed them some jam that they had stolen somewhere else. Most importantly, they wrote out a pass that allowed the group to move through the remainder of the Soviet-held area unmolested.

As they walked toward Wedding, the Beleskis and their companions crossed back and forth between Soviet-held territory and neighborhoods that were still held by SS units. At one point, a group of SS men stopped them and threatened to shoot them. The girls feared that their Jewish identities would be uncovered; they knew that Jews were being shot by the SS. Moreover, if the SS were to discover the pass the Russian soldiers had given them, there was no doubt that they would be executed as spies. Fortunately, the SS men were sufficiently confused and preoccupied with the ongoing battle that they let them go without discovering that they were Jews and without searching them.

As the group neared the hospital, they realized that they had arrived at a street that constituted a battle line. The side of the street from which they were coming was held by German troops, but the Russians were holding positions on the other side. A streetcar was stopped in the middle of the street, and both sides were firing upon it.

Ruth Beleski approached a German officer, explained that they were fleeing from the Russians who had occupied the suburb where they had lived, and asked how they could get to the hospital. The officer said that during the night they carried wounded people across to the hospital and offered, if the group would wait, to let them go with a stretcher that night. They were desperate to reach their refuge, however, and, rather than waiting, made a run for the hospital. As they dashed across the street, shooting erupted at them from both sides. By some good fortune, all the bullets missed, and they made it across the street and in through the hospital gate without injury.

When they finally entered the hospital, the buildings and grounds were deserted. For a moment, they thought that they had made a mistake, that all the Jews had been killed and the buildings abandoned. But then they discovered that the entire population was living underground. They joined their friends and colleagues in the basements and, with considerable fear, once again awaited the arrival of the Soviet troops.

The advent of the liberators did not put an end to the fighting. While the Soviets held the hospital's side of Iranischestrasse and Schulstrasse, SS men still held the other side of those streets, where they hid in the houses and fired on everything that moved. It became even too dangerous for German women from the neighborhood to try to get water from the pump in the street. They, too, had recourse to the hospital's well, which the hospital buildings sheltered from the snipers' line of sight, but the journey there and back was extremely dangerous.

Even with the Soviets on the grounds, the food situation was desperate, and the medical supplies of the hospital and the *Lazarett* were approaching exhaustion. The Soviet troops somehow managed to procure a pig, which they gave to the Jews. Nothing could have been less kosher, but all except the most rigidly observant were happy to see meat of any kind. There was no bread, however. The administrators of the *Lazarett* discovered that there was a bakery about ten minutes' walk away at which bread was still being baked. But the bakery was in territory still under SS control. There was no chance that it would provide any bread to Jews or to anyone who came in the name of the Jewish hospital. However, all the Germans at the *Lazarett* were Soviet prisoners confined to quarters. Finally, it was agreed that the *Lazarett* would order a quantity of bread by telephone, ostensibly for the use of the *Lazarett* alone, and would supply twenty volunteers from the hospital with false identity cards showing them to be *Lazarett* employees so that they could venture forth to collect the bread. Equipped with the false papers and wearing Red Cross armbands as an additional precaution, the twenty Jews set out at 10:00 A.M., dodging sniper fire, to find the bakery.

Hilde Kahan, who had negotiated these arrangements, remembers waiting anxiously as hours passed without any sign of the volunteers. By 2:00 P.M. she was beside herself with worry. She managed to reach the bakery by telephone and, pretending to be calling from the *Lazarett*, asked about the people who had been sent for the *Lazarett*'s bread. She was told that they had loaded up the bread and departed but had been stopped at the nearest SS command post and were being held there. Realizing that a disaster could be imminent, Kahan got Lustig to call the *Lazarett*'s director, who in turn telephoned the SS. His intervention was just in time. The Jews had been arrested as spies and were about to be stood up against a wall and shot. The head of the *Lazarett* managed to persuade the SS commandant to release them, and shortly both the hospital and the *Lazarett* were enjoying fresh bread.

On May 2, 1945, the guns finally were silent in Wedding. After twelve days and eleven nights living in the basements, the hospital's population finally could emerge into the daylight and resume life above ground. The Soviet commandant of Berlin had annulled all of the Nazi legislation pertaining to the Jews, but even before this official action the hospital's occupants had torn off their yellow stars. Now they were free to drop their compulsory Jewish middle names, free to go anywhere and to do whatever they wanted. The question was where to go and what to do in the country that had mistreated them so horrendously. For those who had been lodged in the hospital only because they were defined as Jews under the Nazi racial laws and who never had had any interest in being Jewish, the decision was easier. Most returned to their homes as soon as they could and resumed living as members of the German population. As quickly as possible, they put all question of Jewish identity behind them.

For those who felt themselves to be Jewish, however, the choices were not as easy. Some resumed their lives in Germany and remained there, at least long enough to aid in rebuilding some semblance of the Berlin Jewish community and to provide assistance to Jewish displaced persons. But, as soon as they could, most left a country they had come to hate, one in which they felt that they would forever be the objects of anti-Semitism, to seek true freedom in other countries, primarily the United States.

The immediate tasks, however, were survival and rebuilding. When the guns fell silent, Berlin was a city of ruins and shortages, a situation that persisted for several years, during which the city suffered through some of the coldest winters in its history. One of the first challenges facing the hospital was to deal with the people who had survived deportation.

Rosemarie H., by then functioning as a full-fledged nurse although she still was too young to receive her legal certification, looked out the window of her room at the hospital one Sunday and saw trucks arriving. Her first reaction was to be puzzled and somewhat concerned. For the preceding several years, the arrival of trucks in front of the hospital had meant only one thing: deportations. She realized what was happening as the first emaciated survivors, some of them still in their striped concentration camp uniforms, began to descend from the trucks. Some were in such terrible physical condition that they had to be lifted down on stretchers.

Rosemarie was the first among the nurses to make it downstairs. Chaskel, one of the hospital's administrative officers, was supervising the unloading of the trucks, and he immediately assigned her to take care of the returnees. By then, the Wehrmacht had evacuated the *Lazarett*. Rosemarie's first action was to go into the empty pavilions that the Wehrmacht had occupied, determine the number of usable beds, and report back to Chaskel. On the basis of the number of available beds, he assigned her most of the passengers on the trucks. While inspecting the *Lazarett,* Rosemarie came across a man wearing the trousers from a Wehrmacht uniform but no coat who apparently was living in the building. When she asked him what he was doing there he replied, "I was a doctor here; I don't know where to go." Rosemarie promptly informed Chaskel, who co-opted the Wehrmacht physician and put him in charge of triage of the returnees who had been entrusted to her care. Once the doctor had identified the people who needed medical treatment, especially those with communicable diseases like typhoid and tuberculosis, the most seriously ill were taken to the hospital; the rest were installed in the *Lazarett.* Thus the hospital was launched on the role it was to play for many months after the end of the war, caring for displaced persons — helping to rebuild their lives, as well as curing their illnesses and rehabilitating their damaged bodies. In the hospital offices that since 1942 had been occupied by the *Reichsvereinigung,* the surviving communal employees, their numbers gradually reinforced by returnees from the camps, struggled to reconstitute Jewish communal life in Berlin and to provide social services to the survivors.

For the observant Jews among the hospital population, an early order of business was to give thanks to God for their deliverance and to say memorial prayers for the many who had perished. Bruno Blau was there:

> On May 6th, the chief rabbi of the Polish army, Kahane, who had arrived in Berlin with the Red Army, gathered around him a group of Jews in the rooms of the Reichsvereinigung. Although the event was completely improvised, the room was not big enough to hold the deeply moved multitude; part of those who had come had to remain in the adjoining rooms and hallways. First the rabbi said the *Mincha* [afternoon] prayer and then he briefly and concisely described the situation. He pointed out that the Nazi regime had cost six million Jews their lives, of them three and a half million in Poland alone. In remembrance of the victims the *chasan* [cantor], who also belonged

to the Polish army, sang *El mole rachamim* [a prayer said at funerals and memorial services] which was interrupted by the sobs of the stirred listeners.

Soon thereafter, the hospital's synagogue was repaired and reconsecrated in another moving ceremony. Within the months following the end of the war the synagogue witnessed several weddings, as well as Klaus Zwilsky's Bar Mitzvah.

As life returned to a semblance of normality in occupied Germany, survivors in the hospital and those who had succeeded in getting away resumed contacts with each other. Dr. Conrad Gossels and his wife wrote from the United States to their old friends Helmuth and Meta Cohen, who had remained at the hospital throughout the war. (Dr. Cohen had succeeded to the position of head of internal medicine, which formerly had been held by Gossels's mentor, Professor Hermann Strauss.) The Gosselses asked how their friends and former colleagues had fared during the war years. Meta Cohen's reply, dated December 30, 1945, although generally matter-of-fact and unemotional, serves as a reminder both of the suffering the hospital had witnessed and of the improbable survival that had occurred there.

After commiserating with Gossels over the improbability that his sister Lotti, who had remained in Germany, would be heard from again (in fact she had been murdered in Auschwitz), Mrs. Cohen begins by describing the period in 1942–43 when suicide cases overwhelmed the hospital. She names doctors, nurses, and hospital staff members who themselves committed suicide: Dr. Silberberg, Fräulein Stettiner, Fräulein Gatt, Fräulein Berlowitz, nurse Giesela and nurse Elli Lennhoff and her mother, Irene . . . The names flow on and on down the page of tightly packed single-spaced typing. There follows the list of those who were deported and died, some in Auschwitz, a few in the dreaded "Little Fortress" prison at Theresienstadt, and the short tally of those who survived in Theresienstadt: Hilde Fischer, a handful of the nurses, the groundskeeper and his family. There is a pitifully short list of those who returned from Auschwitz alive. She mentions those who went into hiding. Some disappeared without a trace; some were betrayed and killed. A few made it through to the end of the war.

In the letter, Meta Cohen names the nurses who remained at the hospital through the entire period. Their number is fewer than twenty. "From among all of our doctors (full Jews)," she writes, "the following survived the entire period: Rosenberg, Heumann, Segall, Wolfsohn, Hirschfeld, Cohen and poor Elkan who has died since then." Of the doctors she names three more, Helischkowski, Markuse, and Meyer, who were there until the end and who were protected by living in mixed marriages. She writes not a word about Lustig. She then describes her own family's situation in words that could have been used by almost any of those who survived in the hospital while their colleagues were being deported: "Can you understand how it was here? Every time a piece of our hearts left with them, and the fear that the next time it would be one of us. As for our plans, dear Gossels, we are now physically and psychologically ready to go on. We are certain of only one thing: to leave this ghastly country."

The widespread desire among the hospital staff to leave Germany was natural in light of what they had endured under the Nazis. It undoubtedly was fortified by postwar conditions. Being freed from the constant fear of deportation was a significant improvement, as was the elimination of the yellow star and other anti-Semitic indignities. Yet the anti-Semitism still was there, even though so many Germans were disclaiming any role in the Nazis' crimes that one might have thought that there never had been any Nazis at all, except for the small number whom the Allies had arrested. Many of the same bureaucrats who had delighted in harassing the Jews under the Nazi regime remained in office and continued to do so under the Allied occupation.

"Anti-Semitism has been injected into the German people to such a degree," Ehrich Zwilsky wrote in 1945 in an appeal for help addressed to the Joint Distribution Committee in Paris, "that . . . in all branches of the German administration it is still visible today." In this letter and other contemporaneous documents, Zwilsky, then head of the hospital, painted a compelling picture of the plight of the hospital and Berlin's surviving Jewish population. Conditions in Berlin were appalling, he pointed out, because of the vast physical destruction the war had caused, the shortages of food, clothing, and fuel, and the virtual cessation of economic activity. But the impact of all these things fell hardest on the Jews, and, despite the oppression they had suffered, they were being refused any special help.

"Even the Jewish returnees from the concentration camps cannot get support or help," he wrote about the same time, "since they are not recognized as Victims of Fascism because they were not politically active but were persecuted 'only as Jews.'" Nor was any special treatment extended to the Jews who had remained in Germany. In this appeal to "the entire world" and in his contemporaneous letter to the Joint Distribution Committee and other Jewish organizations, Zwilsky detailed how the Nazi persecutions had left Berlin's remaining Jews especially unprepared to deal with the postwar privations. All bank and savings accounts were blocked. The rest of the population was trying to make do by selling valuables on the black market or using hoarded cash; the Jews, however, had no cash and nothing to sell. They systematically had been despoiled of everything by the Nazi confiscations. Food was another problem. During the last years of the war, everyone in Berlin had been short of food, but, under the Nazi rationing regulations, Jews had received inferior rations. For years their diets had been deprived of meat, fats, and other nourishing foodstuffs, leaving them significantly more undernourished and debilitated than the Aryan Berliners. Yet no allowance was being made in the immediate postwar distribution of available food supplies for the special health needs of these victims of Nazi persecution.

The blocking of financial assets was a particular problem. The reconstituted *Gemeinde* had money in the bank, but it could not touch it. Meanwhile, it was being overwhelmed by the welfare requirements of Berlin's remaining Jews and the returning survivors. The German government had established places where the concentration camp returnees could go for temporary shelter, but refugees were allowed to stay there only for two days. Consequently, the *Gemeinde* found itself responsible for operating and financing a number of camps for survivors and several rest homes for the aged Jews who had returned from Theresienstadt, as well as the hospital. The hospital was short of everything: beds, medications, especially vaccines against typhoid, diphtheria, and dysentery, insulin and narcotics, bandages, thermometers, sheets, towels, and blankets. Conditions in some ways were worse than they had been under the Nazis. At least then the hospital had received operating funds from the Gestapo.

In light of these conditions, it is a tribute to the efforts of the hospital staff that in August 1945, just as Zwilsky was drafting his appeals for help, returnees like Harry Rosenthal and visitors like Ernie Mayerfeld found the hospital to be an oasis of cleanliness and order in the chaos that characterized the defeated city.

13

THE TRIAL OF DR. DR. LUSTIG
AND OTHER QUESTIONS

JUNE 1945. RUTH BELESKI, still working at the hospital as a secretary in the *Reichsvereinigung* office, glanced out the window onto Iranischestrasse. A large official Soviet limousine stood waiting at the curb in front of the administration building. Minutes later she saw Walter Lustig, accompanied by two uniformed Soviet officers, leave the building and get into the car. Nothing seemed unusual or alarming about the scene. Just the preceding month, after all, Lustig had been appointed by the occupation-controlled local government as the director of health services for the Wedding district and had turned over the administration of the hospital to his aide Ehrich Zwilsky. He had remained as head of the *Reichsvereinigung* and recently had petitioned the Soviet authorities to convert it into the new Jewish *Gemeinde*, with himself as its head. He was, in short, a figure of importance in the emerging structure of postwar Berlin. Nothing could have been more normal than for him to leave the office with an honorific military escort to meet a Soviet occupation official on business.

As far as is known, this was the last time anyone connected with the hospital or the *Reichsvereinigung* ever saw the man. Virtually every memoir and published report says the same thing: that the Soviets took Lustig to the concentration camp at Sachsenhausen, which the Soviets had appropriated for the same use as the Nazis, and that there he was either shot or beaten to death without any form of inquiry or hearing. This story of Lustig's end was given an official cast when it was adopted by a Berlin criminal court, not in a proceeding directly involving Lustig, but rather in one involving Fritz Wöhrn. Too minor a functionary to have been tried at Nuremberg or in subsequent war crimes trials, Wöhrn was not brought to justice until the late 1960s, when he was tried before a Berlin state court and convicted of complicity in murder for his wartime acts. The court's judgment in that case contains a lengthy and largely irrelevant disquisition concerning Lustig's personality, actions, and demise.

The court's conclusion as to Lustig's fate has been widely repeated, yet corroboration is singularly lacking. There are no eyewitness accounts and no records. A footnote in Peter Wyden's *Stella* indicates that a Canadian political science professor named Klaus J. Herrmann had managed to follow Lustig's trail as far as the Rummelsburg police prison in East Berlin, where Lustig was brought after his arrest, but that trail is a dead end. All other reports are that Lustig was taken to Sachsenhausen. There the Soviets maintained a surprisingly complete set of records on their prisoners, records that can be consulted in the archive of the present Sachsenhausen memorial. That archive states, however, that it has no record whatsoever of Lustig. Since Lustig was born in 1891, by now the report that he is dead must be true, but when, where, and why he died remain a mystery. However, there are theories that seem more probable than the unverified account that appears to have gained unquestioning acceptance.

What is significant about the trial of Lustig is that there never was one. That leaves it to us to put the man on trial, both as an alleged anti-Semite and as an alleged abuser of his role as the wartime leader of the hospital and of Germany's remaining Jews, and, using the available evidence, to draw our own conclusions as to his purported execution by the Soviets and as to his actions during the war.

Did Lustig's "Execution" Ever Happen?

One scholar comments that Lustig openly enjoyed the power and position he held, as demonstrated by his postwar behavior. It would seem even more to the point to say that Lustig's actions after the liberation showed that vanity and lust for power were ineradicable elements of the man's psychological makeup, to such an extent that they overwhelmed his good sense. Lustig seems to have been unaware that his actions as director of the hospital, and even more so as the Gestapo's handpicked head of the *Rest-Reichsvereinigung*, might subject him to criticism. Even less did he suspect that his life might be in danger. Someone more perceptive would have realized that some of the Jews whose names he had put on deportation lists might have survived the camps, that some of the subordinates whom he had treated harshly during the war years might harbor resentments, and that these people would be gunning for him. In Lustig's case, however, instead of discreetly fading into obscurity, as would have been prudent, he made a brazen power play.

First, as we have seen, he was successful in lobbying the occupying forces to appoint him as head of health services and official doctor for the Wedding district. He was not to hold this position for long. By itself, Lustig's securing of a government post probably would not have been fatal, but it was coupled with another grab for power that may have cost him his life.

On June 6, 1945, he sent a letter to the *Oberbürgermeister* (Lord Mayor) of Berlin in which he claimed that the *Reichsvereinigung* should be recognized as the legitimate and authorized body representing all of Germany's Jews but that it should be renamed the *Jüdische Gemeinde Berlin*, since its activities had come to be concentrated in the Berlin area. He also proposed that he and his associates who constituted the personnel of the *Reichsvereinigung* should be recognized as the senior officials of this new *Gemeinde*. In the same letter, acting as if he already held the

position to which he aspired, he asked for various actions to be
taken vis-à-vis the Jewish population, including preferential allo-
cations of food, clothing, and footwear and exemptions from the
debris-removal work other Berliners were being required to perform.

The letter included a sycophantic paean of praise to Stalin:
"The few surviving Jews of Berlin," Lustig wrote, "thank you,
Marshal, with all their heart for liberation by the glorious Red
Army from the terrible Nazi regime." Meyer describes this statement as particularly cynical because, she alleges, "Lustig at the
time of the occupation of the hospital by the Red Army saved
only his own head, while he left the inmates of the prison ward
(and presumably also the other departments of the hospital) to
their own fate. The Soviet soldiers arrested these prisoners once
again and transported them to Weissensee in order to shoot
them. Only with difficulty did they succeed in explaining their
situation as arrested Jews and thereby escape with their lives."
(Meyer cites no source for this assertion, however, nor is credible
corroboration to be found in the written memoirs of hospital survivors or the recollections of people interviewed for this book
who were present when the Soviet soldiers arrived.)

Lustig's letter was all the more audacious in that the
Berlin Jewish *Gemeinde* already had been reestablished in the
prior month by former *Gemeinde* officials and other Jews who had
survived underground. To say the least, they did not welcome
Lustig's attempt to supplant them. Together with some of the
Jews who at the time of liberation had been prisoners in the
Sammellager on the hospital grounds and some among the few
former *Gemeinde* and hospital employees who had survived the
camps and made their way back to Berlin, they began to file complaints with the occupation authorities accusing Lustig of collaboration with the Nazis. Whether Lustig would have been attacked in this fashion if he had not thrust himself into a battle for
control of the *Gemeinde* is an open question.

The story of Lustig's demise raises many such questions, including the most important: did it ever happen? It is perfectly plausible that complaints by other Jews could have led the Soviet occupation authorities to arrest Lustig. No real explanation exists, however, for why the Soviets would have killed him immediately without at least an investigation of the charges, if not a trial. This purported treatment of Lustig is in stark contrast to that afforded the notorious *Spitzel* Stella Kübler, for example. While Lustig's alleged crimes against fellow Jews were open to substantial doubt, Stella's were not. For years, she had acted as a notorious Gestapo informant. The facts were known to the population at the hospital, who could observe her daily, since she and her fellow renegades were housed there with Dobberke in the *Sammellager*. The facts also were known to the few survivors of the many Jews she had tracked down in hiding and betrayed to the Gestapo.

Like Lustig, Stella Kübler also was arrested by the Russians. Amazingly, also like Lustig, she had so little understanding of her position that she put her own head in the noose. Having run away from the *Sammellager* in the confusion of the final days of the war, she came out of hiding after the war ended and applied at her local police station for a card recognizing her as a "Victim of Fascism." This quickly led to her undoing. She was tried by a Soviet military tribunal and imprisoned. After her release she was tried again by the West German government, although the ten-year sentence she received was remitted on account of the time she had already served. Why did the same not happen to Lustig? With a deep strain of anti-Semitism infecting the Russian authorities from Stalin on down, the Russians had no interest in concealing the crimes of those Jews who had collaborated with the Nazis. Nor did they have any strong motive to avenge the crimes against the Jews by lynching a man like Lustig. While the Soviet authorities might have looked the other way if Lustig's "arrest" and murder were an unauthorized initiative by Soviet Jewish soldiers, the Soviets thought they had more than enough to avenge in terms of Nazi crimes against the Soviet peoples, a vengeance

214 • REFUGE IN HELL

they tended to effect by raping German women and pillaging German property.

It seems unlikely that Lustig's death at the hands of the Soviet authorities occurred as reported. There are two hypotheses that would more plausibly explain the small body of known facts. One is that Lustig became aware of the hostility that was mounting against him, including the very real risk that outraged returning Jewish deportees might murder him, and decided to arrange for his own disappearance in a way that would not encourage anyone to look for him. (Presumably, now that the war was over, he was aware of how Dr. Schönfeld's mistress successfully had used her faked suicide for the same purpose.) As a clever, resourceful man, it should have been possible for him, probably with the aid of a few bribes, to stage the whole thing and ensure that believable rumors of his demise were circulated.

A second hypothesis is that the "arrest" was indeed staged, but at the behest of Lustig's enemies, not Lustig himself. Again, bribery or the connivance of Jewish officers in the Soviet forces (or both together) could have made it possible. There is no indication that Lustig even knew that he was being arrested when the Soviets came for him at the hospital. All we really know is that he left the hospital in an official Soviet car. By appealing to his sense of self-importance, people could well have misled him into coming along voluntarily in the belief that he was being taken for an important official meeting. Once away from the hospital, it would have been easy to turn him over to his real captors and for them to murder him without anyone's being the wiser.

Annemarie Lustig apparently had no less gall than her husband. She applied for a survivor pension as the widow of a victim of Nazi persecution and tried to convince the authorities that Walter Lustig had been arrested in 1943, sent to a *Sammellager*, and never heard from again. Although a few of the Jews who considered themselves Lustig's victims attempted to oppose this request, the authorities declined to institute an inquiry that could have clarified Lustig's real role. The most that happened was rejection of the patently false claim that Lustig had been taken to a Nazi concentration camp. Nonetheless, acting on Annemarie Lustig's application, the Berlin district court declared him officially dead, effective as of December 31, 1945.

Was Lustig an Anti-Semite?

As we have seen, Lustig was harshly criticized for his attitude toward his fellow Jews. Some charge that he was indifferent to the fate of the Jews and avoided organized Jewry until opportunism drove him to employment with the Berlin *Gemeinde*. Others, including the Berlin court that tried Fritz Wöhrn, call him an out-and-out anti-Semite and a Gestapo collaborator, a characterization that the Berlin court adopted largely on the word of Hildegarde Henschel. How justified are these accusations?

The characterization of Lustig as a Jewish anti-Semite is at odds with the reaction of his distant cousin Ernst Lustig. In a brief and anguished commentary on the judgment in the Wöhrn trial, Ernst Lustig expresses surprise and shock at the unfavorable way Walter Lustig is described. "What is difficult for me to comprehend," he writes, "is how this man could develop such a horrible attitude toward Jews when he himself was a flawless Jew." He remembers his cousin as a man who maintained friendly relations with his Jewish relatives, a man whom he knew as "Uncle Walter," and a man who once provided Ernst's father with a genealogical sketch of the branch of the family that descended from Dr. Lustig's great-grandfather Abraham, who had lived in the town of Adamowitz. This seems out of character with the picture of Walter Lustig as a man who took no interest in his Jewish roots, although it is true that the time in question, 1937–38, was already after the date when Walter Lustig decided to throw his lot in with the Jewish community to which the Nazis in any event had irrevocably assigned him.

There are other indications that cast doubt on Lustig's purported anti-Semitism. In 1935 he published a short article entitled "Health Care and Judaism" in the *Gemeindeblatt,* the newspaper of the Berlin *Gemeinde.* In it he lauds the way the Jewish religion has translated the concept of brotherly love into a duty that is not merely personal but communal, leading to the obligation to maintain communal social welfare institutions such as hospitals. The article is replete with references to the Torah, the Talmud, Rabbi Akiba, the *Shulchan Aruch* of Joseph Caro, and other Jewish sources, giving the impression that the author is a devout Jew steeped in Jewish knowledge.

It is hard to know what to make of this article. It is tempting to see it as an example of opportunism. The cynical view is that, defined as Jewish whether he liked it or not and with his prospects in the larger world blocked by Nazi legislation, the ever ambitious Lustig decided to aim for the top in the one sphere that was left to him, Jewish communal medicine. To this end, he put on a show of piety. That seems to be the implication of at least one set of commentators when they describe the article as having "constructed an ideological bridge for [Lustig's] entrance into community health services." On the other hand, this cynical view of Lustig's motives is not the only one possible, or even the most persuasive.

Probably the fact that is the least consistent with the view of Lustig as an unmitigated opportunist who became a Jewish official only because he had no other choice is that he seems to have been active in the Berlin *Gemeinde* well before his dismissal from public service, indeed before the Nazis took power. In 1931 and 1932 he was listed as a member of the *Gemeinde* Relief and Welfare Committee. If this rapprochement with the Jewish community at a time when Lustig was still a high government functionary occurred entirely for the purpose of preparing the way for a change of career should the Nazis come to power, Lustig must be credited with an almost superhuman degree of prescience.

In fact, it is unlikely that Lustig, any more than most other successful and assimilated German Jews, believed in 1931 that the Nazis would gain and hold on to power or, if they did, that they really meant what they said and would eliminate Jews from public life. Thus his voluntary and unpaid participation in the *Gemeinde* before the Nazi era seems unlikely to have been a purely cynical ploy, leading one to wonder if possibly Lustig always had been more connected with the Jewish community than is claimed by his detractors, who cite no evidence for their sweeping statements that he had avoided organized Jewish life. And even if Lustig previously had distanced himself from his Jewish roots, the growth of anti-Semitism in the late 1920s and early 1930s may well have brought him closer to his fellow Jews, without any conscious scheming or ulterior motive on his part. All over Germany, during the 1930s, Jews, marginalized in German society and deprived of outward social relations, turned inward to the Jewish community. Many assimilated Jews with little previous participation in Jewish religious or communal life became more observant. Synagogue attendance "increased dramatically, as Jews, depicted as evil and inferior by the government and the media, sought balm for their raw nerves and affirmation of their identity." It is impossible to determine whether Walter Lustig fell into this category, whether his apparent newfound interest not only in the Jewish community but also in Jewish culture was a genuine evolution in his thinking or merely a calculated ploy to advance his career. Most probably, there were elements of both in Lustig's mind, so complexly intermingled that he himself could not have said which predominated.

Was Lustig a Nazi Collaborator?

The crime for which Lustig purportedly was executed by the Soviets was collaboration with the Nazis. His detractors have asserted, in various ways, that he had improperly close relations with the RSHA and the Gestapo and that he used them to his own benefit to the detriment of the Jews for whose lives he was responsible, the patients and fellow workers at the hospital. How substantiated are these accusations?

It is obvious that Lustig became head of the hospital only because the RSHA and the Gestapo wanted him to have the position. It was not through the usual procedures by which the *Vorstand*, the governing body of the *Gemeinde*, had named hospital directors in the past. Depending on when he took over (that is, whether it was before or after June 1942), there may have been other members of the governing bodies of the *Gemeinde* and the *Reichsvereinigung* still in office and still in Berlin. By the time the deportations began in late 1941, however, the two intertwined organizations were so firmly under the thumb of the Nazi authorities that their leaders could not have made any independent judgment on a matter as important as appointing a new head of the hospital. The interesting question, therefore, is whether the fact that Lustig was approved, perhaps even chosen, by the Nazi authorities automatically made him their cat's-paw. Coupled with that is the question of whether Lustig abused his powers or whether he did what he was compelled to do but in a manner that served the good of the hospital community to the best of his abilities.

An aspect of Lustig's personality that seems especially pertinent to evaluating his actions in connection with his Gestapo bosses and his role as the hospital's director was his punctilious devotion to order. Many who were at the hospital describe him as zealous in carrying out the orders of his Nazi superiors. In the early phase of the mass deportations, when medical exemption certificates were still being granted, he warned the physicians involved that they should adhere scrupulously to the Gestapo's guidelines and wrote in favor of punishing doctors who repeatedly made unjustified decisions in favor of medical exemption. When the Gestapo banned Jewish religious observance at the hospital, it continued in secret, but the participants felt it necessary to hide their actions from Lustig as carefully as they concealed them from the Gestapo. Those who participated said that they "were less afraid of the Gestapo than of . . . Dr. Lustig, who saw to it that the orders of the Gestapo were not violated."

That fear, whether or not well founded, was widespread. Carry Friedlander, after she disappeared from the hospital and went into hiding with her husband, was riding a streetcar one day when she noted, to her horror, that Lustig had boarded the other end of the car. She and her husband managed to get off the train before Lustig spotted them, but she had no doubt, had he seen her, that he would have turned her in.

A slavish devotion to authority, a willingness to enforce every jot and tittle of the Nazis' directives — these are characteristics, some say, that made Lustig acceptable to the RSHA and the Gestapo, that secured him his posts as head of the hospital and the rump *Reichsvereinigung* and kept him firmly in place through the end of the war. These assertedly were deep-seated traits. According to one author, "He had acquired the necessary 'virtues' of subordination and integration into authoritative systems not only at the Police Presidium but also in the military, as well as during medical training under a strictly hierarchical medical system."

The trouble with this hypothesis is that it is not borne out by the evidence of how Lustig actually behaved. We already have seen, from the testimony of others who participated, that he influenced the medical exemption process in favor of Jews to the limited extent that he thought he could get away with doing so. Other incidents also demonstrate that at times Lustig was willing to bend the rules and take risks to preserve Jewish lives. One incident centered on his extraordinary efforts, as described earlier, to obtain approval to perform surgery on Ursula Finke. Another involved Rosemarie H., who had been sent to the hospital to do forced labor. One day, Rosemarie was on her lunch break, a welcome respite in a twelve-hour workday. She and a group of other young workers were warming themselves on the sun deck that stood on the roof of the main medical building. Gestapo officers suddenly appeared and began to shout at the Jews, castigating them for loafing on the job. The Gestapo men placed them all under arrest and marched them down the staircase. Being intimately familiar with the ins and outs of the hospital buildings,

Rosemarie knew that there was a doorway on the main staircase from which one could get access to another staircase that led directly down to the bomb shelter in the basement. Lagging behind, she seized the opportunity to slip into the doorway, run down the stairs, and make her escape. Although the Gestapo complained to Lustig that one of the prisoners had eluded them, Lustig professed to be unable to identify the culprit and did not take any action to discover who it might have been. Later, however, he told Rosemarie, "I knew it had to have been you."

The Lustig who was more Nazi than Hitler, the man who is said to have enforced his instructions from Fritz Wöhrn "to the letter, occasionally even anticipating them," is difficult to recognize in the Lustig who winked at Rosemarie's escape and subtly manipulated medical examinations to delay the deportation of Jews. Conceivably, one picture or the other might be incorrect, but it is more likely that both are true. Indeed, his former superior in the *Gemeinde* health service, Erich Seligmann, described him as "internally so torn up and externally so inhibited," characteristics of an individual who is psychologically primed to act in inconsistent ways.

Perhaps the most balanced psychological profile of Lustig relevant to his wartime official conduct is that given by Beate Meyer. She notes that Lustig's remoteness from his colleagues and his womanizing evidence an inherent problem with relationships. She also points out, however, that in the environment in which he was operating, where every move could be a life or death issue, it was dangerous to open oneself up too much to personal relationships. She notes that Lustig guarded the exclusivity of his relationship with Fritz Wöhrn. Whenever the Nazi overseer appeared in the hospital, he would retire to some private place for a conversation with Lustig from which others were excluded, and Lustig carefully controlled how much information from Wöhrn he passed on to others at the hospital. Keeping intelligence closely held may have been Lustig's way of ensuring that the information continued to flow; he may have seen this as a way of protecting the hospital and its population, rather than a mere form of ego gratification. Meyer admits that Lustig intervened to save Jews from deportation, but she notes that each such successful incident affirmed Lustig's feelings of power. This may be true, but it does not gainsay the fact that Jewish lives were saved.

That Lustig enjoyed being what one might crudely call "Top Jew" seems clear, but it is worth noting that, while his fellow Berlin Jews may have thought that he lived a privileged existence, Lustig did not escape any of the indignities of being a Jew in Nazi Germany. These included, among other things, the confiscation of a large part of his property through the tax on Jewish assets (the tax he paid was equal to almost four years of his pension) and the blocking of the remainder of his assets in a special account, the confiscation of his fur coat and gold jewelry, his skis and his radio, and the prohibition on his using an automobile. He was compelled to wear the yellow star and was unable even to prevent the Gestapo from requiring that it be worn by the hospital population while on hospital premises. For all his purported influence with the Gestapo, he was unable to save his own father from being deported to Theresienstadt in 1943. Moreover, the government assigned his wife to work far away from Berlin; if he tried to prevent this, he certainly failed.

What, then, can be said about his purported villainy? Was he in reality an ignoble instrument of the Nazi authorities who was responsible for the deaths of his fellow Jews? Or was he an unsung hero who cleverly manipulated the Nazis, within the narrow limits of the possible, in order to save as many lives as he could? Was he, as some have claimed, a "one-man *Judenrat*," or Jewish council?

It is noteworthy that, unlike many of the so-called Jewish notables who have been tarred with the reputation of "collaboration," Lustig was not imposed on the Jewish community from above. He was an authentic part of the Berlin *Gemeinde* executive structure well before all its decision making fell under the Gestapo's control in 1938. His case was not like that of the notorious

Georg Kareski, a Zionist leader who apparently was under Gestapo control. The Gestapo tried unsuccessfully to force Kareski's
appointment to the governing board of the *Reichsvertretung* in
1935. (The attempt was thwarted by Leo Baeck's threat to resign
as president of the *Reichsvertretung*.) The RSHA and the Gestapo
may have chosen Lustig as their puppet, but they did so only after
he voluntarily had been made a leader of the *Gemeinde/Reichs-
vereinigung*. At most, they ensured his rise to the top by deporting
everyone else.

The RSHA and the Gestapo may have chosen Lustig because
he appeared the most malleable of the available Jewish leaders.
Or he may have been favored because he had known both Wöhrn
and Wöhrn's boss, Günther, during his years in the Police Presidium and — despite the reputation he earned at the hospital as a
man who mistreated his subordinates — had enjoyed good relations with them.

In terms of how Lustig comported himself in the role the Nazis assigned him, one of the principal facts is beyond dispute:
Lustig was ordered by the Gestapo to designate specific numbers
of hospital staff and patients for deportation, and he complied
with these orders. He personally chose the victims of the 50 percent staff reduction in March 1943, and he did the same every
time he was ordered to in connection with a Gestapo "purge."

Had Lustig declined to make the selection, however, the Gestapo would have made it themselves, or they would have found
someone else to do the job. Many accused of collaboration raised
this defense. In most cases the claim rang hollow, because generally the Nazis could not have operated against the Jews without
Jewish help as effectively as they did with it. But this was not true
of deportations from the hospital. Unlike the actions of many
Judenräte, even of the *Gemeinde/Reichsvereinigung* in 1940 under
Rabbi Baeck's leadership, Lustig's role did not make it any easier
for the Nazis to find or deport Jews. They had no need of Lustig
to tell them who was at the hospital; the Gestapo had full access
to the staff and patient records. Wöhrn — and even Eichmann

himself on numerous occasions — circulated through the hospital, personally selecting deportees. Lustig could legitimately have believed that it would have been worse for the hospital and its population to experience even more of this direct RSHA and Gestapo selection or to have some other Jewish official making up the deportation lists. He may genuinely have thought — and he may have been right in so thinking — that, more than any other Jewish figure remaining in Germany, he had a chance of having his choices accepted by the Gestapo. He may have believed that he more than anyone else who might have been acceptable to the Gestapo had the knowledge that permitted him to preserve the essential core of the hospital's medical staff despite repeated Gestapo depredations.

Some of Lustig's contemporaries, not least Hilde Kahan, give him credit for taking on the burden of making choices as a way to save the hospital and to fight for the survival of the greatest number of its staff and inhabitants. Making life and death decisions, viewed in that light, must have been a lonely and anguishing task.

Rosemarie H. believes that Lustig tried to refuse when the Gestapo first ordered him to draw up a deportation list. "He said, 'I'm the first one.' He wanted to be the first one taken to a concentration camp. I remember that very, very well." No one else shares that memory, but others speak of the distress his responsibilities caused Lustig. Ruth Beleski says: "I think they did Lustig wrong. He had the worst job possible. And who was saved was saved by him. Without him we wouldn't be there anymore. He was a difficult person, but I have seen him cry. It was not an easy job."

Even if the mere fact of having acceded to the Gestapo's demands should not subject Lustig to condemnation, he would be subject to legitimate criticism if the way in which he made choices was self-interested, corrupt, or unethical. Many have so charged, although with little confirmatory evidence. His actions are suspect in three areas: first, turning over Jews to the Gestapo as punishment for violating the Gestapo's rules; second, choosing to deport the patients who were the least likely to survive; and, third, letting his mistresses guide the deportation decisions to the ruination of those who incurred their animosity.

On the first point, little is known. One witness accuses Lustig of having listed a nurse named Ilona because she had helped hide Jews from the Gestapo. Nothing else is known about this incident. Another nurse was deported when she left her post on the prison ward without authorization and two prisoners managed to escape in her absence. It is not known, however, if it was Lustig who put her name on the list or, as seems likely, the Gestapo discovered her involvement through its own investigation of the escapes and directly decided to punish her. Moreover, just as with Lustig's endeavors to maintain the honesty of the medical exemption process (or, at least, to ensure that all decisions to distort the outcome be concentrated in his own hands), enforcing the Gestapo's rules was not necessarily unjustifiable. Actions by individual hospital staff members to help Jews to escape, while laudable in motive, also risked the entire existence of the institution and its hundreds of inhabitants.

The issue of choosing the very sick for deportation is another charge for which almost no evidence can be found. Elkin cites a single source for this accusation. No one else, in describing the making of lists, suggests that Lustig deliberately sacrificed the sickest patients. Indeed, several witnesses say that Wöhrn, and even Eichmann himself, would sweep through the hospital wards and choose the patients who were to be deported. Lustig's role may have been confined to selecting hospital employees.

Even if it were true that Lustig chose patients and selected the most seriously ill among them for deportation, the moral and ethical issues involved are quite difficult. The same accusation was made against a Dr. Tuchmann, the director of Vienna's Rothschild Hospital, another Jewish institution that barely managed to survive through the Nazi era. After the war, Dr. Tuchmann was tried for his alleged offenses. His defense was that it was correct to send the sickest patients on the transports because the healthiest had the best chance of surviving until the war ended. This is similar to the rationale that a number of hospital doctors and nurses used in deciding to save the lives of young people who had attempted suicide and to allow elderly suicide patients to die in peace. Elkin questions the propriety of Lustig's choice, suggesting that his conduct, for which he presumably would have made the same defense as Dr. Tuchmann, "undermines the very foundation of a medical facility; the contradiction inherent in his choice calls into question the meaning of the institution as a hospital in this period. Did not the hospital, whose purpose was to treat the sick, become instead primarily a place where Jews were concentrated under the watchful eyes of the National-Socialist authorities?"

The answer to Elkin's question is probably "yes," but it must be remembered that it was not Lustig who was responsible, but rather the RSHA and the Gestapo. The transformation of the hospital from a purely medical institution to one that served a variety of purposes — prison, ghetto, *Sammellager,* and hospital — was an externally imposed reality with which Lustig was compelled to deal. Looking at the evidence, one can conclude that Lustig did everything he could to keep the hospital functioning as a place of medical treatment, to save it from becoming merely a jail and a ghetto. Faced with a requirement that he could not refuse without jeopardizing the hospital's existence, compelled to choose from among the patients those who would be deported — if indeed that choice was thrust upon him — what other principle of selection would have been any better? He could have chosen the healthiest on the theory that they had the best chance of surviving in the camps, but he almost certainly knew that this chance was at best minimal. He could have chosen patients at random, a method that would have had no arguable benefit to anyone. Whatever principle of selection he used, he would have been open to the same criticism that Elkin has made, that he perverted the hospital's medical mission. In short, from the comfortable perspective of those who were not there and did not have to make the choices, Lustig would have been damned whatever he did. Even if he had refused to act as the Nazis ordered, there undoubtedly are those who would have criticized him for abdicating his function and turning the responsibility over to another.

The most troubling of the accusations against Lustig is that he allowed personal preferences to influence his choice of deportees. On this score, the story that Lustig caused Dr. and Mrs. Fischer to be deported because Dr. Fischer criticized Lustig's sexual conduct is quite damning. One of the points that can be cited in Lustig's defense, regarding his role in selecting coworkers for the transports, is that he endeavored to ensure that the hospital's medical needs would still be met. It would not necessarily be inconsistent with this objective for Lustig on occasion to have been guided by his personal predilections or his mistresses' suggestions if he had to choose between two individuals who both filled the same need and were equally qualified. However, for him to accede to Illa's request that he deprive the hospital of a competent surgeon when no replacement was available would seem to be a completely indefensible abuse of power. The problem is, once again, that there is no fire to go with the smoke. Mrs. Fischer sincerely believes that Illa was the instigator of the deportation, but proof is lacking. Many of Lustig's subordinates at the hospital were firmly convinced that his mistresses had the power to put peoples' names on the deportation lists, but no one actually witnessed whatever pillow talk was involved. In weighing the charges against Lustig, the best one can do in the end is to render the old Scottish verdict of "not proven."

Moreover, without questioning the good faith of most of those who were at the hospital and later had unfavorable things to say about Lustig, it seems clear that a certain amount of scapegoating has occurred. Lustig was a man whose personality made him easy to dislike, and his sexual conduct was reprehensible. He disappeared and thus could not speak in his own defense. It is not surprising, as a consequence, that he became an easy symbol of everything that was terrible about the hospital during the time he directed it or that a number of otherwise kind and gentle people exult in the fact that, as they believe, the Russians killed him. Objectively, it seems unlikely that Lustig could have been fairly convicted in a court of law of anything beyond a vile temper and bad sexual morals.

While Lustig never had occasion to speak in his own defense, others who had worked with him in the hospital were conscious after the war that they were being criticized for alleged "collaboration" with the Gestapo. Dr. Helmuth Cohen retained among the papers he brought with him to the United States a small collection of testimonials from former patients thanking him for helping them during the Nazi period. Whether these were solicited or offered spontaneously we cannot know, but one, dated July 1, 1945, was written by a former police prisoner who was still a patient in the hospital. She says that she unfortunately is forced by her illness to spend some more time in the hospital, but hopes "you will succeed in making me completely healthy soon" so that she can prove her gratitude. Based on the date and circumstances, one cannot help suspecting that Dr. Cohen, shaken by Lustig's recent mysterious disappearance, may have asked certain patients to help him arm himself with defensive materials.

In a more direct approach, Ehrich Zwilsky in late August 1946 composed a two-page document intended "to confront unjustified accusations that have been spread against the Jewish staff of the Jewish hospital." The central theme of his defense is that the staff members acted selflessly and put themselves in considerable danger by carrying out their duties in a manner intended to help the unfortunate Jews who were prisoners or were awaiting deportation. He points out that the doctors wrote medical evaluations that justified long hospital stays for patients who otherwise would have been on their way to a prison or death camp. The risk of doing this was considerable, he says, because the hospital's activities were constantly monitored — through visits from the SS, through inspections, through the presence of the Gestapo who lived on the premises, and through the introduction of informers into the prison ward masquerading as sick people. Everyone on the staff, he says, worked tirelessly and were often required to toil through the night to meet the Gestapo's short deadlines on "statistical tasks." It is absurd to accuse people of collaboration with the Gestapo, he writes, who dutifully carried out their tasks for months without a day off, for years without a vacation, people who considered the hospital's survival to be vital and who personally carried out the firefighting, cleanup, and repair work after each bombing raid. "No one on the staff has any consciousness of guilt, because they fought to keep the Jewish hospital open and they dedicated their professional activity to the service of Jews."

Why Has the Hospital's Story Drawn So Little Attention?

At first blush, it is somewhat surprising that the unique persistence throughout the Hitler era of an identifiably Jewish institution in the very heart of Nazi Germany has not been adopted as a symbol of Jewish survival. For, in a post-Holocaust world where, once again, Jews feel besieged by threats to their existence, there is a yearning to find occurrences that can stand as examples of the hope-inspiring principle of *Am Yisrael Chai*, the resilience of the Jewish people even in the face of apparently endless persecution. The story of the hospital's survival has been known since the end of World War II to a small circle of survivors and Holocaust scholars and has been given passing mention in numerous books about the Nazis' treatment of German Jews. Yet it never has attained prominence or been invoked as a sign of hope or an occurrence in which to take pride. Why? There is no clear answer, but there are several factors that might contribute to an explanation.

For one, only recently has the story of the limited degree of Jewish survival in Nazi Germany begun to emerge from a silence that lasted some four decades. The growth of interest in this subject is part of an evolution of Jewish attitudes toward the Holocaust. Painting with a broad brush, it can be said that, for the first decade or so after the end of the war, writing about the Holocaust received somewhat muted attention among Jews, especially in America, notwithstanding a considerable body of literature on the subject. Jews were focused on succoring the survivors and building the State of Israel, which would largely serve as a refuge for Holocaust victims and other Jews in danger around the world. It was only slowly that the Holocaust emerged as a central Jewish preoccupation, entering, for some congregations, the religious liturgy as well as the secular culture. And, when it did, attention was mainly directed toward the extermination of Jews in the countries occupied by the Germans, particularly in Eastern and Central Europe.

There were a variety of reasons for this focus. In both Israel and the United States, the two most vibrant centers of postwar Jewish culture, people descended from Eastern European Jews far outnumber those descended from German Jews. Second, Jews in countries that were overrun by the Nazis had little chance to escape (although some did). In Germany and Austria (which was incorporated into the Reich), however, a period of six years intervened between Hitler's rise to power and the beginning of World War II, a period during which a substantial number of German and Austrian Jews departed for places where they survived the war. In percentage terms, therefore, the number of Jews originating in Germany and Austria who were killed during the Holocaust was lower than in most other Nazi-controlled countries. Lucy Dawidowicz estimates that 210,000 German and Austrian Jews were annihilated. This constitutes 90 percent of an estimated 240,000 who were in Germany and Austria before the extermination began, but less than 31 percent of the more than 685,000 Jews living in Germany and Austria at the time Hitler came to power. In contrast, 90 percent of the Jews in Poland and the Baltic countries were exterminated. This has made the story of German and Austrian Jews seem, to some people, less compelling than other aspects of the Holocaust. Finally, in prewar Europe, and even to a degree in the United States, there was a tension between German Jews and Eastern European Jews arising from differences in the level of assimilation and economic success and from a perceived "superiority complex" on the part of German Jews. While this has diminished over time, it, too, probably contributed to a dampening of interest in the German Jewish Holocaust experience.

In recent years, the situation has changed. Interest in the Holocaust has spread beyond the Jewish community to the general population. The publication of Victor Klemperer's diaries, which were bestsellers in both Germany and the United States, awakened readers to the fact that there were Jews who survived in Nazi Germany and who suffered greatly in the process. Martin Goldsmith's story of the *Kulturbund*, a tender and moving portrait of his German refugee parents, both musicians, and the families they left behind, is but one of a recent crop of excellent books about the German Jewish experience under the Nazis that reflect a growing popular interest, among Jews and non-Jews alike, in the tragic drama of German Jewish life in the Nazi era.

A second factor that may explain why the hospital has not attained symbolic importance is that the story is fraught with too many negative elements from a Jewish perspective. For one, the survival of the hospital and of the small population of German Jews who lived openly in Germany throughout the war almost entirely was attributable to intermarriage. This is a phenomenon that many committed Jews in the English-speaking world today consider the ultimate threat to Jewish survival. (Interestingly, committed German Jews thought the same way in the early twentieth century about the wave of intermarriage that was affecting their community.) Thus it may not be "politically correct" in some Jewish circles to acknowledge that intermarriage contributed, even to a minor degree, to Jewish survival in Germany.

Closely related is the fact that, while the group who survived at the hospital contained many people who were proud to consider themselves as Jews, some of whom also were religiously observant (to the extent that the Nazis did not make it impossible), a substantial percentage had had their identity as Jews forced upon them by the Nazis. Some had been born and raised as Christians or had long since converted to Christianity; others had merely fallen by the wayside, abandoning both Jewish religious practice and participation in organized Jewish life. It is, of course, morally untenable to think that the survival of people who were Jews against their will was any less important than the survival of Jews who were fully integrated into the Jewish community. Nonetheless, it is understandable that their fate commands less interest in the Jewish community than that of other European Jews.

Third, the story of the hospital carries an unavoidable odor of wrongdoing — whether justified or not. Those who survived there and were in positions of authority automatically fell under suspicion of "collaboration." The mere fact that they remained in Berlin and lived when so many others were deported to the East and, for the most part, died made all the hospital survivors targets of envy and doubt. This doubt can only be reinforced by the fact that the most ignoble among Germany's Jews — the small number of *Greifer* and *Spitzel* and those *Ordner* who treated other Jews badly — ended up living on the hospital grounds during the last year of the war. To be sure, to connect the rest of the hospital population with this handful of renegades, who lived a separate existence on the other side of the barbed wire that fenced off the *Sammellager*, is unfair. But it is likely that many of those who have become familiar with the story of the hospital and its association with the embarrassing phenomenon of Jewish betrayers, and who have taken at face value the accusations that Lustig was a "collaborator," have shied away in distaste from further inquiry.

Why Did the Hospital Survive?

On first hearing about the hospital's survival under the Nazis, many have asked whether the Nazis allowed it to exist for show purposes, to delude the world as to what was happening to Germany's Jews. The assumption is natural, but the hypothesis is untenable.

Except for the fact of the genocide itself, the Nazis made little serious attempt to hide from the world the extent of their atrocities against German Jewry. As a public relations gesture, the worst excesses of the anti-Semitic campaign were put into temporary abeyance for several months at the time of the 1936 Olympics. All that meant, however, was that foreign visitors were spared the sight of the most vicious forms of anti-Semitic propaganda and harassment, that public acts of violence against Jews were reduced, and that no new repressive decrees were issued while the world's eyes were turned toward Germany. By 1936, however, the decrees that already had been issued, including the 1935 Nuremberg Laws, were more than enough to persuade any open-minded observer that Germany had left the path of civilized conduct. So, too, were the atrocities that already had taken place and had been amply reported by foreign journalists. Nor had the Nazis made any secret of their intentions. Hitler's goals had been laid out as early as the publication of *Mein Kampf* and confirmed in myriad speeches, newspaper articles, and other declarations by Hitler and other Nazi leaders.

By the beginning of the period in which the hospital's continued existence becomes truly difficult to understand or explain, from 1942 to the end of the war, the fate of Germany's Jews had become clear beyond hope of concealment. Everyone knew that the German Jews were being expelled from the *Alt Reich* and "resettled" in the East. Nor was the Nazi plan to exterminate the Jews any secret. That fact had been known to perceptive American and European observers like William Shirer as early as 1939. As we have seen, by the end of 1943, all Jewish institutions in Germany were out of existence, except for the hospital (including the rump *Reichsvereinigung* that it housed) and the Weissensee cemetery. To have closed those as well could not have had a significant impact on either foreign or domestic views of what was happening to the Jews inside Germany.

What the German government did wish to hide was the precise fate of the mass of German Jews who had been deported.

Their efforts at deception centered on Theresienstadt, where they maintained the fiction that at least some German Jews — primarily the elderly and the Jewish notables whose fate might be of interest in foreign circles — were living in humane conditions under a form of self-government. For the visit of an International Red Cross delegation, the Germans briefly created a Potemkin Village out of the Theresienstadt ghetto that managed to delude the credulous visitors.

Nothing in the history of the hospital suggests that the Nazi government ever used it as a similar showplace. There is no record that any foreign delegation was brought there to demonstrate that Germany was treating Jews in a humane fashion. It certainly is conceivable, as it became clear to all but the most devoted Nazi fanatics that Germany was going to lose the war, that some German officials might have thought that leaving the hospital in existence could provide useful cover should they ever be called to account for their actions against German Jewry. If so, however, there is no known record of such thoughts. The idea is at best speculation, and not even very probable speculation at that. The hospital, after all, held the largest and best-positioned body of Jewish witnesses to the deportations remaining in Germany. The hospital staff had been intimately involved in the entire deportation process, and its medical records documented the mistreatment of Jews at the hands of the police, SS, and Gestapo — in jails, German concentration camps, and *Sammellager.* The last Berlin *Sammellager,* as we have seen, was right there on the hospital's grounds. One would think that fear of postwar repercussions would have led Nazi officials not only to burn records, as they did, but to eliminate the entire institution and all its surviving occupants. Indeed, in the last days of the war they reportedly planned to do so.

Some people, on hearing of the hospital's survival, instinctively have concluded that the Nazis kept it in existence so that highly placed Nazis could secretly avail themselves of the services of the outstanding Jewish doctors who worked there. This is en-

234 · REFUGE IN HELL

tirely incorrect. The whole notion painfully recalls the initial assumption of many German Jews at the outset of the Nazi regime that ultimately they would be safe because Jews were making an indispensable contribution to German industry, science, and the arts. The reality is that the Nazis' anti-Semitic mania precluded them (with only a few exceptions) from using the services of Jews, no matter how valuable they might have been. For example, and luckily for the rest of the world, they gladly drove out the most valuable potential Jewish scientific contributors, like Einstein, who could have helped them realize their dream of world domination. The fact that the Nazis had no interest in using the hospital's medical resources is shown by the fact that world-famous experts on the staff like Professor Hermann Strauss were among the first to be deported. There is no indication that any high Nazi official ever sought medical care from the hospital or any of its doctors. It was only close to the end of the war that a few Aryans who lived in the neighborhood or were wounded there began, in desperation, to have recourse to the hospital's medical services. One was Dobberke, who insisted that Dr. Elkan examine the Gestapo commandant's ill child. These individuals, however, including Dobberke, were not the ones who had made decisions regarding the hospital's fate during the crucial period from 1941 to the end of the war.

Another explanation offered by many of the survivors is that the hospital was necessary to the Nazis for pubic health reasons, since the remaining Jewish population in Berlin, under Nazi law, could not be treated anywhere else. Fear of epidemics that might affect the Aryan population, it is said, account for the fact that the hospital and its medical staff were allowed to remain. This explanation is more persuasive than others, but it is far from satisfactory, because it flies in the face of the overwhelming Nazi passion for exterminating Jews.

The Jewish population who would not have had a hospital available to them were it not for the Berlin Jewish Hospital consisted principally of Jews living in mixed marriages and their half-Jewish children, plus a handful of "full Jews" who had escaped deportation for one reason or another. We already have seen that the limited protection that Jews in these categories received was highly unpopular with the Nazi authorities and that lower-level officials tried to circumvent it whenever possible. Jews who were supposed to be exempt from deportation were harassed by the Gestapo, the SS, and the police. Their Aryan spouses were put under enormous pressure to divorce them so that the Jewish partner could be deported. The authorities, especially in cities other than Berlin, devoted considerable attention to devising ways to break up intermarried couples that insisted on staying together. More than a few protected Jews were arrested on spurious charges and sent to concentration camps or deported to death camps in the East.

In light of the profound hatred that the Nazis — not to speak of a huge number of Germans who were not party members — directed at Jews, one is compelled to wonder why the authorities, having decided reluctantly to let some Jews remain in Germany because it was politically risky to deport them, did not do their best to ensure that these Jews would die as quickly as possible. An effective strategy to that end would have been to deny them hospital services entirely, just as the denial of ambulance services to Jews ensured that many seriously ill Berlin Jews died despite the existence of the hospital. Indeed, elimination of the hospital appears to have been what the Berlin Gestapo headquarters had in mind in 1943 when it sent trucks to the hospital and ordered that the entire population prepare for immediate evacuation. It is true that there could have been a risk of epidemics if Jews with communicable diseases in Berlin and elsewhere had been left untreated, but that risk could have been mitigated in other ways by a government that was totally inhumane and unscrupulous in its treatment of Jews. Sick Jews could have been consigned to special quarantined "Jew houses" and left there to die without treatment.

236 • REFUGE IN HELL

Or, as the Gestapo secretly ordered in the case of the hospital's mental patients, they could have been quietly taken to the woods outside Oranienburg and shot.

The epidemic-avoidance hypothesis falls particularly short with reference to Jews in places other than Berlin. Victor Klemperer's diaries, which recount in great detail the life that he and a handful of other Jewish men married to Aryans led in Dresden during the Nazi years, make it clear that for these Jews, with rare exceptions, no hospitalization was available in Dresden. The only hope of hospital treatment was if the Gestapo would grant the necessary permits to use the train so that the patient could get himself or herself to the Jewish hospital in Berlin. Even when permission was granted, the trip was impossible for a patient without considerable stamina, since generally he or she was not allowed to have a seat on the train or to use any but the slow trains. Going to Berlin under these conditions may have been possible for a few Jews who needed surgery, but waiting for Gestapo permission and making such a trip obviously would not have been feasible in the case of a condition requiring emergency attention, least of all a debilitating infectious disease. Moreover, while Dresden lies reasonably close to Berlin, which somewhat alleviated the rigor of making a journey under such trying circumstances, the same lack of local hospital care pertained to Jews in much more distant German cities and, for them, must have put hospitalization in Berlin entirely out of the question, even for people who were no more ill than their fellow Jews in Dresden.

In short, the Nazis put so many obstacles in the way of Jews who needed medical care, especially if they lived outside Berlin or were not ambulatory, that it is hard to imagine that the hospital served as much of a protection against the spread of infectious diseases that might have cropped up among the remaining Jewish population — even in Berlin, let alone in other parts of the country. In 1938 the Jewish authorities did maintain that the hospital was needed for such a purpose and asked that therefore it might receive a generous allocation of *Krankenbehandler*. Apparently this argument carried some weight at that time; by 1943, however, it seems not to have held water, and it is hard to believe that this consideration alone accounts for the hospital's survival.

Some survivors believe that the Gestapo and RSHA kept the hospital going to provide themselves with something to do, to create soft billets in Berlin for officers who otherwise might have been sent to the front. This may have played a minor role, but it seems unlikely to have been a major contributor to the hospital's continued existence. The only Nazi officials for whom the hospital, in any sense, was a full-time job were Dobberke and his Gestapo contingent in the *Sammellager*. But the *Sammellager* was only coincidentally lodged on the hospital's grounds and could have operated independently — as, indeed, it had until it was moved to the *Pathologie* in 1944. Of the RSHA officers who were responsible for the hospital, only Fritz Wöhrn seems to have spent much time on it, and even he did not attend to hospital matters on a daily basis. It seems unlikely that Wöhrn singlehandedly could have kept the hospital from being closed.

What, then, did account for the hospital's survival? My conclusion is that it was the product of a confluence of factors, among which must be counted the inexplicable. Perhaps public health considerations played some role. If so, however, that likely was the case only while a large and concentrated Jewish population remained in Berlin, before the *Fabrikaktion* and subsequent deportations in the early months of 1943.

Possibly the two most important factors were bureaucratic convenience and ambition. On the first score, it must be remembered that the hospital served the interests of the RSHA and Gestapo in various ways connected with the deportations — providing doctors and nurses in the *Sammellager* and serving as a commissary, to mention only two. This accounts, in large part, for its survival at least until the end of the *Fabrikaktion* in 1943. Even after that, the hospital continued to prove useful, if only as a locale in which the Gestapo could establish a kind of ghetto.

As to ambition, the RSHA apparently coveted the land and

buildings the hospital occupied. The real estate, however, had been transferred to the Academy of Youth Medicine. As long as the hospital remained in existence as an instrument of the powerful security apparatus headed by Heinrich Himmler (to which both the RSHA and the Gestapo belonged), it was easy for the RSHA to fend off any claim by the academy that its legal title should give it the right to occupy the premises.

Elkin suggests that Eichmann's office stage-managed the entire transaction with the academy specifically in order to preserve the hospital. In 1942, when the first steps in the transfer of title took place, other Jewish communal assets that had not already been the subject of forced sales were in the process of being confiscated by the Finance Ministry. The forced sale to the academy, Elkin says, was engineered by the RSHA as a preemptive strike that kept the hospital's premises out of the hands of the Finance Ministry. Subsequently, the RSHA mounted a successful exercise in foot-dragging by withholding the necessary authorizations for the evacuation of the hospital's inhabitants, staff, and patients. Thus the official registration of the title transfer did not occur until May 1944, and even then, although the academy had formulated plans to establish its own hospital for young people on the site, the Jewish hospital continued to occupy the premises. No one knows how long the RSHA could have kept this exercise in bureaucratic frustration going; the arrival of the Soviet troops put an end to it before the internecine conflict had been resolved.

There is no proof that the RSHA chose the organization to which legal title to the hospital would be conveyed, but it seems likely that it did. If so, the choice of the academy was astute, if not brilliant. The academy was a new organization, formed late in 1942, that was jointly run by the head of the Reich's health services and the head of the Nazi Party's youth leadership and directed by the chief physician of the *Hitlerjugend* (Hitler Youth) organization. While these were influential members of the Nazi hierarchy, they were not in the inner circle of cabinet officers and Hitler confidants. Nor did the academy, as a recently created entity, occupy an established place in German officialdom. In short, it was a relatively powerless organization. Still, its legal title to the property served to block other, potentially more powerful, organs of the German government from trying to take possession. At the same time, the academy's lack of clout and low prestige ensured that the RSHA could count on being able to thwart the academy's desire to take actual control of the property.

The RSHA's desire to keep the hospital's land and buildings out of the hands of other bureaucratic entities required that the *Reichsvereinigung* and the hospital continue to use the property. In addition, there were other functions the premises could fill which bolstered the RSHA's argument that actual occupancy of the hospital grounds could not be surrendered to the academy. These additional functions included playing the role of a kind of ghetto to house, as we have seen, a disparate assortment of Jews. As time went by, it seems likely that the medical role the hospital played grew increasingly less important in Eichmann's eyes than these other functions. Had the medical aspect of the institution not remained, however, the RSHA's claim to retain the premises simply for use as a ghetto would have been hard to defend. There were many other buildings in Berlin — including several that had been confiscated from the former Jewish *Gemeinde* — that could have been turned to that use. Given that the safety and comfort of the Jewish occupants would not have been deemed a relevant consideration, almost any kind of structure would have done. Thus it was necessary to the RSHA's objective that a medical facility continue to function at the Iranischestrasse site.

There is nothing to indicate what the RSHA expected to do with the hospital property after the appropriate moment finally arrived to get rid of the Jews who were there, as surely must have been contemplated. Nor is it clear how Eichmann and his RSHA colleagues planned to fend off the academy once that event occurred. Perhaps no one had thought that far ahead. It is nonetheless plausible that the RSHA's desire to retain control of the property for its own eventual use led Eichmann and his colleagues to conclude that the hospital had to be kept in medical operation, even if only at a reduced level, and that the premises also should be devoted to as many other purposes relating to the Jews as possible, so that no more confiscations, like the Wehrmacht's creation of the *Lazarett*, would be possible.

It was not a certainty that the desire of Eichmann's department to keep the hospital open for ulterior motives would prevail over the zeal of others in the German government to eliminate the Jews. Consequently, substantial credit must be given to Dr. Lustig for his ability to manipulate the German bureaucracy in the interest of preserving the hospital. The most dramatic example is Lustig's facing down of the contingent sent by the Berlin Gestapo headquarters in March 1943 to close the hospital. His adroit handling of his RSHA and Gestapo masters, however, must have extended beyond that one day. Lustig's frequent interchanges with Eichmann, Günther, and Wöhrn largely took place over the telephone or behind closed doors, and no notes appear to have survived, if any ever were made. Consequently, we never will know how he managed to achieve what he did — to protect key staff members from deportation, in some cases even after they had been rounded up, and to keep the hospital functioning as a medical organization. But there can be no doubt that Lustig's relationships with these key officials, his knowledge of the workings of German bureaucracy, his negotiating skills, and his adroitness all played an important role in the hospital's survival.

Finally, one must give due credit to another factor. At various junctures, right up to the very end, a slightly different turn of events could have brought disaster to the hospital. If Eichmann, Günther, and Wöhrn all had been unavailable on March 10, 1943, when the Gestapo arrived to liquidate the hospital, Lustig and all his colleagues and patients might have been in a *Sammellager* before nightfall. Who knows whether the RSHA would have intervened at that stage to undo the Gestapo's actions? Dobberke could very well have followed his instructions to kill the entire hospital population, instead of letting himself be persuaded to flee. The deceptions used by hospital staff to protect certain patients from deportation could have been uncovered and could have led the Nazis to retaliate by closing the hospital. The defeat of Germany could have happened later than it did. For it is clear that time was playing against the survival of the hospital — indeed of all the Jews remaining in Germany. Almost certainly the hospital and its occupants would have been eliminated eventually.

None of these things happened, and the hospital survived. Everyone must decide independently whether this was a matter of blind luck or of divine intervention — whether there really occurred the miracle that so many who lived through the last years of the war in the hospital believe they witnessed.

AFTERWORD

The Hospital Today

THE HOSPITAL REMAINS on the same site today and continues to function under the name *Jüdisches Krankenhaus Berlin*, but it has been vastly altered, both organizationally and physically, the latter by the construction of new buildings and the remodeling of old ones. It continues to assert a claim to Jewish identity, albeit to an attenuated degree, in three ways. One is signage: the official name, *Jüdisches Krankenhaus Berlin*; the continued presence of the legend KRANKENHAUS DER JÜDISCHEN GEMEINDE on the pediment over the door of the main building on Iranischestrasse; and, in the lobby of the principal medical pavilion, a wall devoted to a display on the hospital's prewar and wartime history. The second is the small synagogue attached to one end of the main administration building. The continuing existence of a working synagogue in this space is due to the efforts of a Berlin nonprofit group, *Freunde des Jüdischen Krankenhauses Berlin* (Friends of the Berlin Jewish Hospital), that has devoted itself to preserving the Jewish character of the institution. (Among other things, this organization has underwritten the publication of several German-language books on the hospital's history.) The third sign of Jewishness is a section of the administration building adjacent to the synagogue that has been turned into a small old age home. There, Berlin's Jewish *Gemeinde* cares for several dozen aged Jews in space provided to it by the publicly endowed foundation that now owns and operates the hospital.

Like the current Jewish presence in Berlin, the residual Jewish character of the hospital is only a shadow of the pre-Nazi era. The physical traces are there — the lobby display and a handsome bronze plaque at the entrance, in Hebraic-style letters, proclaiming the Jewish character of the institution and summarizing its long history. These are reminiscent of the numerous memorials, restored Jewish buildings, and museums throughout the city that attest to the fact that Jews once played a major role in the city's life and at the same time poignantly underscore how reduced the vitality of Jewish life in the city is today in comparison with the pre-Nazi past.

The inscription over the hospital's main entrance is no truer today than it was after the Nazis took control of the hospital and dissolved Berlin's Jewish *Gemeinde*. Although the hospital was restored to the *Gemeinde* when the war ended, the impoverished and shrunken Jewish community could not afford to subsidize its operation, and in the 1950s the city (then West Berlin) took over the hospital and provided an independent, publicly sponsored foundation with a sufficient endowment to continue running it as part of the city's medical services. The hospital still employs a few Jewish doctors, including the current medical director and chief surgeon, Dr. Uri Schachtel, the Israeli-born son of German refugees who fled to Palestine in the mid-1930s. These doctors are beneficiaries of a provision in the charter of the foundation that gives preference to Jews in the hiring of staff members. Few, if any, Jews are to be found, however, in the hospital's beds. Ironically, most of the patients are Muslims. Located in a working-class section of the city and part of the municipal health and welfare system, the hospital today principally serves Turkish and Arab "guest workers."

The Postwar Lives of the Principal Sources of Information

After the war, the survivors among the hospital's staff and their families, patients, and prisoners scattered all over the globe. Here is what happened to some of those who left behind memoirs or were interviewed for this book.

Eva Beleski remained at the hospital after the war, along with her mother and her sister, Ruth. A brother of the girls' grandfather had immigrated to England in the nineteenth century. After the war ended a distant English cousin, Leslie Wills, became aware that he had relatives who had survived in Germany and began a correspondence with the Beleskis. A romance by mail developed between Leslie and Eva. One day Eva left for England, quite suddenly, and never returned. Her mother and sister in Germany soon learned that she had married Leslie. Today they live in Christchurch, Dorset, a smallish town on the outskirts of Bournemouth.

Ruth Beleski remained behind in Berlin after Eva left for England. Her plans to marry Dr. Heinz Elkan had been cruelly ended by his untimely death. She continued to work at the hospital and eventually became involved with Dr. Winterfeld, a staff member who had lived at the hospital throughout the war with his first wife but who had parted company with her when the war ended. Eventually Ruth married Dr. Winterfeld, and they immigrated to the United States, where they lived in Salt Lake City until Dr. Winterfeld died. Ruth now lives with her daughter in the suburban town of St. Charles, Missouri.

Bruno Blau immigrated to the United States in 1947 and became a librarian at the YIVO Institute in New York, where he remained until 1953. He wrote a number of articles on German Jewry under the Nazis. In 1953 he returned to Germany and died there shortly afterward.

Cordelia Edvardson went to Sweden after the war as part of a contingent of surviving Auschwitz prisoners who were given

shelter by Swedish benefactors. She married a Swede, joined his
Lutheran church, and had two children. She became a journalist
of some prominence. In her thirties, in connection with her attempts to deal with serious psychological problems arising from
her childhood experiences, she began to develop an interest in
her Jewish roots. This led ultimately to a decision to convert to
Judaism and move to Israel, where she became the Israeli correspondent for a major Swedish newspaper. In recent years, Edvardson has been a controversial figure in Israel because of her
outspoken positions in favor of Palestinian causes.

Hilde Fischer and her husband were deported to Theresienstadt in 1943, but in 1944 they were separated. Dr. Fischer was
sent to Auschwitz and never returned. Mrs. Fischer recounts that
he was sent from Auschwitz to various outlying labor camps to
serve as a doctor. About two or three months before the end of
the war, she says, Dr. Fischer was sent from one of those camps,
accompanied by a guard, to Berlin to bring back medical supplies
from the Jewish hospital. Although he could have escaped, he was
too honorable to expose the guard to punishment. While at the
hospital he left a letter for his wife in the custody of the pharmacist, Kantelberg. Kantelberg told her this, but when she returned
to the hospital after the war, the letter had disappeared.

When the war ended, Mrs. Fischer and other prisoners in
Theresienstadt each were given a small sum of money, either by
the Soviets or by a Western aid organization. She and several
other Berliners used their money to secure places aboard a truck
that was taking sacks of flour to Berlin. On her arrival at the hospital, she was put to work preparing the *Schwesternheim*, which
had been reclaimed from the Wehrmacht, for use as housing for
returnees from Theresienstadt and other concentration camps.
After working as a nurse at the hospital for several years in the
postwar period, Mrs. Fischer immigrated to the United States.
She was taken in by a distant relative in New York, who gave her a
place to live while she studied to obtain her nursing qualification

there. She found employment as a nurse and eventually retired to a Quaker-operated continuing care community in Medford, New Jersey.

Carry Friedlander and her husband lived in hiding from the time of the *Fabrikaktion* to the end of the war. They owe their lives to a non-Jewish German woman and her husband whom they had not previously known. The couple who helped them lived in a tiny flat consisting only of a bedroom, a kitchen, and a bathroom with toilet and sink but no bathtub. They could not hide anyone in their own home, but they had a wide circle of friends who were willing to assist in their efforts.

For more than two years the German couple managed to find places where the Friedlanders could stay, usually as paying lodgers of someone who did not know, or chose to pretend not to know, that they were Jewish. They had no papers and no ration cards, but their benefactors managed to get them sufficient food to keep from starving, although they were constantly hungry. Their experiences while in hiding were extraordinary. During the daytime they generally could not stay indoors because the apartments were subject to being visited at any time by the building superintendent. So they spent most of their days wandering in cemeteries, which they thought were the places where they were least likely to encounter the Gestapo and the *Greifer* and *Spitzel*. At one point Mrs. Friedlander contracted hepatitis. She had to recover entirely without medical attention, since there was no way to obtain treatment without being exposed. She also became pregnant and had no choice but to obtain an abortion. In this case, she ran the risk of appealing for help to a non-Jewish friend who was a nurse.

After the war, the Friedlanders went to Switzerland for a time and then came to the United States. They lived in the New York area, where Mrs. Friedlander worked as a nurse for many years before they moved to Florida. When Mr. Friedlander became seriously ill, they moved to a continuing care community in North

Andover, Massachusetts, to be close to one of their daughters who lives nearby. Mr. Friedlander died several years ago.

"Rosemarie H." initially worked in the pediatric department. After the war, she stayed in Berlin long enough to complete formal nurse's training and obtained her nursing license in 1947. During the immediate postwar period she helped in setting up the residence in the former *Schwesternheim* to care for returnees from Theresienstadt.

Rosemarie moved to New York, obtained her U.S. certification, and began to work as a nurse. She married a physician, also an émigré from Germany, and has two children and three grandchildren.

Hilde Kahan would have liked to emigrate as soon as possible after the war, but she promised Ehrich Zwilsky that she would remain at the hospital as long as he was its director. In 1946, when the Zwilskys left for Sweden en route to the United States, she was recruited by her former boss from the *Hilfsverein*, who had returned to Germany as a representative of the Hebrew Immigrant Aid Society (HIAS). She worked for HIAS in Berlin and then in Stuttgart. She then immigrated to New York City. She worked there as a stenographer while studying accounting and then went to work for the New York City government as an accountant. She retired as a senior group chief supervising a staff of fifty people. After her retirement, Hilde Kahan left the United States and moved to Israel. I made unsuccessful attempts to locate her over the last few years. The only information I could obtain was from the Israeli Holocaust memorial, Yad Vashem (which had interviewed Hilde Kahan for a videotaped oral history), where it was believed that Ms. Kahan had returned to the United States during the Gulf War because she was afraid of the Scud missile attacks from Iraq. If still alive, she now would be in her early nineties.

Ruth Lebram married Dr. Hans Knopp and lived with him in Mainz until he died. She then returned to the United States and

248 · AFTERWORD

took up the nursing profession again. Mrs. Knopp now lives in retirement in Red Bank, New Jersey.

Inge London continued to work at the hospital as a manual laborer until the end of the war. She left Berlin afterward and immigrated to the United States, where she married a Jewish refugee from Germany named Lewkowitz. Her husband had managed to escape to Shanghai, where he had earned his living as a prizefighter, engaging in more than 120 bouts. Mrs. Lewkowitz, now a widow with several children and grandchildren, lives in Flushing, New York. She has been trying for many years to obtain compensation for the years of forced labor she had to perform at the hospital but so far has been unsuccessful because the hospital is not recognized as falling into any of the categories for which compensation is available.

Margot Neumann left her job at the hospital during the battle for Berlin and never returned. She married a non-Jew, becoming Margot Frey, and had one child, a son. She decided to raise him as a Christian and, as far as could be told from what she said in her interview, has maintained little or no contact with the Jewish community or anything Jewish since the war. She lives today in a modest apartment in a blue-collar neighborhood in the former East Berlin that is largely populated by immigrants.

Hermann and Herta Pineas went underground in March 1943. They left Berlin and were given shelter, at times separately and at other times together, by clergymen of the Protestant Confessing Church, pupils of the renowned Karl Barth. Hermann Pineas managed to obtain false identity papers, obtained a job in a tool manufacturing company, and even made business trips on behalf of his employer to the Ministry of War Supplies in Berlin. The couple survived in hiding to the end of the war. After the war, they immigrated to the United States, where Dr. Pineas worked as a neurologist in a Veterans Administration outpatient clinic in New York.

Klaus Zwilsky and his parents remained in Berlin until 1946. They continued to live at the hospital, where Ehrich Zwilsky had become director in May 1945. In August 1945, the *New York Times* published an article by Drew Middleton under the headline "Jews in U.S. Zone of Reich Find Conditions Improving — Status in Other Countries Surveyed." The article referred to the hospital and quoted Klaus's father. For the family's relatives in the United States, this was the first indication that the Zwilskys had survived. Eventually, the relatives in New Jersey were able to make contact with Ehrich Zwilsky and help the family to immigrate to the United States. Because of delays in obtaining the necessary papers, the family first went to Sweden, where they stayed from June 1946 to January 1947.

In America, they initially stayed with their relatives on a farm in New Jersey. Klaus's mother was able to use her experience as a slave laborer in a German uniform factory to obtain a job as a garment finisher. Ehrich Zwilsky ultimately benefited from a New Jersey law that enabled foreign-trained medical personnel to work in state institutions without passing new qualifying examinations. He became a pharmacist in a New Jersey state hospital and worked there until his death. Klaus attended high school in New Jersey and was admitted to MIT, where he received his undergraduate education and a doctorate in engineering. He worked for various U.S. government agencies and for the National Academy of Sciences, for which he still acts as a consultant in his retirement.

NOTES
BIBLIOGRAPHY
GLOSSARY
ACKNOWLEDGMENTS
INDEX

Notes

Preface

PAGE

xviii *An interesting example:* Meyer, "Reichsvereinigung," p. 14.

xix *Hartung-von Doetinchem records:* Hartung-von Doetinchem, "Zerstörte Fortschritte," p. 174.

1. Nichts Juden. Juden Kaputt

1 *A spokesman stepped forward:* This somewhat dramatized account is drawn from several survivors' interviews. Hilde Kahan says that there were several fluent Russian speakers on the hospital staff. Hilde Kahan, videotaped interview, undated, Yad Vashem Archives, Jerusalem.

2 *There were some eight hundred Jews:* A number of published sources estimate the hospital's population at around eight hundred at the time of liberation. See, for example, Ball-Kaduri, "Berlin Is 'Purged,'" p. 316; and Blau, "Last Days," p. 204. Many of the people whom I interviewed who were there at the time of liberation seemed doubtful about this estimate and thought that there probably were fewer. Hilde Kahan gives the number of five hundred in her videotaped interview.

2 *The tally on February 28, 1945:* Elkin, "Survival," p. 192, n. 217.

3 *Astonishment over the still functioning:* Rowe, "Memoir."

3 *"As we exited":* Ibid.

4 *"I asked people":* Personal communication.

4 *There, a handful of Jewish employees:* Marriage to an Aryan spouse, protection by Nazi officials, imprisonment in a concentration camp in Germany, such as Oranienburg or Sachsenhausen, and various other circumstances kept certain German Jews from being deported. This

led to the continued presence in Germany of a minuscule number of registered Jews. In some cases, when one of these Jews died, burial in the Weissensee cemetery was permitted.

4   *The cemetery served:* The Nazis desecrated Jewish cemeteries elsewhere in Berlin and throughout Germany. The survival of the Weissensee cemetery, like that of the hospital, was an aberration.

6   5,100 MEMBERS: The 5,100 figure is lower than the 6,284 Jews recorded in February 1945 by Fräulein Raphael for the Gestapo. Several factors may account for the discrepancy. One is mortality during the last three months of the war. Another is that some of the "Jews" whose numbers were being tracked by the Gestapo were defined as such only in Nazi terms, such as Jewish converts to Christianity who were married to non-Jews. These people had not been members of the Jewish *Gemeinde* before the Nazi racial laws came into force and were unlikely to have been counted as members once the war ended.

6   *At the war's end:* See Gross, *Last Jews.* The book recounts the experiences of a handful of Berlin Jews who survived in this manner.

6   *It has been estimated:* Kaplan, *Between Dignity,* p. 203.

10 *Like her boss:* For information in this paragraph, see Hilde Kahan, videotaped interview, undated, Yad Vashem Archives, Jerusalem.

11 *Of the rest:* Ibid.

2. The Hospital and the Berlin Jews

15 *It took all of everyone's time:* Inge Berner, interview by Ernest Mayerfeld and the author, Reston, Virginia, December 5, 2000.

15 *The founding of the city of Berlin:* For information in this and the following paragraph, see Richie, *Faust's Metropolis,* pp. 23, 28, 42, 57.

16 *It was in this period:* Elkin, "Survival," p. 157.

16 *The true origins of the hospital:* For information in this paragraph, see Philipsborn, "Jewish Hospitals," pp. 220–21.

17 *The organizations employed:* Ibid., p. 222.

17 *In the ensuing half century:* Ibid., pp. 222–23.

18 *Indeed, as a leading:* Richie, *Faust's Metropolis,* p. 151.

18 *It was in the flush:* Elkin, "Survival," p. 157.

19 *The new hospital was:* At the time the hospital was built, Iranischestrasse was called Exerzierstrasse.

21 *The hospital's survival:* The historical summary in this paragraph is drawn principally from Laqueur, ed., *Holocaust Encyclopedia,* pp. xxi–xxvii.

21 *April and May 1933:* For information on the Aryan clause, see Dawidowicz, *War,* pp. 58–59.

22 *Under the Nazi measures:* Kaplan, *Between Dignity,* p. 24.

22   *One of the most highly placed:* The information in this chapter about Lustig's background and career is drawn primarily from Nadav and Stürzbecher, "Walter Lustig," and from Meyer, "Gratwanderung," the section entitled "Der 'Ein-Mann-Judenrat': Dr. Dr. Walter Lustig" (The "one-man Jewish council": Dr. Dr. Walter Lustig), pp. 325–30. These two essays are the most complete and extensively researched published accounts about Lustig. Because they largely contain the same information, drawn from the same sources and phrased in similar language, specific citations to either are omitted except where an observation or item of information is unique to one or the other.

23   *Commentators on Lustig's character:* Nadav and Stürzbecher, "Walter Lustig."

23   *His military work:* Ibid.

24   *Another of his works:* Ernst Lustig, "Zur Strafsache," p. 2.

26   *His physical appearance:* Eva Wills, interview by the author, Christchurch, England, July 31, 2001.

26   *To Margot Neumann:* Margot Frey, interview by Gerald Liebenau and the author, Berlin, April 12, 2002.

26   *Lustig's most memorable feature:* Inge Lewkowitz and Rosemarie H., interview by Ernest Mayerfeld and the author, New York City, January 12, 2001.

26   Schwester *Carry remembers:* Carry Friedlander, interview by the author, North Andover, Massachusetts, February 28, 2002.

26   *Another forced laborer:* Ruth Abrahamsson, interview by the author, Stockholm, Sweden, July 4, 2002.

26   *According to one source:* Meyer, "Gratwanderung," p. 325.

26   *One of the harshest:* Ibid., p. 326.

26   *He is said to have:* Nadav and Stürzbecher, "Walter Lustig," p. 223.

26   *The head of:* Pineas and Pineas, "Our Fortunes," p. 452.

27   *This depiction:* Henschel was the wife of Moritz Henschel, who served as the last president of the Berlin *Gemeinde*. She was deported with her husband to Theresienstadt in 1943 and survived there.

27   *She describes Lustig:* Henschel, "Gemeindearbeit," p. 4.

27   *As a young man:* Meyer, "Gratwanderung."

27   *He had a "querulous and autocratic nature":* Nadav and Stürzbecher, "Walter Lustig," p. 226. On the description of Lustig as "distant and reserved," Hildegarde Henschel says that he drank heavily, which she thought might explain what she describes as his bad behavior (Henschel, "Gemeindearbeit," p. 4). No other contemporary, however, corroborates this claim, including the secretaries who were with him most often.

27   *In the words of:* Hildegarde Fischer, interview by the author, Medford, New Jersey, March 8, 2001.

27 *"He was famous"*: Carry Friedlander, interview by the author, North Andover, Massachusetts, February 28, 2002.

27 *In her written memoir:* Kahan, "Chronik," p. 34. See also Elkin, "Survival," p. 187.

28 *She makes it clear:* In its judgment in the Wöhrn case, the court had this to say: "Dr. Dr. Lustig was an enigmatic personality. He was nimble and good at negotiating. However he was also arrogant and driven for prestige. . . . Many Jews at the hospital as well as those working in the Reichsvereinigung were afraid of Lustig. . . . Although Dr. Lustig himself was a full Jew he had anti-Semitic sentiments. . . . The statements of Frau Henschel regarding Dr. Lustig's personality and his anti-Semitic views have already been established by statements of witnesses Hilde Kahan and Kleemann." Landgericht Berlin, "Strafsache," pp. 32, 35.

28 *"He was a very courageous man"*: For Hilde Kahan's statements in this paragraph, see Hilde Kahan, videotaped interview, undated, Yad Vashem Archives, Jerusalem.

28 *"He was a very intelligent"*: Ruth Winterfeld, interview by the author, St. Charles, Missouri, April 4, 2001.

28 *"Everybody lived in absolute dread"*: Eva Wills, interview by the author, Christchurch, England, July 31, 2001.

29 *Even as early as July 1933:* "Jüdische Krankenhaus in Gefahr!"

3. The Beginning of the End

32 *Although by then:* Kaplan, *Between Dignity*, p. 132.

32 *Jews were forbidden:* Ibid., pp. 145–46.

32 *A series of post-Kristallnacht decrees:* Ibid., p. 146.

33 *Despite continual Nazi harassment:* Baker, *Days of Sorrow*, p. 154.

34 *There even was Jewish entertainment:* See Goldsmith, *Inextinguishable Symphony*, for a moving portrayal of the *Kulturbund.*

35 *"The 'Jewish star'"*: Klemperer, *Witness 1933–1941*, p. 433.

35 *In 1940 groups of Jews:* Kaplan, *Between Dignity*, p. 179.

37 *The hospital had been built:* Elkin, "Survival," pp. 159–60.

38 *Rabbi Leo Baeck became:* The material that follows on Rabbi Leo Baeck is drawn primarily from Baker, *Days of Sorrow*, the preeminent biography of Baeck.

38 *When on March 13, 1938:* Ibid., p. 201.

39 *The next step:* The information in this paragraph is drawn primarily from Cochavi, "Berlin," p. 72.

40 *Indeed, the fact:* Elkin, "Survival," p. 159.

40 *The underutilization:* The crisis of underutilization reported in the hos-

pital's July 1933 appeal in the *Gemeindeblatt* seems to have ebbed and flowed (see p. 29 of this book). While in 1933 it looked as if non-Jews would permanently be precluded from using the hospital, in 1935 an article in the *Gemeindeblatt* reported that 30 percent of the hospital's patients were non-Jews. Nonetheless, the hospital's situation continued to be precarious until 1938. See G.H., "Jüdische Krankenhaus."

40 *A photograph:* Elkin, *Jüdische Krankenhaus,* p. 23.

41 *Thus the Jewish population:* Elkin, "Survival," p. 161, n. 31.

42 *They were kept under guard:* A typical case of this came to my attention in response to our *Aufbau* advertisement looking for people who had been at the hospital during the war years. One survivor of Auschwitz called from St. Louis to say that he had been a patient in the hospital for a short time. He was already on a train bound for Auschwitz when he suffered an attack of acute appendicitis. The guards took him off the train and delivered him to the hospital's police ward, where an appendectomy was performed. After a few days of recuperation, he was dragged away and put on another train to Auschwitz. The Nazis' practices in this regard were truly unpredictable. At almost the same time as the man in St. Louis was having his appendix out, another Jew, John Fink, was in the "free" part of the hospital, also undergoing an appendectomy. While recovering, he was arrested in his bed, taken to the Grosse Hamburgerstrasse *Sammellager,* and shortly thereafter shipped to Auschwitz. Letter to Ernest Mayerfeld from John Fink, November 12, 2000.

42 *In 1933 Jewish doctors:* Elkin, "Survival," p. 163.

43 *Indeed, after* Kristallnacht: Ibid., pp. 165–66.

44 *The German health authorities:* For information in this paragraph, see ibid., pp. 164–65.

45 *In 1940 there were:* Hartung-von Doetinchem, "Zerstörte Fortschritte," pp. 175–76.

45 *Even in that year:* Ibid., pp. 174–75.

45 *"I . . . then created":* Holzer, "Bericht."

4. The Nazis' Intermarriage Quandary

46 *Rosemarie H.:* "Rosemarie H." is a pseudonym adopted at the request of the interviewee to protect her privacy. Also pseudonymous are her uncle's name, "Fritz," and her brother's name, "Hans," used in Chapter 7. Her story in the following paragraphs is based on Rosemarie H., interview by the author, New York State, May 29, 2001.

47 *Rosemarie's story is typical:* The information in this chapter is drawn from various sources. One stands out, however: Nathan Stoltzfus, *Re-*

sistance of the Heart. This careful, insightful, and very complete study of intermarriage and of the Rosenstrasse demonstration (discussed in Chapter 8 of this book) is both scholarly and highly readable.

47 *By 1927:* Kaplan, *Between Dignity,* p. 11.

48 *They had welcomed:* Ruth Abrahamsson, interview by the author, Stockholm, Sweden, July 4, 2002.

48 *The hospital's Dr. Hans Knopp:* Ruth Knopp, interview by Ernest Mayerfeld and the author, Red Bank, New Jersey, January 11, 2001.

50 *The next significant increase:* The description of the Nuremberg Laws is based primarily on Fraenkel, "Nuremberg Laws," pp. 451–55; and Friedländer, "Nazi Policy," pp. 427–37.

51 *The term, which can be translated: The Pocket Oxford German Dictionary* (Oxford: Oxford University Press, 1980), p. 229.

52 *Estimates range:* See, for example, Kaplan, *Between Dignity,* pp. 75–78.

52 *As Nathan Stoltzfus has emphasized:* For this and the next sentence, see Stoltzfus, *Resistance of the Heart,* p. 5.

54 *They received the same food rations:* Blau, "Fourteen Years," p. 466.

54 *The distinctions among mixed marriages:* Kaplan, *Between Dignity,* p. 149.

54 *The effect of the "privileged Jew" rules:* Blau, "Fourteen Years," p. 466.

55 *As a survivor:* For Cordelia Edvardson's story, see Edvardson, *Burned Child.*

57 *These minighettos:* Numerous examples can be found in Klemperer, *Witness 1933–1941* and *Witness 1942–1945.*

57 *Ruth Beleski, who worked:* The rest of this paragraph is based on Ruth Winterfeld, interview by the author, St. Charles, Missouri, April 4, 2001.

5. The Deportations

59 *The services:* The description of Yom Kippur 1941 is based on Baker, *Days of Sorrow,* p. 270.

60 *In the end, despite Baeck's misgivings:* The decision to cooperate with the authorities in the hope of easing the plight of the deportees was controversial at the time and led to disagreement between Baeck, the president of the *Reichsvereinigung,* and the organization's executive director, Paul Eppstein. According to Baker, ibid., Rabbi Baeck was troubled by the degree of cooperation between the *Gemeinde/Reichsvereinigung* (by this time the boundary between the central organization and its subunit, the Berlin *Gemeinde,* was already blurred) and the Nazi authorities, but he was powerless to do anything about it. He let himself be pushed into acquiescence by Eppstein, feeling that he was unable to do otherwise.

60 *"When the question arose"*: Ibid., p. 272.
61 *Hannah Arendt:* The following quotations are from Arendt, *Eichmann in Jerusalem*, p. 117. Raoul Hilberg, in his magisterial book *The Destruction of the European Jews*, pp. 293–305, notes the enormous contribution that cooperation by Jewish communal organizations made to the Nazi process of destroying the Jews and says that the instinct of Jewish communal leaders to cooperate with the oppressor in hopes of mitigating the severity of the attacks, which arose from traditional Jewish modes of adapting to anti-Semitic oppression and violence in the European past, proved fatally misguided in the context of the Nazis' genocidal aims. With the benefit of hindsight, one can see that, instead of alleviating Jewish suffering, such cooperation enabled more Jews to be killed faster than otherwise would have occurred and at less cost to the Germans.
63 *As a result:* This sentence and following quotation are from Carry Friedlander, interview by the author, North Andover, Massachusetts, February 28, 2002.
63 *Dr. Hermann Pineas:* This paragraph is based on Pineas and Pineas, "Our Fortunes," pp. 450–51.
65 *These two officers:* Kahan, "Chronik," p. 8.
65 *However, although there are accounts:* But see Blau, "Fourteen Years," p. 464. Blau says that some Berlin *Ordner* stole from deportees.
66 *As the deportations took their toll:* Pineas and Pineas, "Our Fortunes," pp. 448–49.
67 *Herta Pineas, Dr. Pineas's wife:* This paragraph is based on ibid., p. 449.
68 *She attributed the authorities' action:* Kahan, "Chronik," p. 9.
68 *There were still:* Blau, "Last Days," pp. 198, 200.
69 *The board was staffed:* Henschel, "Gemeindearbeit," p. 4.
69 *If the initial result:* Hilde Kahan, videotaped interview, undated, Yad Vashem Archives, Jerusalem.
69 *The workload of the board:* Most of the information in this and the next paragraph is from Henschel, "Gemeindearbeit," pp. 4, 5.
70 *"I was a secretary"*: Ibid., p. 5.
71 *"During the medical examinations"*: Kahan, "Chronik," pp. 9–10.
71 *Henschel hints:* This paragraph is based on Henschel, "Gemeindearbeit," p. 4.
71 *The number of operations performed:* The information in this paragraph is based on Hartung-von Doetinchem, "Zerstörte Fortschritte," pp. 175–76. The "all-time high" observation is based largely on her review of the hospital's operating room statistics.
72 *As Hilde Kahan remarks:* Hilde Kahan, videotaped interview, undated, Yad Vashem Archives, Jerusalem.
72 *Moreover, in many cases:* Elkin, "Survival," p. 173.

73 *The rate of suicides rose dramatically:* Ibid., p. 175 and n. 117.
73 *Bruno Blau estimates:* Blau, "Last Days," p. 200.
73 *As many as seven thousand Jews:* Hartung-von Doetinchem, "Zerstörte Fortschritte," p. 179.
73 *One hospital nurse remembers:* This sentence and the following quotation are from Kraft, "Mrs. A," p. 5.
74 *Indeed,* Schwester *Carry:* This sentence and the following quotation are from Carry Friedlander, interview by the author, North Andover, Massachusetts, February 28, 2002.
74 *At the height of:* This paragraph is based on Hartung-von Doetinchem, "Zerstörte Fortschritte," pp. 179–80.
75 *One nurse never withheld treatment:* Kraft, "Mrs. A," pp. 5–5a.
75 *One describes an incident:* Hartung-von Doetinchem, "Zerstörte Fortschritte," p. 180.
75 *Obviously, no records were kept:* The Holocaust presented Jewish health care workers with many agonizing dilemmas of this type. Even more extreme than the question of providing medical attention to suicide patients was the question of whether to euthanize patients to spare them the torments they would suffer at the hands of the Nazis. For an interesting survey of some of these issues, see Nevins, *Moral Dilemmas,* and the works cited there.
75 *Hilde Kahan remembers:* The following story is found in Kahan, "Chronik," pp. 41–42.

6. The Assault on the *Gemeinde* and the Hospital

77 *Since then, each transport:* Kahan, "Chronik," p. 13.
77 *Such strict orders could only:* Ibid.
78 *As 7:00 A.M. came and went:* This and most of the next three paragraphs are based on ibid.
78 *According to one account:* This account of Günther's actions is based on Hartung-von Doetinchem, "Zerstörte Fortschritte," p. 187, quoting interview with Margot Brenner (Berlin), May 1988.
79 *The Gestapo appointed Walter Lustig:* Lustig probably was appointed as the director of the hospital in 1942, although the exact date is in doubt. Confusion arises on this point because two events occurred in 1942, both requiring the appointment of a new "director" at the hospital. One was the deportation of Dr. Hermann Strauss, who had been the medical director or chief of medicine. The other was the suicide of Dr. Schönfeld, who had been the hospital's administrative director. Some accounts indicate that Lustig was appointed his successor, as stated in the text. Others indicate that Schönfeld was replaced as administrative director by Selmar Neumann (Elkin, "Survival," p. 178). It may well

be, however, that Lustig first became administrative director in place of Schönfeld and shortly thereafter medical director, replacing Strauss, and that he then appointed Neumann, who was not a doctor, as hospital administrator. The exact sequence of events is immaterial. It is clear that by the end of 1942 Lustig was firmly entrenched as the hospital's top official, with Selmar Neumann as his subordinate. After June 1943, he also was the head of the *Reichsvereinigung*, which had been officially dissolved and unofficially revived.

79   *A similar mass arrest:* This account is based on Baker, *Days of Sorrow*, pp. 276–77 and n. 40; and Cochavi, "Berlin," p. 74. Curiously, both times one hundred people reportedly were deported, leading one to wonder whether these really were two separate events. The reports of eyewitnesses, as well as the descriptions in secondary sources, are less than entirely clear, so it is conceivable that the June and October 1942 actions against Jewish community officials were one and the same. This does not appear likely, however. Two people in a position to know the facts both wrote detailed descriptions of the October roundup. These were Hilde Kahan, who was a *Gemeinde/Reichsvereinigung* employee and Dr. Lustig's secretary, and Hildegarde Henschel, the wife of the last president of the Berlin *Gemeinde* before it was officially dissolved. Their accounts of the October action are sufficiently circumstantial and different enough from others' accounts of the June action to suggest that the repetition of the number one hundred was either coincidence or the result of a consistent Gestapo policy.

80   *The Gemeinde continued:* The man appointed to succeed Baeck as nominal head of the community, Moritz Henschel, was able to accomplish nothing useful during his brief tenure before he and his wife were arrested and sent to Theresienstadt in June 1943.

81   *The hospital was moving:* The phrase "one-man *Judenrat*" was coined by Meyer, "Gratwanderung," p. 325.

81   *The other was Ehrich:* The information on Ehrich Zwilsky is based on Klaus Zwilsky, interview by the author, Scientists' Cliffs, Port Republic, Maryland, July 23, 2002; and the *Arbeitsbuch* (official German work carnet) of Erich Zwilsky, collection of Klaus Zwilsky.

82   *Professor Martin Jacoby:* The information on the hospital's doctors in this paragraph is taken from Elkin, *Jüdische Krankenhaus*, pp. 102–10.

82   *A 1938 photograph:* Hartung-von Doetinchem, "Zerstörte Fortschritte," p. 165.

83   *Still active in his seventies:* This sentence and the rest of the paragraph are based on Gossels, *Hermann Strauss*.

83   *In July 1942, Strauss was deported:* Elkin, *Jüdische Krankenhaus*, p. 110.

83   *The circumstances of his deportation:* Elkin (ibid.) claims the confronta-

262 · NOTES

tion was with the Nazi authorities; Blau ("Vierzehn Jahre," p. 61)
claims it was with a German soldier.
84 Many believed: See Gossels, Hermann Strauss, p. 6; Blau, "Vierzehn
    Jahre," p. 61; and Strauss, "Hermann Strauss," p. 8.
84 Like Leo Baeck, he declined: Wulman, "On the Death," pp. 4–5.
84 In an obituary: Dr. Strauss was eulogized in print on at least two differ-
    ent occasions. In 1942, shortly after he had been deported to The-
    resienstadt, an untrue newspaper account reported that he had com-
    mitted suicide there. This occasioned the publication of various
    obituary notices and articles of appreciation for his accomplishments.
    His actual death occurred two years later in 1944 and elicited similar
    publications. See Gossels, "On the Death," p. 9.
84 In Schwester Carry's eyes: Carry Friedlander, interview by the author,
    North Andover, Massachusetts, February 28, 2002.
85 The hospital's chief neuropsychologist: Pineas and Pineas, "Our Fortunes,"
    p. 452.
86 Dr. Pineas's epiphany: This and the next two sentences are based on
    ibid., pp. 451–52.
86 Dr. Hans Knopp, as a half-Jew: Ruth Knopp, interview by Ernest
    Mayerfeld and the author, Red Bank, New Jersey, January 11, 2001.
86 Bruno Blau describes: The radiologist's story is from Blau, "Fourteen
    Years," p. 461.
86 Another of the radiological assistants: This story is based on Blau, "Vier-
    zehn Jahre," p. 84.
86 Writing to Conrad Gossels: Letter from Meta Cohen to Conrad Gossels,
    December 31, 1945, Archives of the United States Holocaust Memo-
    rial Museum, Washington, D.C., Eva Fischer Collection.
87 One apparent suicide case: Carry Friedlander, interview by the author,
    North Andover, Massachusetts, February 28, 2002.
87 By the end of 1942: This paragraph is based on Elkin, Jüdische
    Krankenhaus, pp. 30–40.
88 One of the repositories: Pineas and Pineas, "Our Fortunes," p. 451.
88 Most of the asylum's staff members: Hartung-von Doetinchem, "Zer-
    störte Fortschritte," p. 184.
89 There were about thirty patients: This and the next two sentences are
    based on Kahan, "Chronik," p. 10.
89 Jewish patients from other: Elkin, Jüdische Krankenhaus, p. 129.
89 Notably, in October 1942: Information on orphanages is from ibid.,
    pp. 129–30.
89 Although the hospital: Schwester Carry's story in based on Carry Fried-
    lander, interview by the author, North Andover, Massachusetts, Feb-
    ruary 28, 2002.
91 Moreover, relations between: Kahan, "Chronik," p. 14.

7. Making a Life for Oneself in the Hospital

93 *The two young women:* This episode is based on Ruth Knopp, interview by Ernest Mayerfeld and the author, Red Bank, New Jersey, January 11, 2001. I have taken the liberty of somewhat dramatizing the bare facts as Ms. Knopp recounted them.

96 *"It was like a small island":* Eva Wills, interview by the author, Christchurch, England, July 31, 2001.

96 *Most of the Jews:* Statements about who lived at the hospital and who did not are tentative, at best. Although the hospital and the *Reichsvereinigung* kept records methodically, large portions of those records did not survive the war. In addition, of those documents that did, the bulk of the hospital's records were not available in the course of my research for this book. When I visited the hospital in April 2002, I was received with great cooperation and courtesy but was told that all the hospital's records, as well as those of the Jewish *Gemeinde*, had recently been transferred to the Stiftung Centrum Judaicum in Berlin. However, I was unable to obtain access to them, although the Stiftung Centrum Judaicum eventually reviewed some for me. Fortunately, earlier authors had the opportunity to examine most of these records before they passed into the hands of the Stiftung Centrum Judaicum, so at least some of the information they contain is available.

97 Schwester *Carry, who had married:* Carry Friedlander, interview by the author, North Andover, Massachusetts, February 28, 2002.

97 *To avoid such incidents:* Ruth Winterfeld, interview by the author, St. Charles, Missouri, April 4, 2001.

98 *One story involving the Neumanns:* Inge Lewkowitz, interview by Ernest Mayerfeld and the author, New York City, January 12, 2001.

98 Schwester *Carry says:* Carry Friedlander, interview by the author, North Andover, Massachusetts, February 28, 2002.

98 *Bruno Blau charges him:* Blau, "Fourteen Years," p. 462.

98 *From the lowly perspective:* Margot Frey, interview by Gerald Liebenau and the author, Berlin, April 12, 2002.

99 *A hospital nurse, Gerda Haas, writes:* Haas, "Leben der Juden."

99 *Hilde Fischer says that:* This paragraph is based on Hildegarde Fischer, interview by the author, Medford, New Jersey, March 8, 2001.

102 *Ruth and Lotte came even:* This story is based on Ruth Knopp, interview by Ernest Mayerfeld and the author, Red Bank, New Jersey, January 11, 2001.

103 *An even more dramatic:* The story of Schwester Ada's adventure is a slightly dramatized composite of two accounts. One of the nurses whom I interviewed told the story essentially as recounted here and said that it had happened to her. But Schwester Carry also told the same

story, although with fewer details, and said that it had happened to a friend of hers named *Schwester* Ada. She then showed me a picture of herself and another nurse whom she identified as Ada. It was taken in the hospital's garden shortly after the incident on the S-Bahn. The bandage on "Ada's" leg is clearly visible, but the "Ada" in the picture does not appear to be the nurse from whom I heard the story. Although the identity of the nurse in question is unclear, there is no reason to doubt that the incident occurred.

105 *The same, unfortunately:* Ruth Knopp, interview by Ernest Mayerfeld and the author, Red Bank, New Jersey, January 11, 2001.

105 *Eva describes Ruth:* Eva Wills, interview by the author, Christchurch, England, July 31, 2001.

105 *Ruth says that Eva:* Ruth Winterfeld, interview by the author, St. Charles, Missouri, April 4, 2001.

106 *"My poor mother nearly died":* This quotation and the following paragraph are based on Eva Wills, interview by the author, Christchurch, England, July 31, 2001.

106 *One of the boldest forays:* This account is from Rosemarie H., interview by the author, New York State, May 29, 2001.

108 *There they could hear:* See Goldsmith, *Inextinguishable Symphony.*

109 Schwester *Carry looks back:* This and the next paragraph are from Carry Friedlander, interview by the author, North Andover, Massachusetts, February 28, 2002.

109 *Margot Neumann, one of the hospital's:* This paragraph is from Margot Frey, interview by Gerald Liebenau and the author, Berlin, April 12, 2002. (Translated for this book by Gerald Liebenau.)

110 *There was a 10:00 P.M. curfew:* This information comes from Carry Friedlander, interview by the author, North Andover, Massachusetts, February 28, 2002.

111 *Having lived on the hospital premises:* Hilde's recollections are from Hildegarde Fischer, interview by the author, Medford, New Jersey, March 8, 2001. (Bracketed translations of Yiddish and German words added.)

111 *Another longtime hospital nurse:* Lisa Theresa Meyersohn, interview by Tatiana Bacal, Rio de Janeiro, Brazil, May 13, 2001.

112 *"From time to time on holidays":* Blau, "Fourteen Years," p. 471. A *minyan* (plural: *minyanim*) is the quorum of ten adult (i.e., post–Bar Mitzvah) Jewish males required under Jewish law for the conduct of a Jewish service. By extension, the word *minyan* sometimes is used to refer to the service itself, especially one of the three daily services that observant Jews attend. In contemporary Reform congregations and many Conservative Jewish congregations, full equality between the

sexes has been established, so that women are counted as part of the *minyan.*

112 *One of the young women:* Rosemarie H., interview by the author, New York State, May 29, 2001.

113 *Klaus Zwilsky was a boy:* This paragraph is based on a conversation with Klaus Zwilsky, April 14, 2001.

113 *Klaus's mother was:* This paragraph is based on an e-mail message to the author from Klaus Zwilsky, February 18, 2002.

113 *As we have seen:* Cordelia Edvardson, *Burned Child,* pp. 55–57.

114 *As for cigarettes:* Ruth Winterfeld, interview by the author, St. Charles, Missouri, April 4, 2001.

115 *In a passage on "love":* This and the next paragraph are based on Blau, "Vierzehn Jahre," p. 107.

116 *All we know:* The story of Hans Knopp and Ruth Lebram could provide a plot line for a writer of romantic fiction. In 1942 Hans decided that it was too risky to rely on either his half-Aryan descent or his job as a surgeon at the hospital to protect him against being deported. He returned home to Mainz, went into hiding with the help of his Aryan family, and survived the war. In August 1943 Ruth was one of a group of about twenty hospital employees who were taken one day by the Gestapo and interned in the *Sammellager* on Grosse Hamburgerstrasse. After several days the group was marched on foot to the Grunewald railway station, one of the departure points for transports to the camps. There are two parallel tracks at Grunewald. One carried trains to Theresienstadt, the other to Auschwitz.

Ruth had the good fortune to be sent to Theresienstadt. (Others say that it was not a matter solely of luck but was due to the intervention of the hospital's dentist, Chapski, who reportedly had an "in" with the Gestapo. Ruth had become friendly with Chapski and his wife.) In Theresienstadt she had the further luck, if one can call it that, to fall deathly ill as the result of malnutrition and the effects of working day after day in the laundry washing the sheets of people who had dysentery. In that job she had to stand much of the time with her feet, on which she had only clogs, in cold, filthy water. While in the infirmary being treated by a Czech Jewish doctor, she mentioned that she was a trained nurse who had worked in Berlin's Jewish hospital. The doctor not only brought her back to health but, when she had recovered, arranged for her to be transferred to work as a nurse in the infirmary. This transfer saved her from being sent to a death camp, the fate of most Jews sent to Theresienstadt.

The war ended. In Mainz, Hans Knopp returned to his medical practice. In Theresienstadt, Ruth was one of a group of liberated prisoners who were given refuge in Sweden. From there she immigrated to the United States, without ever returning to Berlin. In the chaos of postwar Europe, the two sweethearts failed to make contact with each other. Years passed. Ruth obtained a nursing license in the United States, established herself as a nurse, and began to remake her life. One of her passions was skiing, and from time to time she traveled with friends to ski in Switzerland, where she became friendly with a German couple from Karlsruhe. Her friends urged her to visit them at their home. Unwilling to return to the country where she had seen and endured so much suffering, Ruth initially refused, but after several years she finally accepted.

In the years since the war's end, Ruth had heard a rumor that Hans had survived, but she had done nothing about it. She assumed, if indeed he were living, that he had long since married. Once in Karlsruhe, however, her curiosity and the urgings of her German friends, to whom she had told the story, finally impelled her to call directory assistance in nearby Mainz and see if there was a telephone listing for a Dr. Hans Knopp. Indeed there was. She called the number and was told that the doctor was in surgery but that she could leave her name and number. In a little while the telephone rang at her friends' house in Karlsruhe.

"Ruth, where are you?" a voice said. "I'm coming right now to get you." Within a few months she and Hans were married. (Ruth Knopp, interview by Ernest Mayerfeld and the author, Red Bank, New Jersey, January 11, 2001.)

116 *Another Ruth, Ruth Beleski:* Ruth Beleski's story is from Ruth Winterfeld, interview by the author, St. Charles, Missouri, April 4, 2001.

117 *Hilde Kahan, for example:* Hilde Kahan, videotaped interview, undated, Yad Vashem Archives, Jerusalem.

118 *Inge London remembers:* The story of the salami is from Inge Lewkowitz, interview by Ernest Mayerfeld and the author, New York City, January 12, 2001.

118 *Gallows humor persisted:* This anecdote is from Ruth Knopp, telephone conversation with the author, January 13, 2002.

8. The Factory Raid and the *Frauenprotest*

119 *Swaying with fatigue:* The description of Inge's experiences is from Inge Lewkowitz, interview by Ernest Mayerfeld and the author, New York City, January 12, 2001.

122 *Hilde Kahan witnessed:* The description of Hilde Kahan's experiences is

drawn from an account by Hilde Kahan quoted in Hartung-von Doetinchem, "Zerstörte Fortschritte," pp. 187–89.

125 *It had recently been closed:* War crimes trial testimony of one Alexander Rotholz identifies a fifth hastily improvised *Sammellager* as the former Jewish old age home on Gerlachstrasse. "Anklageschrift in der Strafsache gegen Otto Bovensiepen und sieben weitere Angeschuldigte," document, undated, Yad Vashem Archives, Jerusalem, No. TR. 10/662 I, p. 135.

125 *Gerda Haas, then a twenty-year-old nurse:* Haas, "Leben der Juden."

126 *"I report this event to you":* Letter of Rudolph aus den Ruthen, reproduced in Jochheim, *Frauenprotest*, p. 120, and taken by Jochheim from Robert M. W. Kempner, "Die Ermordung von 35,000 Berliner Juden," in *Gegenwart und Rückblick: Festgabe für die Jüdische Gemeinde zu Berlin 25 Jahre nach Neubeginn* (Heidelberg: 1970).

126 *On February 27, 1943:* Rosemarie H., interview by Ernest Mayerfeld and the author, New York City, January 12, 2001, and interview by the author, New York State, May 29, 2001.

126 *They shivered in the bitter winter cold:* Description of this scene is based on Jochheim, *Frauenprotest*, p. 117.

127 *"It's funny; people always know":* Eva's recollections from Eva Wills, interview by the author, Christchurch, England, July 31, 2001.

128 *Rosemarie H. saw the entire* Frauenprotest: This and the next paragraph are from Rosemarie H., interview by the author, New York State, May 29, 2001.

129 *"Nothing to eat":* Ruth Winterfeld, interview by the author, St. Charles, Missouri, April 4, 2001.

131 *Rosemarie remembers that:* This incident is from Rosemarie H., interview by Ernest Mayerfeld and the author, New York City, January 12, 2001, and interview by the author, New York State, May 29, 2001.

131 *Day after day:* Most of the details of this event are given in Stoltzfus, *Resistance of the Heart*, pp. 242, 243.

132 *On Thursday, March 4:* Or possibly Friday, March 5. Ibid. (p. 238) indicates that the event occurred "on or about March 5."

132 *A non-Jewish woman:* Ibid., p. 243.

133 *"Murderers, murderers, murderers":* This and the next paragraph are based on ibid., pp. 252–54; and "Anklageschrift in der Strafsache gegen Otto Bovensiepen und Sieben Weitere Angeschuldigte," document, undated, Yad Vashem Archives, Jerusalem, File No. TR-10/622 II, p. 213.

133 *"Schacht gave me a long lecture":* Quoted in Jochheim, *Frauenprotest*, p. 133.

135 *There, as the mopping-up phase:* The Beleskis' experiences are drawn

from Ruth Winterfeld, interview by the author, St. Charles, Missouri, April 4, 2001, and Eva Wills, interview by the author, Christchurch, England, July 31, 2001.

136 *When Ruth had completed:* Stoltzfus identifies a Karl Krell, an unemployed baker who joined the Gestapo and became the director of the detention center at the Göring barracks during the *Fabrikaktion* (Stoltzfus, *Resistance of the Heart*, p. 217). It is not certain that this was the same Krell whom Ruth Beleski met at the Rosenstrasse, but it seems likely.

137 *In the end, because of Lustig's:* Ruth Winterfeld, interview by the author, St. Charles, Missouri, April 4, 2001.

137 *Ever feisty, Rosemarie H.:* Rosemarie H., interview by the author, New York State, May 29, 2001.

137 *"On April 3, 1943, Dr. Lustig":* Quoted in Hartung-von Doetinchem, "Zerstörte Fortschritte," pp. 200–201.

9. The Continued Assault on the Hospital

140 *Hilde Kahan comments:* This and the next two paragraphs are based on Kahan, "Chronik," p. 21.

142 *The disappearance of the Gestapo:* The facts of this incident are based on ibid., pp. 21–22.

142 *They were the head:* Ibid., p. 21. Kahan does not name the director of the Berlin *Sammellager*, but presumably it was Walter Dobberke, who was to become a prominent figure in the life of the hospital when the last *Sammellager* was relocated to the hospital's grounds.

144 *Hilde Kahan reports that:* Hilde Kahan, videotaped interview, undated, Yad Vashem Archives, Jerusalem.

145 *Once the deportation notices:* Ibid.

145 *"The consciousness of our helplessness":* Kahan, "Chronik," p. 22.

146 *Even though she escaped deportation:* Ibid., pp. 22–23.

147 *Instead, she asked Kantelberg:* Hilde Kahan, videotaped interview, undated, Yad Vashem Archives, Jerusalem.

147 *There they encountered:* Kahan, "Chronik," pp. 23–24.

147 *She had reason:* Lustig's warnings are related in Landgericht Berlin, "Strafsache," p. 33.

148 *Lustig and the Ordner:* Kahan, "Chronik," pp. 23–25.

148 *The Zwilskys also were beneficiaries:* Conversation with Klaus Zwilsky, Rockville, Maryland, April 14, 2001.

148 *He does recall, however:* Dr. Rosenberg, the head of the pediatric service, was deported to Theresienstadt, where he survived the war. After the war, he returned to Berlin and resumed his position at the hospital.

When Dr. Helmuth Cohen left to immigrate to the United States, Dr. Rosenberg became the hospital's chief of medicine.

148   *Far less fortunate:* The story of Golly Grünberg and Sally Herzberg is based on an e-mail message dated November 9, 2002, from Golly (Grünberg) Dowinsky to her nephew Klaus Zwilsky, retransmitted to the author on November 11, 2002, by Klaus Zwilsky with Mrs. Dowinsky's permission.

150   *"Sally was sitting on the floor":* Ibid. (Words capitalized for emphasis in the original have been replaced with lowercase italics.)

151   *The raids on the Auguststrasse:* This and the next two sentences are based on Elkin, "Survival," p. 177.

152   *According to Kahan:* Kahan, "Chronik," p. 29.

152   *The authorities moved:* This paragraph is based on ibid., p. 26.

152   *In the two hours allotted:* Hartung-von Doetinchem, "Zerstörte Fortschritte," p. 178.

153   *"Give them a kick in the ass":* Kahan, "Chronik," p. 27.

153   *"The facilities of the ward":* Pineas and Pineas, "Our Fortunes," pp. 451–52.

154   *Notwithstanding its limitations:* Kahan, "Chronik," p. 16.

154   *Hilde Kahan remembers two:* Ibid.

155   *The Gestapo issued an ultimatum:* Elkin, "Survival," p. 178, and sources cited there in n. 137.

155   *The patients' foreign passports:* Kahan, "Chronik," p. 33.

155   *Hilde Kahan tells of receiving:* Ibid., p. 42. Oranienburg is a town north of Berlin, today the last stop on one of the S-Bahn lines. It housed the Oranienburg concentration camp, and the adjacent forest became notorious as the site of the Sachsenhausen concentration camp. Sachsenhausen was used by the Germans primarily for the detention, torture, and in many cases murder of political dissidents, members of the resistance in occupied countries, and captured Russian and other Allied troops. Although not a death camp on the scale of those in the East, Sachsenhausen did have its own gas chamber and crematorium, which were used in wholesale killings. It also housed many Jews who were arrested during the November 1938 pogrom and at other times. Hundreds of Jews who were held there eventually were transported to the death camps in Poland. Hundreds more were killed at Sachsenhausen. As the war neared its end, the prisoners at Sachsenhausen were forced to participate in a death march toward the sea, in which large numbers perished. After the Allied victory, Sachsenhausen, which is situated in what became East Germany, was turned into a prison camp by the Soviets. Later it was transferred to the East German government, which continued to use it as a prison.

155 *To Hilde Kahan the piece of paper:* Ibid., pp. 42–43.
156 *This was an example:* See, for example, Stoltzfus, *Resistance of the Heart,* pp. xxii, 203–5.
156 *In 1943 a number of Jews:* Blau, "Fourteen Years," pp. 468–69.
157 *To Bruno Blau:* This paragraph is from ibid., p. 469.

10. Prisoners and Survivors

159 *On a cool Berlin summer's day:* The description of Wöhrn's visit and the disastrous consequences it had for Ruth Ellen Wagner is taken from Landgericht Berlin, "Strafsache," pp. 27–31.
162 *For example, in June 1943:* Ibid., p. 24.
162 *His favorite response:* Ibid.
162 *Another of Wöhrn's arrests:* Ibid., pp. 24–25.
163 *On another occasion:* Hilde Kahan, videotaped interview, undated, Yad Vashem Archives, Jerusalem.
164 *"I always tried to stay away":* Ruth Winterfeld, interview by the author, St. Charles, Missouri, April 4, 2001.
164 *"When quotas were not being met":* Brod, "Lasting Legacy," p. 337.
166 *Bruno Blau counted:* Information on the police ward and its patients in the following paragraphs is taken from Blau, "Fourteen Years," pp. 461, 464, 467, 468.
167 *Although the hospital itself:* Some of the hospital survivors believe that the Allies intentionally targeted the hospital because they knew that a portion of it had been turned into a Wehrmacht hospital. This, if true, would have been a violation of the international law of war and seems unlikely, especially in view of the amazing fact that not a single person was killed on the hospital's premises as a result of the bombings. Conversely, others of the survivors believe that the Allies knew that the hospital still was occupied by Jews and deliberately tried to avoid bombing it. Probably neither story is correct.
168 *One of the lucky ones:* The Fildermann story is taken from Blau, "Vierzehn Jahre," pp. 79–80.
169 *Another survivor in the police ward:* The story of Ursula Finke and quotation are from Benz, *Juden in Deutschland,* pp. 692–93.
171 *On one occasion, the nurse on duty:* Rosemarie H. and Inge Lewkowitz, interview by Ernest Mayerfeld and the author, New York City, January 12, 2001.
171 *One who did:* Jim's story is taken from Kraft, "Mrs. A." Jim's parentage is not identified in this source, but it seems that he must have been a *Geltungsjude* with an Aryan mother, since his mother was able to visit

him when he was in the police ward, something that would have been less likely were she Jewish.

172 *Not all attempted escapes:* Ruth Winterfeld, interview by the author, St. Charles, Missouri, April 4, 2001.

172 *Documents from the 1930s:* See "Jüdische Krankenhaus in Gefahr!"

172 *Most of these people figured:* Kahan, "Chronik," p. 33.

172 *The "patients" in the* Extrastation: Most of the information on Schiffer is from Ruth Winterfeld, interview by the author, St. Charles, Missouri, April 4, 2001. See also Blau, "Vierzehn Jahre," p. 62.

173 *Since every morning he took his constitutional:* Kahan, "Chronik," p. 33.

173 *Reportedly, there were several members:* Harry Brod, telephone interview with the author, recounting information obtained from his late mother, Lotte Schüfftan, April 4, 2001.

174 *Perhaps the most mysterious:* This paragraph is from Ruth Winterfeld, interview by the author, St. Charles, Missouri, April 4, 2001.

174 *Among the luckiest:* For information in this paragraph, see Blau, "Fourteen Years," p. 470.

174 *A final group:* This paragraph is based on Kahan, "Chronik," p. 34.

175 *For those who cared:* The story of the Rosenbergs is from Rosemarie H. and Inge Lewkowitz, interview by Ernest Mayerfeld and the author, New York City, January 12, 2001.

11. The Work of the *Reichsvereinigung* and the Hospital

177 *Some assert that:* Hans-Erich Fabian, quoted in Ball-Kaduri, "Berlin Is 'Purged,'" p. 300.

178 *Publicly abolishing the last:* The following figures are from Kahan, "Chronik," p. 29.

179 *It was suggested that:* Ibid., p. 30. Kahan attributes this idea to the Gestapo office in Breslau.

179 *One aspect of the compromise:* Hilde Kahan, videotaped interview, undated, Yad Vashem Archives, Jerusalem.

180 *Despite an air raid:* Microfilmed copies of these files are located in the Archives of the United States Holocaust Memorial Museum, Washington, D.C.

180 *These, together with interviews:* See Ball-Kaduri, "Berlin Is 'Purged.'" Unless otherwise noted, the discussion of the *Reichsvereinigung* in this chapter is based on this article.

182 *Thus one of the* Reichsvereinigung *officials:* Quoted in ibid., p. 303.

182 *Accordingly, Hilde Kahan had:* Hilde Kahan, videotaped interview, undated, Yad Vashem Archives, Jerusalem.

183   *So Lustig sought the help:* Letter from Lustig to RSHA, dated February 4, 1943, Yad Vashem Archives, Jerusalem.

183   *Among the last* Reichsvereinigung: See letter from Hans-Erich Fabian to Kurt J. Ball-Kaduri, dated July 6, 1947, Yad Vashem Archives, Jerusalem, No. 01/50.

185   *Bruno Blau, who was in:* Blau, "Fourteen Years," p. 470.

185   *The hospital's surgical register:* This information is derived from an examination of the surgical register of the Berlin Jewish Hospital conducted for the author by Mr. Thorsten Wagner.

185   *By way of confirmation:* Elkin, *Jüdische Krankenhaus,* pp. 102–10.

186   *A rough guide to the size:* Undated three-page document, first page headed "Im Hause Iranischestr. 2 wohnhafte Mitarbeiter," Yad Vashem Archives, Jerusalem, No. 08/287.

187   *Another indication of the hospital's:* Norbert Opitz, "Untersuchung." Opitz, as a German Ph.D. candidate at the Berlin Free University's Institute for the History of Medicine, made a comparative study of the hospital's mortality statistics from 1935 to 1945, based on a combination of municipal vital statistics and the hospital's own records. The hospital's mortality records (ibid., Table II, p. 76) show the following total numbers of deaths during the ten-year period: 1935 — 443; 1936 — 502; 1937 — 499; 1938 — 695; 1939 — 790; 1940 — 844; 1941 — 1,005; 1942 — 1,321; 1943 — 425; 1944 — 124; and 1945 — 567.

187   *How did the hospital fare:* Opitz's study shows that from 1922 to 1938 the ratio of deaths to admissions to the hospital varied from year to year, ranging from 8.55 to 15.8 percent. Apparently Opitz did not have access to the hospital's patient registers for the years after 1938, since he does not provide any information on the ratio of deaths to admissions for those years. Nor has information on hospital admissions, such as the patient registers for 1941 and 1942, been found elsewhere.

        Rough estimates of hospital admissions in the years for which patient registers are missing can be made by extrapolating from the ratios of deaths to admissions in earlier years. Estimating admissions in 1941 is problematic because it is not certain whether the lower mortality rates that prevailed up to 1938 continued up through 1941 or whether it would be appropriate to use the higher rates that characterized the 1943–45 period. The latter reflect, among other things, a high number of suicide attempts in response to the deportations, which began only in the latter part of 1941, as well as deteriorating food and sanitary conditions for Berlin's Jews as the war situation grew more desperate for Germany. During most of 1941, conditions for the Jewish population, both physical and psychological, were not as bad as they later became, so mortality probably was not as high as in the last three years of the war. By blending mortality experience in both earlier and later years, the number of admissions in 1941 can be estimated in the range of 4,000 to 6,000. Surviving surgical records examined for this book by Thorsten Wagner indicate that 1,722 surgical procedures were performed in the hospital in that year, which seems consistent with a high rate of patient admissions.

By 1942 the conditions for Jews in Berlin probably were about as bad as they continued to be for the rest of the war. Thus, an estimate of the number of patients admitted in 1942 can be extrapolated from Opitz's mortality statistics by applying a deaths:admissions ratio of 25 percent, the average of the years 1943–45. The result would be approximately 5,284 admissions. Although this is higher than the hospital's highest previous recorded number of admissions (4,854 in 1930), in light of what we know was going on in 1942 the estimate does not seem improbable. That was, after all, a year in which more than two-thirds of Berlin's Jews were deported and the remainder were overworked (and not infrequently mistreated) in forced labor, while being given inadequate rations, subjected to crowded living conditions, and, in many cases, made to walk everywhere regardless of weather conditions. It also was the year in which most of the approximately 7,000 or more Jewish suicides and attempted suicides took place. A large percentage of the suicide victims were admitted to the hospital, even though many already were beyond help when they arrived there. In addition, as Opitz's study demonstrates, the number of deaths from many categories of ailments and events other than suicide skyrocketed during 1942 and 1943. It is evident that the psychological and physical pressures under which Berlin's Jews were forced to live were taking their toll.

187 *Surviving patient registers show:* Information from the hospital's patient registers for 1943, 1944, and 1945 was made available through the kind assistance of the staff of the archives of the Stiftung Centrum Judaicum in Berlin, the institution that currently has custody of these materials.

187 *This compares to an annual average:* Opitz, "Untersuchung," Table I, pp. 69–70. Admissions in the years leading up to and including *Kristall-nacht* were as follows: 1932 — 3,372; 1933 — 3,085; 1934 — 2,841; 1935 — 3,730; 1936 — 3,394; 1937 — 3,040; and 1938 — 4,585.

188 *If overall admissions were low:* Statistics in this paragraph are from ibid.

188 *Admissions during the first four months of 1945:* Information on admissions in 1945 is based on the hospital's patient register and was kindly provided by the Stiftung Centrum Judaicum in Berlin.

188 *Although all of Germany:* Hilde Kahan, videotaped interview, undated, Yad Vashem Archives, Jerusalem.

189   *Its birth register:* The information is derived from a photograph of the register page in Elkin, *Jüdische Krankenhaus,* p. 73.

12. The Twilight of the Nazis

190   *Edith, well known as a tomboy:* Rosemarie H. and Inge Lewkowitz, interview by Ernest Mayerfeld and the author, New York City, January 12, 2001.

191   *"We had to protect our hospital":* Ruth Winterfeld, interview by the author, St. Charles, Missouri, April 4, 2001.

191   *The Berlin fire department:* Survivors are unanimous in saying that the Berlin fire department would not serve the hospital. It seems somewhat surprising that this was the case, in light of at least two considerations. One is that the hospital buildings constituted valuable real estate, title to which did not reside in the *Reichsvereinigung* but rather in the *Akademie für Jugendmedizin.* Second, the *Lazarett* occupied three of the hospital's seven contiguous pavilions. It must have been obvious that if the Jewish portion of the buildings were to burn down it would be difficult to keep the *Lazarett* from being consumed in the same conflagration. Perhaps the explanation is that the official firefighters were so overwhelmed by the nightly air raids that it never was possible for them to cover everything in the city. In those circumstances it would not be surprising that the Jews were assigned the lowest priority, effectively meaning that the hospital received no attention.

192   *Eva Beleski remembers that the fire:* Eva Wills, interview by the author, Christchurch, England, July 31, 2001.

192   *Although ostensibly:* Here to the end of the paragraph is from Hilde Kahan, videotaped interview, undated, Yad Vashem Archives, Jerusalem.

192   *Successive bombings blew tiles off:* Ruth Winterfeld, interview by the author, St. Charles, Missouri, April 4, 2001.

192   *Repairing damage to the roof:* Here to the end of the paragraph is from Eva Wills, interview by the author, Christchurch, England, July 31, 2001.

193   *The final drama began:* This paragraph is drawn from Kahan, "Chronik," p. 44; and Blau, "Fourteen Years," p. 472.

194   *Beginning in mid-February 1945:* Kahan, "Chronik," p. 44.

194   *In one particularly heavy air raid:* Here to the end of the paragraph is from Hilde Kahan, videotaped interview, undated, Yad Vashem Archives, Jerusalem.

194   *In mid-April, several:* Blau, "Fourteen Years," p. 472.

195   *The Gestapo began burning:* Here to the end of the paragraph is from Kahan, "Chronik," pp. 44–45.

195 *As Blau notes:* Blau, "Fourteen Years," p. 471.
195 *Even with the Red Army:* Ibid.
196 *Hilde Kahan remembers:* Kahan, "Chronik," p. 45.
196 *Thus began the hospital's final days:* Unless otherwise indicated, the description of the hospital during the battle for Berlin is derived from Kahan, "Chronik," pp. 45–47; and Blau, "Fourteen Years," pp. 471–73.
196 *Someone had had the foresight:* E-mail message to the author from Klaus Zwilsky, February 18, 2002.
197 *Klaus Zwilsky remembers:* Ibid.
198 *There are no records:* The RSHA, SS, and Gestapo destroyed many records at the end of the war. Neither Rivka Elkin nor Dagmar Hartung-von Doetinchem, despite extensive researches preparatory to writing their histories of the hospital in the 1938–45 period, uncovered any official German records indicating either why the hospital was allowed to remain open or what the Germans intended to do with its occupants as the fall of Berlin became imminent. One aspect of the preparation for writing this book was to commission a search by History Associates, Inc., at the United States National Archives in Suitland, Maryland, for possibly relevant files among the voluminous collection of copies of captured German official documents that the U.S. military had assembled after the war in what was called the Berlin Document Center. In the course of this search, no sets of records were identified that seemed to have any likelihood of containing relevant material.
198 *The initial contact:* E-mail message to the author from Klaus Zwilsky, February 18, 2002.
199 *In Weissensee, Ruth Graetz:* Here to the end of the paragraph is from Ruth Abrahamsson, interview by the author, Stockholm, Sweden, July 4, 2002.
199 *In the suburb of Karlshorst:* The account of the Beleskis' experiences is drawn from Ruth Winterfeld, interview by the author, St. Charles, Missouri, April 4, 2001.
201 *The administrators of the* Lazarett: The story of the bread comes from Kahan, "Chronik," pp. 47–48.
203 *Rosemarie H., by then:* This paragraph and much of the next are from Rosemarie H., interview by the author, New York State, May 21, 2001.
204 *"On May 6th":* Blau, "Fourteen Years," p. 473. (Bracketed translations of Hebrew terms added.)
205 *Meta Cohen's reply:* Letter dated December 30, 1945, written by Meta Cohen and Dr. Helmuth Cohen, Archives of the United States Holocaust Memorial Museum, Washington, D.C., Eva Fischer Collection. (Translated for this book by Gerald Liebenau and Peter Werres.)
206 *"Anti-Semitism has been injected":* Letter to the "Joint in Paris" from Ehrich Zwilsky, dated August 3, 1945, Collection of Klaus Zwilsky,

Scientists' Cliffs, Port Republic, Maryland. (Translated for this book by Peter Werres.) The United States–based Joint Distribution Committee was the principal Jewish relief organization that addressed the postwar material needs of the Jewish survivors and displaced persons in Europe.

207 *"Even the Jewish returnees"*: Document signed by Ehrich Zwilsky, headed "Re: Jews in Berlin" and probably dated August 1, 1945, Collection of Klaus Zwilsky, Scientists' Cliffs, Port Republic, Maryland. (The last digit in the date is illegible, but the contents strongly suggest that it was written in 1945.) No addressee shown. (Translated for this book by Peter Werres.)

13. The Trial of Dr. Dr. Lustig and Other Questions

209 *Ruth Beleski, still working:* Ruth Winterfeld, interview by the author, St. Charles, Missouri, April 4, 2001.

210 *The court's judgment in that case:* Landgericht Berlin, "Strafsache."

210 *A footnote in Peter Wyden's:* Wyden, *Stella*, p. 209. Unfortunately, when I tried to track down Professor Herrmann, I discovered that he died several years ago, so this intriguing line of possible inquiry is cold.

210 *That archive states:* Letter to the author from Monika Liebscher, Archivist, Gedenkstätte und Museum Sachsenhausen, dated April 23, 2002.

211 *One scholar comments:* Meyer, "Gratwanderung," p. 330.

211 *First, as we have seen:* Grimm, "Über die Geschichte," p. 18. Lustig turned the directorship of the hospital over to Ehrich Zwilsky. Letter from Walter Lustig to Ehrich Zwilsky, dated May 28, 1945, Collection of Klaus Zwilsky, Scientists' Cliffs, Port Republic, Maryland.

211 *On June 6, 1945, he sent:* The information on this letter is from Meyer, "Gratwanderung," p. 328.

213 *Like Lustig, Stella Kübler:* Wyden, *Stella*, pp. 211–12, 230–31, 254.

214 *There is no indication:* Kahan says, however, that the Soviets examined hospital financial records on the same occasion, a fact that may support the arrest hypothesis. Hilde Kahan, videotaped interview, undated, Yad Vashem Archives, Jerusalem.

214 *She applied for a survivor pension:* Meyer, "Gratwanderung," p. 328.

215 *Nonetheless, acting on Annemarie:* Nadav and Stürzbecher, "Walter Lustig," p. 226.

215 *The characterization of Lustig:* Ernst Lustig's great-great-grandfather was the brother of Walter Lustig's great-grandfather.

215 *"What is difficult for me"*: Ernst Lustig's comments on Walter Lustig are from Ernst Lustig, "Zur Strafsache," pp. 1, 2. Ernst Lustig uses the colorful term *"ohne Webfehler"* (without a flaw in the weave), meaning,

in effect, a dyed-in-the-wool Jew. It is interesting that Ernst Lustig does not call into question the accuracy of the information the witnesses in the Wöhrn trial had provided about Walter Lustig — once again, perhaps, an example of German attitudes to authority. He was, after all, commenting on the official pronouncement of a German court.

215 *In 1935 he published:* Walter Lustig, "Krankenpflege."
216 *That seems to be the implication:* Nadav and Stürzbecher, "Walter Lustig," p. 223.
216 *In 1931 and 1932 he was listed:* Elkin, "Survival," p. 179 and n. 145.
217 *Synagogue attendance:* Kaplan, *Between Dignity*, p. 53.
218 *In the early phase:* Elkin, "Survival," p. 181.
218 *Those who participated said:* Blau, "Fourteen Years," p. 471.
219 *Carry Friedlander, after she:* Carry Friedlander, interview by the author, North Andover, Massachusetts, February 28, 2002.
219 *According to one author:* Meyer, "Gratwanderung," p. 329.
219 *Another involved Rosemarie H.:* Rosemarie H., interview by Ernest Mayerfeld and the author, New York City, January 12, 2001, and by the author, New York State, May 29, 2001.
220 *The Lustig who was:* Meyer, "Gratwanderung," p. 327.
220 *Indeed, his former superior:* Ibid., p. 329.
220 *Perhaps the most balanced:* Ibid.
221 *For all his purported influence:* Ibid., pp. 326–27.
221 *Was he, as some have claimed:* Ibid., p. 325. The term *Judenrat*, literally "council of Jews," refers to the executive committees of Jews that the Nazi authorities forced on the ghettoized Jewish communities in many parts of occupied Europe prior to sending their inhabitants to the death camps. See Laqueur, ed., *Holocaust Encyclopedia*, p. 370. The comportment and role of these councils are controversial and varied from place to place and over time. Because of the harsh and sometimes corrupt tactics used by some *Judenrat* members, however, the term has acquired a pejorative gloss, denoting deluded or self-serving collaboration with the Nazis by Jewish "leaders" who significantly facilitated the annihilation of the Jews.
221 *His case was not like:* Dawidowicz, *War*, pp. 194–95.
223 *Rosemarie H. believes:* Rosemarie H., interview by Ernest Mayerfeld and the author, New York City, January 12, 2001.
223 *"I think they did Lustig wrong":* Ruth Winterfeld, interview by the author, St. Charles, Missouri, April 4, 2001.
224 *One witness accuses:* Elkin, "Survival," p. 183, n. 171.
224 *Another nurse was deported:* Rosemarie H. and Inge Lewkowitz, interview by Ernest Mayerfeld and the author, New York City, January 12, 2001.

224 *Elkin cites a single source:* Elkin, "Survival," p. 184 and n. 175.

224 *Indeed, several witnesses say:* Rosemarie H. and Inge Lewkowitz, interview by Ernest Mayerfeld and the author, New York City, January 12, 2001, and Ruth Abrahamsson, interview by the author, Stockholm, Sweden, July 4, 2002.

224 *The same accusation was made:* The material on Dr. Tuchmann is drawn from Elkin, "Survival," p. 184.

227 *Dr. Helmuth Cohen retained:* Helmuth Cohen documents, Archives of the United States Holocaust Memorial Museum, Washington, D.C., Eva Fischer Collection.

227 *She says that she:* Letter from Käte Bibo to Helmuth Cohen dated July 1, 1945, ibid. (Translated for this book by Ernest Mayerfeld.)

227 *In a more direct approach:* Unsigned two-page document, dated at the end "Berlin August 26, 1945," Collection of Klaus Zwilsky, Scientists' Cliffs, Port Republic, Maryland. (Translated for this book by Peter Werres.) Although the document has no signature, it comes from Ehrich Zwilsky's files, and there is no reason to doubt that he wrote it.

229 *Lucy Dawidowicz estimates:* Dawidowicz, *War,* p. 403.

230 *Martin Goldsmith's story:* Goldsmith, *Inextinguishable Symphony.*

232 *That fact had been known:* Shirer, *Berlin Diary,* p. 250.

234 *One was Dobberke:* Elkan was terrified, knowing that if the child died his life probably was forfeit. He complied, however, and Dobberke's child recovered. Ruth Winterfeld, interview by the author, St. Charles, Missouri, April 4, 2001.

234 *Fear of epidemics:* See, for example, Elkin, "Survival," p. 192.

236 *Victor Klemperer's diaries:* Klemperer, *Witness 1942–1945,* pp. 206, 269–70, 368.

238 *The forced sale to the academy:* Elkin, "Survival," pp. 161–63.

238 *The academy was a new organization:* Ibid., p. 161 and n. 34.

241 *Almost certainly the hospital:* Kahane, *Rescue,* pp. 71–72, reaches the same conclusion and finds the hospital's survival to be "inexplicable."

Bibliography

Arendt, Hannah. *Eichmann in Jerusalem: A Report on the Banality of Evil.* New York: Penguin Books, 1994.

Baker, Leonard, *Days of Sorrow and Pain: Leo Baeck and the Berlin Jews.* New York: Macmillan, 1978.

Ball-Kaduri, K. J. "Berlin Is 'Purged' of Jews: The Jews in Berlin in 1943." *Yad Vashem Studies on the European Jewish Catastrophe and Resistance* 5 (1963), p. 271.

Benz, Wolfgang. *Die Juden in Deutschland 1933–1945: Leben unter national-sozialistischer Herrschaft* (The Jews in Germany 1933–1945: Life under National Socialist rule). Munich: C. H. Beck, 1988. (Translated for this book by Peter Werres.)

"Beobachtungen Einer Englischen Juedin in Deutschland 1943–1945" (Observations of an English Jewish woman in Germany 1943–1945). Oral memoir, undated. Wiener Collection, Sourasky Library, Tel Aviv University, No. 202. (Translated for this book by Peter Werres.)

Blau, Bruno. "Fourteen Years of Misery and Horror." In *Jewish Life in Germany: Memoirs from Three Centuries,* edited by Monika Richarz and translated by Stella P. Rosenfeld and Sidney Rosenfeld. Bloomington: Indiana University Press, 1991.

———. "The Last Days of German Jewry in the Third Reich." *YIVO Annual of Jewish Studies* 8 (1953), p. 197.

———. "Vierzehn Jahre Not und Schrecken" (Fourteen years of misery and horror). Manuscript, undated. YIVO Institute for Jewish Research, New York. (Translated for this book by Peter Werres.)

Brod, Harry. "The Lasting Legacy of Temporary Survival." In *Second Thoughts: Critical Thinking from a Multicultural Perspective,* edited by

Wanda Teays. Mountain View, Calif.: Mayfield Publishing Company, 1996.

Cochavi, Yehoyakim. "Berlin." In *The Holocaust Encyclopedia*, edited by Walter Laqueur. New Haven: Yale University Press, 2001.

Dawidowicz, Lucy S. *The War Against the Jews 1933–1945*. New York: Bantam Books, 1986.

Edvardson, Cordelia. *Burned Child Seeks the Fire*. Translated by Joel Agee. Boston: Beacon Press, 1997.

Elkin, Rivka. *Das Jüdische Krankenhaus in Berlin zwischen 1938 und 1945* (The Jewish hospital in Berlin between 1938 and 1945). Berlin: Edition Hentrich, 1993.

———. "The Survival of the Jewish Hospital in Berlin 1938–1945." *Leo Baeck Institute Year Book* 38 (1993), p. 157.

Fraenkel, Daniel. "Nuremberg Laws." In *The Holocaust Encyclopedia*, edited by Walter Laqueur. New Haven: Yale University Press, 2001.

Friedländer, Saul. "Nazi Policy." In *The Holocaust Encyclopedia*, edited by Walter Laqueur. New Haven: Yale University Press, 2001.

Goldhagen, Daniel Joseph. *Hitler's Willing Executioners: Ordinary Germans and the Holocaust*. New York: Vintage, 1997.

Goldsmith, Martin. *The Inextinguishable Symphony: A True Story of Music and Love in Nazi Germany*. New York: John Wiley and Sons, 2000.

Gossels, Conrad L. *Hermann Strauss — The Scientist and the Man*. Reprinted from (editor unknown) *Victor Robinson Memorial Volume: Essays on Historical Medicine*. New York: Froben Press. Date of reprint and of original publication both unknown, reprint found in personal effects of Dr. Conrad L. Gossels.

———. "On the Death of Professor Hermann Strauss: A Man of Duty." *American OSE Review*, No. 3–4 (March–April 1942), p. 7.

Grimm, Dr. W. "Über die Geschichte des öffentlichen Gesundheitsdienstes in Berlin-Wedding" (On the history of public health services in Berlin-Wedding). In *Festschrift zur Eröffnung des Erweiterungsbaues Haus der Gesundheit Wedding '82*, edited by the Bezirksamt Wedding von Berlin. Berlin: 1982. (Translated for this book by Gerald Liebenau.)

Gross, Leonard. *The Last Jews in Berlin*. New York: Simon and Schuster, 1982.

H., G. (author identified only by initials). "Das jüdische Krankenhaus in der Persichen Strasse" (The Jewish hospital in Persichen Strasse). *Gemeindeblatt der Jüdischen Gemeinde zu Berlin*, April 28, 1935. (Translated for this book by Peter Werres.)

Haas, Gerda. "Das Leben der Juden in Berlin in den Jahren 1940 bis 45" (The life of Jews in Berlin in the years 1940–1945). Memoir, undated. Archives of the United States Holocaust Memorial Museum, Washington, D.C., No. RG-02.016. (Translated for this book by Gerald Liebenau.)

Hartung-von Doetinchem, Dagmar. "Zerstörte Fortschritte." In *Zerstörte Fortschritte: Das Jüdische Krankenhaus in Berlin 1756 — 1861 — 1914 — 1989* (Progress destroyed: The Jewish hospital in Berlin 1756 — 1861 — 1914 — 1989), edited by Dagmar Hartung-von Doetinchem and Rolf Winau. Berlin: Edition Hentrich, 1989. (Translated for this book by Gerald Liebenau.)

Henschel, Hildegarde. "Gemeindearbeit und Evakuierung von Berlin 16. Oktober 1941–16. Juni 1943" (The work of the community and the evacuation from Berlin October 16, 1941, to June 16, 1943). Manuscript, undated. Yad Vashem Archives, Jerusalem, File 01/52. (Translated for this book by Gerald Liebenau.)

Hilberg, Raoul. *The Destruction of the European Jews: Student Edition.* New York: Holmes and Meier, 1985.

Holzer, Charlotte. "Bericht über Margarete Abraham" (Account concerning Margarete Abraham). Memoir, dated February 15, 1957. Wiener Collection, Sourasky Library, Tel Aviv University, No. 511. (Translated for this book by Peter Werres.)

Jochheim, Gernot. *Frauenprotest in der Rosenstrasse* (The wives' demonstration in the Rosenstrasse). Berlin: Edition Hentrich 1993. (Translated for this book by Gerald Liebenau.)

"Das Jüdische Krankenhaus in Gefahr!" (The Jewish hospital in danger!). *Gemeindeblatt der Judischen Gemeinde zu Berlin,* July 1933.

Kahan, Hilde. "Chronik Deutscher Juden 1939–1945" (History of the German Jews 1939–1945). Memoir, dated 1980. Yad Vashem Archives, Jerusalem, File 0.8/190. (Translated for this book by Peter Werres.)

Kahane, Charlotte. *Rescue and Abandonment: The Complex Fate of Jews in Nazi Germany.* Melbourne: Scribe Publications, 1999.

Kaplan, Marion A. *Between Dignity and Despair: Jewish Life in Nazi Germany.* New York: Oxford University Press, 1999.

Klemperer, Victor. *I Will Bear Witness: A Diary of the Nazi Years 1933–1941.* New York: Modern Library, 1999.

———. *I Will Bear Witness: A Diary of the Nazi Years 1942–1945.* New York: Random House, 1999.

Kraft, E. "Mrs. A.: Jewish Hospital Berlin." Report of interview in London, November 1954. Yad Vashem Archives, Jerusalem, File 02/29.

Landgericht Berlin. "Strafsache gegen den Handelsvertreter Fritz Oskar Karl Wöhrn" (Judgment against the commercial representative Fritz Oskar Karl Wöhrn). Document issued in Berlin, April 6, 1971. Leo Baeck Institute Archives, New York. (Translated for this book by Gerald Liebenau.)

Laqueur, Walter, ed. *The Holocaust Encyclopedia.* New Haven: Yale University Press, 2001.

Lustig, Ernst. "Zur Strafsache Wöhrn" (On the Wöhrn judgment). Manuscript, written in Wolfenbüttel, May 1981. Leo Baeck Institute Archives, New York. (Translated for this book by Gerald Liebenau.)

Lustig, Walter. "Krankenpflege und Judentum" (Health care and Judaism). *Gemeindeblatt der Jüdischen Gemeinde zu Berlin*, April 28, 1935.

Meyer, Beate. "Gratwanderung zwischen Verantwortung und Verstrickung — Die Reichsvereinigung der Juden in Deutschland und die Jüdische Gemeinde zu Berlin 1938–1945" (Vacillation between self-defense and entrapment — The Reichsvereinigung der Juden in Deutschland and the Berlin Jewish Gemeinde 1938–1945). In *Juden in Berlin, 1938–1945: Begleitband zur gleichnamen Ausstellung in der Stiftung "Neue Synagoge Berlin — Centrum Judaicum" Mai bis August 2000* (Jews in Berlin 1938–1945: Catalogue for the exhibit of the same name held in the "New Synagogue Berlin — Centrum Judaicum" Foundation from May to August 2000), edited by Beate Meyer and Hermann Simon. Berlin: Philo Verlagsgesellschaft, 2000. (Translated for this book by Gerald Liebenau.)

———. "The Reichsvereinigung of Jews in Germany — A Prototypical Judenrat?" Jerusalem: Yad Vashem, 2000. *http://www.yadvashem.org.il/ research_ publications/research/reichsve.pdf* (downloaded April 30, 2002).

Nadav, Daniel, and Stürzbecher, Manfred. "Walter Lustig." In *Zerstörte Fortschritte: Das Jüdische Krankenhaus in Berlin 1756 — 1861 — 1914 — 1989* (Progress destroyed: The Jewish hospital in Berlin 1756 — 1861 — 1914 — 1989), edited by Dagmar Hartung-von Doetinchem and Rolf Winau. Berlin: Edition Hentrich, 1989. (Translated for this book by Gerald Liebenau.)

Nevins, Michael. "Moral dilemmas faced by Jewish doctors during the Holocaust. *http://www.usisrael.org/jsource/Judaism/dilemma.html* (downloaded March 31, 2000).

Opitz, Norfried. "Untersuchung über die Todesursachen der Verstorbenen aus dem Jüdischen Krankenhaus zu Berlin für die Jahre von 1935 bis 1945" (Investigation into the causes of death at the Jewish hospital in Berlin for the years from 1935 to 1945). Doctoral dissertation, Institute for the History of Medicine of the Free University of Berlin, 1997. Collection of Dr. Uri Schachtel, Berlin. (Translated for this book by Gerald Liebenau.)

Philipsborn, Alexander. "The Jewish Hospitals in Germany." *Leo Baeck Institute Year Book* 4 (1959), p. 220.

Pineas, Hermann, and Herta Pineas. "Our Fortunes After January 30, 1933." In *Jewish Life in Germany: Memoirs from Three Centuries*, edited by Monika Richarz and translated by Stella P. Rosenfeld and Sidney Rosenfeld. Bloomington: Indiana University Press, 1991.

Richie, Alexandra. *Faust's Metropolis: A History of Berlin*. New York: Carroll and Graf, 1999.

Rowe, Harry. "Memoir of Harry Rowe." Manuscript, undated. Collection of Harry Rowe, Port St. Lucie, Florida.

Shirer, William L. *Berlin Diary: The Journal of a Foreign Correspondent 1934–1941.* New York: Alfred A. Knopf, 1941.

Stoltzfus, Nathan. *Resistance of the Heart: Intermarriage and the Rosenstrasse Protest in Nazi Germany.* New Brunswick: Rutgers University Press, 2001.

Strauss, Walter. "Hermann Strauss." Document. Leo Baeck Institute Archives, New York, No. MM 76 (undated).

von Lang, Jochen, in collaboration with Claus Sibyll. *Eichmann Interrogated: Transcripts from the Archives of the Israeli Police.* New York: Vintage Books, 1983.

Wulman, Dr. L. "On the Death of Professor Hermann Strauss: A Tragic Conflict." *American OSE Review,* No. 3–4 (March–April 1942), p. 3.

Wyden, Peter. *Stella: One Woman's Tale of Evil, Betrayal and Survival in Hitler's Germany.* New York: Anchor Books Doubleday, 1993.

Glossary

Akademie für Jungdmedizin (German): Academy of Youth Medicine. The German government organization to which legal title to the hospital premises was transferred under the Nazis.

Aktion (German): An action or operation. Used in Nazi Germany to refer to police, SS, and/or Gestapo roundups of Jews.

Alt Reich (German): The original German territory before incorporation of Austria and parts of Czechoslovakia.

Am Yisrael Chai (Hebrew): Literally, "the people Israel lives." Used metaphorically to refer to the survival and resilience of the Jewish people through millennia of adversity.

Arbeitsamt (German): Labor Bureau. Used in this book to refer to the Jewish Labor Bureau set up by the Nazis to assign otherwise unemployed German Jews to forced labor, typically in war-related industrial establishments.

Aufbau (German): Literally, "reconstruction." The name of the German-language newspaper published in the United States to serve the community of German-speaking Jewish émigrés.

Behörden-Liste (German): Literally, "authorities' list." Name given in the hospital to a list of patients, some of them not ill, who, under some form of official protection, lived in the hospital over an extended period and were entitled to special treatment.

Berliner Tageblatt (German): The name of one of Berlin's leading newspapers during the Weimar period.

Bikur Cholim (Hebrew): An association typically found in Jewish communities for visiting and aiding the sick.

Chevra Kadishah (Hebrew): An association typically found in Jewish communities for ensuring appropriate burial rites for the Jewish dead.

El mole rachamim (Hebrew): Prayer used in Jewish funeral and memorial ceremonies.

Extrastation (German): Literally, "extra ward." The name given at the hospital to the ward reserved for first-class patients, those paying for and receiving a higher level of care than the public welfare patients.

Fabrikaktion (German): Literally, "factory operation" or "factory raid." The name popularly given to the February 1943 roundup of Berlin Jews, which occurred primarily at their places of work.

Förderverein Freunde des Jüdischen Krankenhauses Berlin e.V. (German): Foundation of the Friends of the Berlin Jewish Hospital, a charitable organization that helps to maintain the Jewish character of the hospital in modern-day Berlin.

Frauenbund (German): See *Jüdischer Frauenbund.*

Frauenprotest (German): Literally, "women's demonstration" or "wives' demonstration." Name given to the successful demonstration by Aryan wives and relatives of detained Jewish spouses and part-Jewish children arrested in the *Fabrikaktion.*

Gauleiter (German): District leader. In Nazi Germany, a significant position of regional authority.

Geltungsjude (plural: *Geltungsjuden*) (German): Under Nazi racial laws, a half-Jewish person (a person with two Jewish grandparents) who was treated as equivalent to a full Jew.

Gemeinde (German): A community, municipality, parish, or congregation. In Germany the term was used to refer to an organized religious denomination with official status that was supported by public funds. In this book, the term *Gemeinde*, standing alone, refers to the Jewish *Gemeinde* of Berlin.

Gemeindeaktion (German): The Nazi roundup of the Berlin Jewish *Gemeinde* officials in October 1942.

Gemeindeblatt der Jüdischen Gemeinde zu Berlin (German): The gazette of the Berlin Jewish *Gemeinde.*

Gesundheitsdezernent (German): Health department head.

Greifer (German): Literally, "grabber" or "catcher." Used in this book to refer to one of the renegade Jews who assisted the Gestapo in arresting Jews who had gone underground in Berlin.

Heimeinverkaufsverträge (German): Nazi program under which elderly Jews "purchased" life care in Theresienstadt in return for surrendering all their assets to the government. In reality, a ruse for seizing Jewish assets with minimal difficulty.

Hekdesh (Hebrew): A hostel for Jewish travelers maintained in premodern times by many synagogues.

Hilfsverein (German): As used in this book, the department of the official Jewish communal organizations during Nazi times that was devoted to helping Jews emigrate from Germany.

Hitlerjugend (German): The Hitler Youth organization.

Judenhaus (plural: *Judenhäuser*) (German): A house or apartment in which the Nazis segregated several different Jewish households.

Judenrat (plural: *Judenräte*) (German): Literally, "council of Jews." A council of Jewish notables or leaders organized by the Nazis in occupied territories ostensibly to govern the Jewish community but in fact exploited by the Germans to facilitate their conduct of genocide.

Judenreferat (German): The Jewish affairs department of the *Reichssicherheitshauptamt.*

Judenrein (German): A Nazi word meaning "cleansed of Jews."

Jüdische Gemeinde Berlin (German): The Jewish Community of Berlin.

Jüdische Kulturbund (German): The Jewish cultural organization established by the Nazis to allow Jewish artists and performers to provide cultural events and entertainment for Jewish audiences after Jews were prohibited from performing in front of, or joining with, Aryan audiences.

Jüdischer Frauenbund (German): Jewish Women's League. The organization of wives of Jewish communal officials that helped prepare food for the deportees during the early stages of the Nazi deportations of Berlin Jews.

Jüdisches Nachrichtenblatt (German): Jewish gazette or information bulletin. The only publication Jews were permitted to publish in

GLOSSARY · 287

Germany after the Nazis suppressed all other Jewish newspapers and magazines. It served principally as a medium for disseminating new anti-Semitic decrees.

Kinderunterkunft (German): As used in this book, the orphanage section of the hospital.

Krankenbehandler (German): Literally, "carer for the sick." After the Nazis deprived all Jewish doctors of their medical licenses, a limited number were allowed to care solely for Jewish patients and to use this demeaning title.

Krankenhaus der Jüdischen Gemeinde (German): Hospital of the Jewish Community.

Kristallnacht (German): Literally, "night of crystal." A term popularly applied to the pogrom of November 1938 because of the vast amount of broken glass that littered German streets after the destruction of synagogues, other Jewish institutions, and Jewish-owned business establishments throughout the country.

Kulturbund (German): As used in this book, the *Jüdische Kulturbund.*

Länder (German): The states making up the German Reich.

Lazarett (German): A military hospital. As used in this book, the military hospital installed in part of the premises of the Jewish hospital.

Mincha (Hebrew): The Jewish afternoon daily service.

Minyan (plural: *Minyanim*) (Hebrew): A quorum of ten adult Jewish men (in current Reform and most Conservative Jewish practice, men and women) necessary to conduct certain Jewish religious services.

Mischling (plural: *Mischlinge*) (German): Literally, "half-breed." The term the Nazis applied to a person of mixed Jewish and Aryan ancestry.

Nachtwache (German): Literally, "night watch." As used in this book, the fire watch mounted by hospital staff during Allied bombing raids.

Oberbürgermeister (German): Lord Mayor.

Oberin (German): Head nurse.

Obermedizinalrat (German): Literally, "chief medical counselor." A German bureaucratic title for a physician of high status in the civil service.

Oberregierungsrat (German): Literally, "chief administrative counselor." A German bureaucratic title for an administrator of high status in the civil service.

Onkel (German): Uncle.

Ordner (German): Police auxiliary. As used in this book, one of the Jewish police auxiliaries pressed into service by the Nazis to aid in rounding up and guarding Jews slated for deportation.

Pathologie (German): Literally, "pathology." As used in this book, the hospital's freestanding pathology pavilion.

Pfennig (German): One hundredth of a reichsmark.

Polizeistation (German): Literally, "police ward." As used in this book, the hospital's locked prison ward.

Rassenschande (German): Racial defilement. The Nazi term for sexual contact between Jews and Aryans.

Reichsbürger (German): A citizen of the Nazi Reich possessing full rights of citizenship. Jews were excluded from this status.

Reichsmark (German): The principal unit of currency in Nazi Germany.

Reichssicherheitshauptamt (German): Reich Security Main Office. An organization within the security services of Nazi Germany. Referred to in text as RSHA.

Reichsvereinigung (German): See *Reichsvereinigung der Juden in Deutschland.*

Reichsvereinigung der Juden in Deutschland (German): Central (or National) Organization of Jews in Germany. The organization established at the government's direction to act as an intermediary in controlling Germany's Jews.

Reichsvertretung (German): See *Reichsvertretung der deutschen Juden.*

Reichsvertretung der deutschen Juden (German): Central (or National) Representation of German Jews. Organization established by German Jews to provide centralized relief activities during the Nazi period and to act as an interlocutor with the government. It was dissolved and replaced by the *Reichsvereinigung der Juden in Deutschland.*

Rest-Reichsvereinigung (German): The rump *Reichsvereinigung.* The term used to refer to the *Reichsvereinigung* as it continued to operate after being officially dissolved by the German authorities.

Sammellager (German): A collection camp for Jewish deportees.

S-Bahn (German): One of Berlin's two public rail transportation systems.

Schwester (German): Sister. The title used for a nurse.

Schwesternheim (German): Nurses' residence.

Siechenheim (German): Nursing or convalescent home.

Spitzel (German): Informer. As used in this book, one of the renegade Jews who assisted the Gestapo and Berlin police in finding Jews who had gone underground.

Staatsangehöriger (German): A German national. Term used by the Nazis to describe German Jews who had lost their citizenship rights but still held German nationality as far as the rest of the world was concerned.

Transportreklamationstelle (German): Literally, "transport claims service." The medical examination panel set up by the Nazis to advise on Jews' claims that they were medically unfit to be deported.

U-Bahn (German): One of Berlin's two public rail transportation systems.

Vorstand (German): Board of directors.

Acknowledgments

Every book is the author's child in some sense. And, while it may take a village to raise the average child, it has taken an international metropolis to bring this one to the point of publication. I have received so much generous help from so many people that in fairness I should label this book a collective effort. However, I bear sole responsibility for whatever errors and shortcomings the book contains.

To my friend Klaus Zwilsky I owe deep thanks. By mentioning his childhood there, he originally made me aware of the Jewish hospital in Berlin and the fascinating story of its survival through the Nazi era. Like many other survivors, Klaus for many years found it difficult to talk about his experiences. I am all the more grateful to him for having overcome his understandable reluctance to revisit painful recollections. He generously shared with me his memories, as well as numerous photographs, documents, and memorabilia in his possession, including his father's papers. He also gave liberally of his time in reading and commenting on the manuscript.

When I set out on the journey to learn the hospital's story, my partner was my dear friend Ernest Mayerfeld. Ernie initially offered to help as a German translator, but he quickly embraced the project with enthusiasm as a full partner and contributed enormously to getting the research under way. His untimely death deprived the work of the invaluable contributions he would have continued to make, as well as cheating Ernie of the satisfaction he would have derived from seeing this book appear in print. His wife, Marilyn, and his children,

Diane and Jamie, have continued to provide support, encouragement, and precious friendship throughout the process of research and writing. I hope that this book, which is dedicated to Ernie's memory, will provide them with at least a fraction of the pleasure it would have given Ernie.

Immediately following Ernie Mayerfeld's funeral, I received a telephone call from Ernie's friend and longtime professional colleague Gerald Liebenau, of whom Ernie had often spoken but whom I did not know. A native of Berlin whose family fled the Nazis, Jerry came to the United States as a teenager and then returned to Germany over the course of several assignments, both as a soldier and a U.S. government official.

"Now that Ernie is gone," Jerry said, "you'll need a translator. I'm offering my services."

From that point on, Jerry became an invaluable source of help and advice, freely making his time available despite a schedule crowded with an impressive array of professional and volunteer obligations. One has only to look at the Bibliography, in which I have identified the individuals who translated relevant portions of various source materials for this book, to realize the enormous amount of time and effort that Jerry contributed to this work. Moreover, not only did he provide indispensable assistance in dealing with a large mass of German-language materials, but he also volunteered to accompany me and my wife to Berlin to visit the hospital and various archives. Our trip, in April 2002, turned into a Liebenau family venture. I am grateful to the other members of the expedition, Jerry's wife, Vivian, and his daughter and son-in-law Elisabeth and Harold Closter, for their help, encouragement, and lively companionship on that trip. Jerry also read the manuscript and made many helpful suggestions and corrections. The friendship that has developed between us is one of the many rewards this project has brought me.

Extending the Liebenau family's contributions to the project, Jerry's son Jonathan Liebenau, temporarily living in New York on sabbatical from his teaching duties at the London School of Economics, volunteered to assist me in finding archival materials at the Leo Baeck Institute in New York. He provided major assistance in that regard.

Numerous librarians and archivists contributed to the research effort. My principal research resources were the library and archives of the United States Holocaust Memorial Museum in Washington, D.C. On every visit, I was extended help and invariably treated with outstanding courtesy by the staff members of that institution. Dana Ledger, archivist at the Leo Baeck Institute in New York, was extremely helpful in steering me to important documents in that institution's collection. I am grateful to Saul Ferrero of the Yad Vashem Archives in Jerusalem and to Tami Sagi, head of the Wiener Collection, Sourasky Central Library, Tel Aviv University, for promptly and efficiently replying to requests for information on their relevant holdings and for supplying copies of documents. In Berlin, I was the beneficiary of courteous and helpful attention from the library staff of the *Jüdische Gemeinde*. For the success of my visit to Berlin, I owe particular thanks to Aubrey Pomerance, director of the Leo Baeck Institute Archives, New York, at the Jewish Museum Berlin, who went out of his way to be helpful and friendly and was of significant assistance in finding archival materials, especially photographs. I am also grateful to the Stiftung Centrum Judaicum in Berlin, whose archives hold most of the hospital's remaining wartime records. The Centrum Judaicum's archivist made available the services of an intern to review the hospital's patient registries and compile data for my use.

While in Berlin I also benefited from the cooperation of many others. Mrs. Genja Katz, president of the *Förderverein Freunde des Jüdischen Krankenhauses Berlin e.V.* (Friends of the Berlin Jewish Hospital Foundation), was helpful in introducing me to Professor Dr. Rolf Winau, one of the editors of *Zerstörte Fortschritte*, and to Dr. Uri Schachtel, medical director and chief of surgery at the hospital. Dr. Schachtel and his colleague Gerhard Nerlich, the hospital's public relations manager, welcomed us warmly and provided invaluable assistance. Their friendliness and enthusiasm for my project were especially welcome at a moment when my spirits were flagging because early setbacks made it appear that the search for material in Berlin might prove fruitless. I am particularly grateful to Dr. Schachtel for giving me his personal copy of an interesting unpublished doctoral thesis by a student at the Free University of Berlin that analyzes mortality at the hospital during the Nazi period. Gerhard Nerlich spent many hours escorting us around the hospital and generously provided contemporary photographs of the buildings and grounds from his files. Professor Winau kindly met with Jerry Liebenau and me at his office in the Free University's Institute for the History of Medicine and provided suggestions and insights. Alexander Pajevic helped me make arrangements for the trip to Berlin. I contacted Mr. Pajevic at a time when he was doing public relations work for the *Förderverein Freunde des Jüdischen Krankenhauses Berlin e.V.*, but he continued to be helpful even after his engagement with that organization ended.

My research both in Berlin and the United States was aided by advice from Dr. William Gilcher, of the Goethe Institute in Washington, and Ms. Katrin Paehler, a scholar of the Nazi period to whom Dr. Gilcher introduced me. In Germany, Manfred Stürzbecher provided helpful advice.

At various points in the research for the book I retained the services of others to do things that were geographically or linguistically beyond my reach. All of them contributed significantly. Peter Werres of McLean, Virginia, provided prompt and effective translations of German documents at a time when I felt that to ask Jerry Liebenau to do more would impose excessively on his generosity. James Lide and Kate Belinski of History Associates, Inc., efficiently performed research on captured German documents found at the United States National Archives. Tatiana Bacal of Rio de Janeiro (whom I found through the good offices of Michael Bell, Ernie Mayerfeld's son-in-law) interviewed one of the hospital's former nurses who lived in that city. Thorsten Wagner of Berlin compiled significant information found in the hospital's surgical registers and aided in other ways in shedding light on the hospital's medical role in the last years of the war.

The most delightful aspect of my research was the opportunity to interview some of the most impressive people I have ever met, survivors of the Nazi terror who lived and worked at the hospital during or immediately after World War II. I am deeply grateful to these women of valor — Ruth Abrahamsson, Inge Berner, Hilde Fischer, Margot Frey, Carry Friedlander, "Rosemarie H.," Ruth Knopp, Inge Lewkowitz, Eva Wills, and Ruth Winterfeld — for their generosity of spirit, their friendliness, their hospitality, and their willingness to revisit a painful period in their lives in the interest of making the hospital's remarkable story known to the English-speaking world. The new friendships these interviews created have been another unexpected benefit of writing the book. Similarly, I am grateful to Harry Brod for sharing with me the stories he remembers from his late mother, a nurse at the hospital, and to Golly Dowinsky for providing a written account of her experiences and those of her late husband, Dr. Sally Herzberg. Two other individuals who provided information, John Fink in Chicago and Lisa Meyersohn in Rio de Janeiro, are no longer living, but their deaths have not diminished my gratitude for their help. I also am grateful to several individuals with whom Ernie Mayerfeld and I spoke by telephone but who wish to retain their anonymity. The widow of Dr. Conrad Gossels, Mrs. Natalie Gossels, generously turned over to me all of her late husband's papers relating to Germany, among which were several important sources of information about the hospital and its medical staff that could not be found anywhere else. Numerous people responded to our Internet posting and our advertisement in *Aufbau* with leads to survivors or other sources of information.

A host of friends and acquaintances have provided assistance, advice, and moral support. I am grateful to David Marblestone for pursuing several research leads and providing books from his own library. My friend and law partner Sara Schotland read the manuscript and made useful suggestions. Tatjana Hendry helped obtain materials in Germany and identified Peter Werres as the excellent translator he proved to be. My friends and neighbors Punch Wray and Dahlia Luttwack introduced me to Walter Laqueur, who in turn shared insights from his vast store of knowledge about Nazi Germany.

I have been blessed with the help of a wonderful literary agency and a superb editor at Houghton Mifflin. Gail Ross of the Gail Ross Literary Agency embraced the idea of this book with enthusiasm. She and Jenna Land, the agency's executive editor, provided the impetus that turned an inchoate idea and a mass of research notes into the structure of a book, and Jenna made valuable editorial contributions throughout. It was a particular joy to work with my talented editor at Houghton Mifflin, Deanne Urmy. Her clear and supportive vision of the book inspired me, and her editorial suggestions, offered with sensitivity and tact, brought great improvements to the manuscript.

My secretary, Jan Madden, entered innumerable changes with unfailing cheerfulness. I am grateful to her and to my law firm of Cleary, Gottlieb, Steen & Hamilton.

Finally, I want to record my loving appreciation for all that my wife, Sybil, did to make this book possible. She accompanied me to several of the interviews, where her gentle presence helped to build confidence and encourage candor. She read repeated versions of the manuscript and provided a finely calibrated mixture of encouragement and constructive criticism. She traveled farther and more often than she would have liked because she knew that her company was important to me. And, as always, she kept me well fed and cared for, and found my eyeglasses innumerable times.

Index

A., Mrs., 171–72
Academy of Youth Medicine, 90–91, 182, 238–39, 274n
Ada, *Schwester*, 103–5, 263–64n
Adlon Hotel restaurant, 93–94, 101, 102
Akademie für Jungdmedizin (Academy of Youth Medicine), 90–91, 182, 238–39, 274n
Akiba, Rabbi, 216
Aktion (operation), definition of, 81
Alcoholic beverages, 192
Altersheim (Jewish old age home), 137
Ambulance service, 75–76
Angress, Dr., 82
Anti-Semitism
  in families, 46–47, 58
  in Germany after war, 203, 206–7
  history of, 16, 18, 47
  of Lustig, 26–27, 215–17, 256n
  of Nazis, 21–22, 25, 29, 31–37, 41, 49–60, 73, 122, 221, 232, 234
  See also Holocaust
Arbeitsamt (Jewish Labor Bureau), 134, 57–58, 84, 132

Arendt, Hannah, 61
Aryans
  ban on sexual relations between Jews and, 21, 50, 52
  bomb shelter for, at hospital, 194
  dating of Jewish women by, 106
  definition of, xxii, 21
  and *Frauenprotest*, 128–35, 138–39, 146, 186
  and hospital, 7, 29, 40, 163, 189, 234, 257n
  intermarriage of Jews and, 8, 12, 22, 24, 27, 36, 39, 43, 46–58, 134, 138–39, 156–57, 168, 178, 230, 235
  purchase of Jewish businesses by, 32, 34
  as *Reichsbürger*, 50
  treatment of, in hospital, 7
Aufbau (newspaper), xiv, 257n
Auschwitz concentration camp, xix, 45, 79, 83, 84, 94, 133, 150–51, 159, 166, 194, 205, 206, 244–45, 245, 257n
Austria, 229
Autobahn system, 182–83

Baeck, Rabbi Leo, 33–34, 38–39, 59–
    61, 80, 84, 86, 150, 222, 258n,
    261n
Ball-Kaduri, K. J., 180
Barth, Karl, 248
Baruch Auerbach Orphanage, 89
Baruth, Bella, 82
Bayer works, 168
Behrend, 170
Beleski, Eva
    and factory raids, 126–27, 135
    and fire watch teams, 192
    as forced laborer in hospital, 136–37
    as forced laborer at I.G. Farben,
        57–58, 127, 135
    postwar life of, 244
    risk-taking by, 105–6
    and roof repair, 192
    and Ruth's typing skills, 135
    as secretary in Lustig's office, 28,
        192
    and Soviet occupation of Berlin,
        199
Beleski, Ruth
    on bombing raids, 191
    and factory raids, 126–27, 129,
        135
    as forced laborer at I.G. Farben,
        57–58, 127, 135
    love between Elkan and, 116–17,
        244
    on Lustig, 28, 223
    marriage of, 244
    postwar life of, 244
    risk-taking by, 105, 136
    at Rosenstrasse camp, 129, 268n
    as secretary in Lustig's office, 28,
        136–37, 146, 164
    and Soviet occupation of Berlin,
        199–201
    as typist for Gestapo, 135–36
    use of public transportation by, 105

Benndorf-Seyn psychiatric asylum,
    88–89
Berlin
    anti-Jewish measures by Nazis in,
        21–22, 25, 29, 31–37, 49–60, 73,
        122, 221, 232
    bombing of, xi, 6, 96, 100, 130, 133,
        166–67, 184, 190–95, 270n
    cooperation of Jews with deporta-
        tion order, 60–61, 64–66, 258n,
        259n
    deportations of Jews from, 59–76
    establishment of Jewish community
        in, 16
    false identities for Jews in or living
        "underground," 6, 7–8, 63, 64,
        69, 72, 79, 84, 86, 107, 108, 134,
        175, 206, 219, 246, 248
    founding of, 15–16
    history of Jewish community in, 16–
        18
    Jewish businessmen in, 18, 32, 34
    Jewish cemetery in, 4, 19, 178, 181,
        197, 232, 254n
    Jewish community organizations in,
        33–34, 36–40, 65–66, 232
    as Judenrein (cleansed of Jews), 4
    orphanage in, 89
    police department in, 24–25
    population of Jews in, 2–3, 5, 41, 59,
        120, 178, 254n
    postwar conditions in, 15, 203,
        207–8
    restaurants in, 93–94, 101, 102
    Soviet liberation of, 1–13, 15
    Soviet occupation of, 198–208
    synagogues in, 33, 59, 65, 66
Berlin Jewish Hospital
    administration of, 37, 40, 62, 218
    admission statistics for, 187–88,
        272–73n
    and ambulance service, 75–76

Berlin Jewish Hospital (*cont.*)
arrests of staff of, 127–28, 135, 140–42
and Aryans, 7, 29, 40, 163, 189, 234, 257n
births recorded in, 189
bombing of, 166–67, 190–95, 270n
and burial of dead, 197
changes in, during war years, 95–96
children's clothing workshop in, 157
community of, 93–118
current situation of, 242–43
daily routines of, 95
and deportation of Jews, 61–62, 66–76, 233
and deportation of nursing home patients, 151–53
deportations of staff of, 28, 79, 81, 83–84, 87–88, 100, 137, 140–51, 161, 163, 226, 234
Eichmann's inspections of, 164–65, 175, 222–24
emigration of staff from, 82–85
escapes and attempted escapes from prison ward of, 171–72
Extrastation (extra ward) of, 9, 118, 172–74
and factory raids, 122–24, 127–28, 135, 136–38, 140–42
final days of, under Nazi rule, 190–98
fire watch at, 191–92, 274n
food and water for, 117–18, 192–93, 196–97, 201–2
founding of, 19
funding for, 37
and Gestapo informers, 107–8, 190, 231
and Gestapo's plans to close hospital and arrest staff, 140–42, 235, 240
heightened use of, in 1938–39, 40–45

Jewish men married to Aryan women living in, 156–57
kitchen of, 98, 110, 111, 147, 172–73
and *Kristallnacht*, 40
lack of attention to story of, 228–31
looting of, by Nazis, xix–xx
Lustig as director of, xvi, 2, 22, 79, 80, 81, 217–18, 260–61n
and medical deferments from deportation, 67–76, 219
medical staff of, 7, 8, 12, 42–45, 79, 82–88, 96–97, 100, 101, 135, 177, 185–87, 205, 206, 243
military hospital in, 7, 91–92, 100, 182, 188, 196, 198, 201–4, 240, 274n
mortality statistics of, 188, 272n
news of war in, 100–101
non-Jewish staff of, 87–88
nonpatients in, 9, 156–58, 172–74, 19
number of beds in, 19, 29, 42, 156
origins of, 15–19
orphanage at, xix, 28, 55–56, 89, 156, 174–75
overcrowding in, 95
patients limited to Jews, 40–41
personal memories of, xvii–xx
pharmacy of, 88, 114, 147, 188–89
physical facility of, x, 6–7, 19–2
population of, 2, 8, 196, 253n
prison ward of, 9, 42, 74, 95, 157, 163, 165–72, 212, 257n
psychiatric services of, 88–89, 153–56, 236
quarantine facility of, 89–90
reasons for survival of, 231–41
records of, 263n, 275n
Reichsvereinigung housed in, 158, 177, 180, 232
repairs of, after bombing raids, 190, 192, 193

sexual liaisons in, xix, 27, 87, 98, 99–
100, 113–17
shortages of medical supplies in,
201, 208
social gatherings at, 109–10
sources of information on, xiv–xvii,
275n
Soviet liberation of, 1–13, 15, 189,
198–99, 253n
and suicide cases, 74–76, 142, 176,
205, 225, 273n
surgeries performed in, 45, 71–72,
170, 185, 219, 257n, 272–73n
survival of, through Nazi era, x–xiii,
1–15, 228, 230–41
survivors from concentration camps
in, 203–4
survivors in, at liberation of, 161,
165–76, 196
synagogue in, 20, 110–13, 204–5,
218
transfer of title of, 90–91, 182, 238–
39, 274n
underutilization of, 1933–1938, 29–
30, 40, 256–57n
Wöhrn's inspections of, 96, 159–65,
175, 193, 222–24, 237
wounded people brought to, 196–97
See also Doctors, Jewish; Nurses,
Jewish
Berliner Tageblatt, 167
Berlin School of Commerce, 168
Berlowitz, Fräulein, 205
Bikur Cholim (fellowship for visiting
and caring for sick), 17
Birkenau death camp, 3
Blau, Bruno
on end of Nazi rule, 195
in hospital prison ward, 9, 157, 166–
69
on hospital staff, 185
on Jewish men separated from
Aryan spouses, 157

on Lustig, 98
memoirs of, 9, 115
physicians treating, 86
postwar life of, 244
and registration of children with
Gemeinde, 54
and religious services, 112, 204–5
and sexual liaisons in hospital, 115
on Strauss's death, 84
and suicides by Jews, 73, 86
B-List, 172
Bombing of Berlin, xi, 6, 96, 100, 130,
133, 166–67, 184, 190–95, 270n
Brandt, Dr., 126
Brod, Harry, 164
Broniakowsi, Frau Dr., 83
Buchenwald concentration camp, 5
Bukofzer, Kurt, 162–63
Burial of dead, 197
Burned Child Seeks the Fire
(Edvardson), xix
Buschke, Abraham, 87
Businesses, Jewish, 18, 32, 34

Caro, Joseph, 216
Carry, Schwester
assignment of, to deportation transport, 84, 85–86
on emigration of hospital staff, 84–
85
and forced labor assignment in factory, 84
and Jüdische Kulturbund (Jewish
Culture Association), 109
on Lustig, 26, 27, 98
marriage of, 97
and scarlet fever, 89–90
on Schwester Ada's accident, 263–64n
and sexual predation by Lustig, 27
and social gatherings in hospital,
110
and suicide cases, 74, 87
use of public transportation by, 97

Cemeteries, 4, 19, 178, 181, 197, 232, 254n
Central Representation of German Jews (*Reichsvertretung der deutschen Juden*), 38–39, 60
Chapski (dentist), 265n
Chaskel, Inspector, 138, 203–4
Chevra Kadishah (fellowship for burial of dead), 17
Children
    arrests of, 125, 129–31, 139, 142
    Bar Mitzvah for, 113, 205
    in orphanage section of hospital, xix, 28, 55–56, 89, 156, 174–75
    registration of, with *Gemeinde*, 54
    schools for, 38, 149, 178
Cigarettes, 114
Clou (restaurant/nightclub), 123–26
Cohen, Eva, 12
Cohen, Helmuth, 12, 86, 170, 173, 186, 205, 206, 227, 269n
Cohen, Meta, 6, 12, 86, 173, 205–6
Community organizations, Jewish, 33–34, 36–40, 41, 65–66, 232
Concentration camps. *See specific camps*
Conversion of Jews to Christianity, xxi, 41, 52–55, 168, 231
Culture Association, Jewish, 34, 108–9

Dachau concentration camp, 5, 21
Dawidowicz, Lucy, 229
Deportations
    bureaucratic process for, 64–66
    certificate of exemption from, 96, 124
    of elderly Jews, 184, 233
    of employees of *Gemeinde/ Reichsvereinigung*, 77–81, 86, 144, 147, 151, 261n
    and fate of Jewish deportees, 64, 232–33
    final deportations of Jews, 194

of forced laborers, 125–26, 139, 141–42
of hospital staff, 28, 79, 81, 83–84, 87–88, 100, 137, 140–51, 161, 163, 222–24, 226, 234
Jews' cooperation with, 60–61, 64–66, 258n, 259n
medical deferments from, 62–63, 64, 66–76, 219
medical staff assigned to transports, 66–67, 84, 85–86
of mentally ill, 153–56, 236
of nursing home patients, 151–53
of seriously ill patients, 224–26
and suicide cases, 69, 73–76, 79, 84–87, 142
violence involving, 125, 126
of Yom Kippur in 1941, 59–60, 66
See also Sammellager (temporary holding camp)
Diphtheria, 169, 208
Divorce, 57, 58, 156, 235
Dobberke, Walter
    drunkenness of, at end of Nazi rule, 195
    and elderly family friend, 174
    escape of, from hospital, 198, 240–41
    and fate of mentally ill patients, 155
    full-time position of, at *Sammellager*, 237, 268n
    and Gestapo informers, 213
    ill child of, 234, 278n
    mistress of, 99, 107, 198
    relationship of, with hospital staff, 107, 190
Doctors, Jewish
    and ban on treating Aryan patients, 40
    conversion of, 53
    deportation of, 66–67, 79, 81, 83–84, 87–88, 100, 152, 163
    emigration of, 82–85

and factory raids, 122–24
at hospital, 43–45, 82–88, 100, 185–
86, 206, 243
labeled *Krankenbehandler* (carer for
the sick), 42, 44, 45, 76, 185, 236
and medical deferments from deportation, 69–76
and medical inspections in
Sammellager, 66
Nazi measures against, 21–22, 29,
40, 42–43
and news of war, 101
sexual liaisons of, 115–17
and suicide cases, 75, 225
suicides of, 84, 86–87, 205
and support of hospital, 29–30
Dresden, 236
Drug use, 113–14
Dysentery, 208

Edith (hospital staff), 190
Education. *See* Schools for Jewish
children
Edvardson, Cordelia, xix, 55–56, 114,
244–45
Ehrenhaft (patient), 174
Eichengrün, Ernst, 168
Eichmann, Adolf, xvii, 24, 40, 61, 96,
141, 143, 151, 160, 161, 164–65,
175, 182, 222–24, 238–40
Einstein, Albert, 234
Eleonora, *Schwester*, 116
Elkan, Heinz, 12, 114, 116–17, 138,
169, 206, 234, 244, 278n
Elkin, Rivka, xv, xvii, 185, 186, 224,
225, 238, 275n
Elli, *Schwester*, 99–100, 149–50, 198
Emigration of German Jews, 5, 11, 32,
39, 43, 59, 82–85
Employment/unemployment of Jews,
10–11, 18, 21, 32, 34, 38, 51, 81–
82. *See also* Forced labor by Jews
Eppstein, Paul, 80, 258n

Eulenberg, Franz, 168
Euthanasia, 260n
Evchen ("little Eve"), 154
Extrastation (extra ward), 9, 118, 172–
74

Fabian, Hans–Erich, 183–84
Fabrikaktion (factory raids), 96, 119–
31, 134, 135–36, 140–42, 193,
237, 268n
Fildermann (police ward inmate),
168–69
Fink, John, 257n
Finke, Ursula, 169–70, 219
Fire watch, 191–92, 274n. *See also*
Nachtwache
Fischer, Erich, 83, 87, 99–100, 111,
226, 245
Fischer, Hilde, 27, 99–100, 111, 205,
226, 245–46
Fliesser, Werner, 82–83
Food, 34, 111, 113, 117–18, 129, 192–
93, 196, 201–2, 207
Forced labor by Jews, 11, 34, 57-58,
73, 84, 98, 113, 120–23, 137–38,
177, 182–83, 187
Frank, Anne, 5
Frank, Johanna, x, 4
Frauenprotest, 128–35, 138–39, 146,
186
Frederick the Great, 16
Frederick William ("Great Elector"),
16
*Freunde des Jüdischen Krankenhauses
Berlin* (Friends of the Berlin Jew-
ish Hospital), 242
Frey, Margot, 248. *See also* Neumann,
Margot
Fridolin, 154
Friedlander, Carry, 219, 246–47
Friedlander, Mr., 246–47
Friends of the Berlin Jewish Hospital,
242

Gatt, Fräulein, 205
Geltungsjuden (persons counted as
    Jews), 51, 55, 57, 96, 106–8, 120,
    126, 128, 135, 137, 149, 160, 190,
    199, 270n
Gemeinde (Jewish community)
    and ambulance services, 76
    dates of operation of, 33
    deportation of employees of, 77–81,
        144, 147, 151
    and deportation of Jews, 60–62, 64–
        67, 69, 72, 77–81
    and director of hospital, 218
    dissolution of, 30, 38, 80, 178
    Gestapo surveillance of, 72
    health department of, 11, 25, 43, 82
    and Jewish converts to Christianity,
        53
    and Lustig, 216–17
    and medical deferments for depor-
        tation, 69
    newspaper of, 29
    number of Jews registered with, 5
    and physicians for hospital, 44
    in postwar period, 80, 184, 208,
        211–12, 243
    records of, 263n
    registration of children with, xxi,
        54
    and social welfare services, 20, 33,
        36–37, 208, 243
    structure and function of, 36–40, 80
    and synagogue at hospital, 110.
    See also Reichsvereinigung
Gemeindeaktion (community raid), 77–
    81, 144
Gemeindeblatt, 216
German Explosive Chemicals GmbH,
    183
Gestapo
    and arrival of Soviet troops, 198
    and bomb shelter for Aryans at hos-
        pital, 194

and children's clothing workshop in
    hospital, 157
closing of synagogue by, 60
and courage of Jews, 28
and deportation of Jews, 65–67, 78–
    80, 96, 143, 146–48, 151–53, 161,
    194, 222–24
and Eichmann, 143
and factory raids, 123–26, 128, 131,
    133, 135–36
and fall of Berlin, 157, 195
and Frauenprotest, 130, 131
and hospital, 80, 85, 90–92, 95, 96,
    98, 99, 135, 140–43, 208, 227–28,
    235, 237–38, 240
and ill or injured Jews, 42
informers for, 107–8, 170, 190, 194–
    95, 213, 231
and intermarriage regulations, 8,
    57, 156–57, 235
and Judenhäuser (Jew houses), 57
and Kareski, 222
looting of hospital by, xix–xx
and Lustig, 217–18, 221–24
and medical deferments from de-
    portation, 69, 71–72
medical staff of, 77
and mentally ill patients, 89, 154–
    55, 236
and orphanage section of hospital,
    xix
and plans to close hospital and ar-
    rest staff, 140–42, 235, 240
prohibition of religious services at
    hospital by, 110, 112, 218
records of, 195, 275n
and Reichsvereinigung, 39, 72, 178,
    181–83
and Sammellager (temporary hold-
    ing camp), 2, 7, 76, 95, 107–8,
    118
search for underground Jews by,
    107

and suicide cases, 75
violence against Jews by, 42, 57,
    131, 169
Giesela (nurse), 205
Goebbels, Joseph, 4, 121, 133–34
Goldschmidt, Georg, 83
Goldsmith, Martin, 230
Gordon family, 174
Göring, Hermann, 121
Gossels, Conrad, 84, 86, 205–6
Gossels, Lotti, 205
Graetz, Frau, 199
Graetz, Ruth, 26, 48, 106, 199
Greifer (catchers), 107, 194–95, 231
Gross, Leonard, xiii
Grossbeeren labor camp, 133
Grosse Hamburgerstrasse camp, 133,
    134, 149, 163, 169
Grünberg, Golly, 148–51
Grynzspan, Herschel, 35
Günther, Rolf, 24, 78–79, 222, 240
Gynecology Outpatient Clinic, 40
Gypsies, xxii, 153

H., Hans, 106–7
H., Rosemarie
    arrest of, by Gestapo, 219–20
    and concentration camp survivors in
        hospital, 203–4
    and deportation of hospital staff,
        223
    and factory raids, 126, 128
    as forced laborer at hospital, 137
    and Frauenprotest, 128
    intermarriage in family of, 46–47
    Lustig's protection of, 219–20
    marriage of, 247
    postwar life of, 247
    at Rathenowerstrasse stable, 126,
        128, 131
    risky behavior of, 106–7
    visit of, to Sachsenhausen concen-
        tration camp, 106–7

Haas, Gerda, 99, 125
Hartung-von Doetinchem, Dagmar,
    xv, xvii, xix, 275n
Health insurance, 22, 182–83
Hebrew Immigrant Aid Society
    (HIAS), 247
Heimeinverkaufsverträge, 184
Hekdesh (hostel for traveling Jews),
    16–17
Helischkowski, Dr., 170, 206
Henschel, Hildegarde, 27, 68–72,
    255n, 256n, 261n
Henschel, Moritz, 151, 255n, 261n
Hepatitis, 246
Herrmann, Klaus J., 210, 276n
Hermann Göring Kaserne, 119–20,
    124, 126, 129, 268n
Herzberg, Sally, 148–51
Heumann, Dr., 206
HIAS. See Hebrew Immigrant Aid So-
    ciety (HIAS)
Hilberg, Raoul, 259n
Hilfsverein, 11, 247
Himmler, Heinrich, 121, 141, 238
Hindenburg, Paul von, 21
Hirsch, Kurt, 83
Hirschfeld, Dr., 72, 206
Hitler, Adolf, 5, 21, 48, 49, 50, 52, 93,
    120–22, 125, 134, 138, 229, 232
Hitlerjugend (Hitler Youth), 238
Holocaust
    literature of, 228–30
    number of Jews killed in, 5–6, 204,
        229
    survivors of, 3–4, 188, 203–8, 212,
        229–31
Holzer, Charlotte, 45
Hostage exchanges, 174
Hostel (Hekdesh), 16–17

I.G. Farben factory, 58, 127, 135
Illa, Schwester, 99–100, 226
Ilona (nurse), 224

Institute for Physiological Chemistry, 82
Insurance. *See* Health insurance
Intermarriage, 8, 12, 22, 24, 27, 36, 39, 43, 46–58, 134, 138–39, 156–57, 168, 178, 230, 235
Israel, 229, 245, 247

Jacoby, Dr., 88
Jacoby, Martin, 82
Jarwitz, Herbert, 82
Jewish Culture Association, 34, 108–9
Jewish Genealogy Net, xiv
Jewish Hospital in Berlin. *See* Berlin Jewish Hospital
Jewish Labor Bureau (*Arbeitsamt*), 11, 34, 57–58, 84, 132
Jewish Museum (Berlin), xvi, 116
Jewish Women's League (*Jüdischer Frauenbund*), 65–67
Jews
   assimilation of, 47, 53
   ban on emigration of, 83
   and ban on marriage and/or sexual contact with Aryans, 21, 50, 52
   community organizations of, in Berlin, 33–34, 36–40, 65–66, 232
   conversion of, to Christianity, xxi, 41, 52–55, 168, 231
   and cooperation with deportation order, 60–61, 64–66, 258n, 259
   definition of term, xx–xxi, 22, 39, 41, 49, 50–51, 54–55
   emigration of German, 5, 11, 32, 39, 43, 59, 82–85
   employment/unemployment of, 10–11, 18, 21, 32, 34, 38, 51, 81–82
   establishment of community in Berlin, 16
   false identities for, or living "underground," 6, 7–8, 48, 63, 64, 69, 72, 79, 84, 86, 107, 108, 134, 175, 206, 219, 246, 248
   food rations for, 117–18, 207
   forced labor by, 11, 34, 57–58, 73, 84, 98, 113, 120, 121–23, 137–38, 177, 182–83, 187
   German citizenship taken from, 50
   as Gestapo informers, 108, 231
   history of Jewish community in Berlin, 16–18
   intermarriage of, 8, 12, 22, 24, 27, 36, 39, 43, 46–58, 134, 138–39, 156–57, 168, 178, 230, 235
   number killed in Holocaust, 5–6, 204, 229
   Polish, 35, 59, 113
   population of, in Berlin, 2–3, 5, 41, 59, 120, 178, 254n
   population of, in Germany, 5, 32, 41, 178, 180
   and postwar conditions in Berlin, 15, 203, 207–8
   and prohibition from using public transportation, 73, 77, 97, 110
   "racial" labeling of and badges for, 32–36, 54, 56, 94, 95, 97, 101–3, 105, 107, 120, 122, 159–60, 162, 173, 202, 221
   under Soviet occupation of Berlin, 202–3
   stereotypical view of physical appearance of, 102
   suicides by, 69, 73–76, 79, 84–87, 119, 142, 176, 205, 225, 260n, 262n, 273n
   survivors of concentration and labor camps, 3–4, 188, 203–8, 212, 229–31
   violence against, 41–42, 57, 64, 125, 126, 131, 232.
   See also Anti-Semitism; Berlin Jewish Hospital; Deportations
"Jim" (prisoner), 171–72, 270n
Joint Distribution Committee, 275n
Judenhäuser (Jew houses), 53–54, 57

Judenrat (Jewish leadership council), 81, 277n
Jüdische Kulturbund (Jewish Culture Association), 34, 108–9
Jüdischer Frauenbund (Jewish Women's League), 65–67
Jüdisches Nachrichtenblatt, 33, 43–44

Kahan, Hilde
and bombings of Berlin, 194
and deportation of employees of *Gemeinde/Reichsvereinigung*, 78, 261n
and deportation of hospital staff, 142–46, 223
and deportation of nursing home patients, 152
employment history of, 10–11
expulsion of, from apartment, 146
and factory raids, 122–24, 128, 137
food rations for, 117–18
and forced labor for hospital, 138
and Gestapo's plans to close hospital and arrest staff, 140, 142
on Lustig, 27–28, 256n
Lustig's protection of, 146–48, 173
and medical deferments from deportation, 68, 70–72
memoirs and videotaped interview of, xvi, xviii
and mentally ill patients, 154, 155–56
and military hospital, 91
mother of, 10–11, 28, 117–18, 123–25, 128, 146–48, 151, 173, 186
on population of hospital, 253n
postwar life of, 247
and release papers for prisoners in *Sammellager*, 198
and retaliation against Germans for crimes against Jews, 193
and RSHA correspondence, 182
and Ruth Ellen Wagner, 159–61

in *Sammellager*, 147–48, 151
as secretary to Lustig, 2, 5, 11, 146
and Soviet examination of hospital financial records, 276n
on Soviet liberation of hospital, 253n
and Soviet troops near Berlin, 196
and suicide cases, 75–76
and ulcer, 117
Kahn, Eugen, 190
Kantelberg, Erwin, 88, 114, 147, 188, 245
Kareski, Georg, 222
Kinderunterkunft (orphanage), xix, 28, 55–56, 89, 156, 174–75
Kleemann (personnel officer), 161, 256n
Klemperer, Eva, 35
Klemperer, Victor, 35, 230, 236
Knopp, Hans, 48, 86, 110, 116, 247, 265–66n
Kosher food, 34, 111, 113
Kozower, Gisela, 150
Kozower, Philipp, 80
Krankenbehandler (carer for the sick), 42, 44, 45, 76, 185, 236
Krebs, H., 183
Krell, Karl, 136, 268n
Kristallnacht, 10–11, 31–33, 37, 40, 41–42, 149, 165
Kübler, Stella, 107–8, 170, 213
Kurmärkischen Wood Fiber and Cellulose Company, 182–83

Labor Bureau, Jewish. *See* Jewish Labor Bureau
Landsberg, Fritz, 83
Law for the Protection of German Blood and Honor, 50–52
Law for the Restoration of the Professional Civil Service, 21, 22, 25
Law on Rental Leases with Jews, 53–54

Lawyers, Jewish, 53
Lazarett (military hospital), 7, 91–92,
    100, 182, 188, 196, 198, 201–4,
    240, 274n
Lebram, Ruth, 93–94, 101, 102–3,
    116, 118, 247–48, 265–66n
Lennhoff, Elli, 205
Lennhoff, Irene, 205
Levy, Else, 86
Lewkowitz, Mr., 248
Liebknecht, Karl, 23
London, Inge, 98, 118, 119–20, 126,
    129, 137, 248
Looting of hospital, xix–xx
Löwenberg, Edith, 82
Lustgarten, 120–21
Lustig, Annemarie, 24, 214–15
Lustig, Bernhard, 22–23
Lustig, Ernst, 215, 276–77n
Lustig, Regina Besser, 23
Lustig, Walter
    anti-Jewish measures against, 221
    anti-Semitism of, 26–27, 215–17,
        256n
    and arrest of Ruth Ellen Wagner,
        159–61
    birth and parents of, 22–23
    death of, 209–15
    and deportation of employees of
        Gemeinde/Reichsvereinigung, 78–
        79, 144
    and deportation of hospital staff, 28,
        142–48, 150, 151, 161, 222–24,
        226
    and deportation of nursing home
        patients, 151–52
    and deportation of seriously ill pa-
        tients, 224–26
    as director of health services for
        Wedding district, 209, 211
    education of, 23
    and factory raids, 123, 124
    and forced labor at hospital, 137–38

    and *Gemeinde*, 216–17
    and Gestapo's plans to close hospital
        and arrest staff, 140–42, 240
    in health department of *Gemeinde*,
        25, 43
    as hospital director, xvi, 2, 22, 79,
        80, 81, 217–18, 260–61n
    and insurance claims, 182–83
    marriage of, 24, 27, 43
    medical career of, 23–26, 42–43
    and medical deferments from de-
        portation, 67, 70–72, 219
    and mentally ill patients, 155
    as Nazi collaborator, 217–28
    personality of, 23, 25, 27, 28, 62,
        98–99, 218–21, 256n
    physical appearance of, 22, 26
    Police Presidium job of, 24, 114,
        141, 219
    positive and negative views of, 26–
        28, 97–99, 215–17, 226–28
    in postwar period, 209–15
    and prohibition against religious
        services at hospital, 112
    protection of Hilde Kahan by, 146–
        48, 173
    and psychiatric services, 88–89
    as *Reichsvereinigung* head, 2, 81, 144,
        158, 178, 184, 209, 211–12, 261n
    as *Reichsvereinigung* health depart-
        ment head, 11, 27, 43, 62, 80
    sexual liaisons by, 27, 98, 99–100,
        114, 226
    and Soviet liberation of hospital,
        11–12
    and Soviet occupation of Berlin,
        202
    surgery performed by, 170, 219
    and survival of hospital, 240
    titles of, 114, 162–63
    in World War I, 23, 25
    writings of, 23–24
Luxemburg, Rosa, 23

Margarete, 106–7
Markuse, Dr., 206
Marriage
   between Aryans and Jews, 8, 12, 22,
      24, 27, 36, 39, 43, 46–58
   before deportation of Jews, 63
   and divorce of mixed-marriage cou-
      ples, 57, 58, 156, 235
   in postwar period at hospital, 205
Maya, *Schwester*, 137
Mayerfeld, Ernie, ix, x, xii, xiv, xv, 4,
   208
Mayerfeld, Herr, ix–x
Medical deferments from deportation,
   62–63, 64, 66–76
Mein Kampf (Hitler), 232
Mental illness, 88–89, 153–56, 236
Meyer, Beate, xviii, 212, 220–21
Meyer, Dr., 206
Meyersohn, Lisa, 12, 111–12
Middleton, Drew, 249
Military hospital (*Lazarett*), 7, 91–92,
   100, 182, 188, 196, 198, 201–4,
   240, 274n
Milwitzki, Heinz, 82
Minyan, 112, 264–65n
Mischlinge (half-Jews), 50–52, 55–58,
   102, 131, 133, 134, 138, 146, 159,
   162, 174–75, 178, 186, 195
Mixed marriage. *See* Intermarriage
Moeller (Gestapo officer), 170
Moses, Jules, 63–64
Müller, Margarete, 87
Muslims, 243

Nachtwache (night watch), 191–92
Nadav, Daniel, xvi
Narcotics, 113–14, 208
Nazis
   anti-Jewish measures by, 21–22, 25,
      29, 31–37, 41, 49–60, 73, 122,
      232
   definition of Aryans by, xxii

definition of Jews by, xx–xxi, 39, 41,
   49, 50–51
and intermarriage regulations, 46–
   58, 156–57, 235
Lustig as collaborator with, 217–28
murder of mentally ill by, 88
propaganda and manipulation of the
   masses by, 52, 101, 178, 196, 198
violence against Jews by, 41–42, 57,
   64, 125, 126, 131, 232
See also Deportations; Hitler, Adolf;
   Holocaust
Neumann, Margot, 26, 98, 109, 248
Neumann, Mrs. Selmar, 98, 186
Neumann, Selmar
   as administrative director of hospi-
      tal, 81, 260–61n
   corporal punishment of staff by, 163
   criticisms of, 98
   and deportations of hospital staff,
      143–45
   and forced labor in hospital, 137–38
   and relative in *Extrastation*, 173
   and religious services, 112
   residence of, at hospital, 186
   and Soviet liberation of Berlin, 12
Neuropsychiatry Department, 63
Night watch (*Nachtwache*), 191–92
Nuremberg Laws, xx–xxi, 21, 39, 42,
   44, 50–53, 232
Nuremberg trials, 164, 165, 210
Nurses, Jewish
   dangerous escapades by, into Berlin
      society, 93–95, 101–8
   deportation of, with transports, 66–
      67, 84, 85–86, 152
   and factory raids, 122–23, 127
   Lustig's sexual predation on, 27, 99–
      100, 114
   and medical deferments from de-
      portation, 69
   and medical inspections in
      Sammellager, 66

Nurses, Jewish (*cont.*)
    residence of, 7, 20, 69, 87, 96, 110
    sexual liaisons of, 27, 99–100, 115–17
    size of nursing staff, 186–87
    and suicide cases, 75, 176, 225
    suicides of, 86–87, 205
    training of, 20, 45, 149
Nursing homes, 151–53, 181
Nursing school, 20, 45, 149

Oberin (head nurse), 111
Old age homes, 20, 124, 134, 137, 151, 181, 243, 267n
Olympics (1936), 232
Opitz, Norbert, 272n
Oppenheimer, Frau, 173
Oranienburg concentration camp, 42, 253n, 269n
Ordner (police auxiliaries), 60–61, 65, 123, 124, 126, 141–42, 148, 152, 231
Orphanage, 28, 55–56, 89, 156, 174–75

Palestine, 174, 243
Pathologie (pathology laboratory), 2, 7, 9, 190, 237
Pharmacy, 88, 114, 147, 188–89
Physicians. *See* Doctors, Jewish
Pineas, Hermann, 63–64, 85, 86, 153–54, 248
Pineas, Herta, 67, 248
Plaut, Max, xviii–xix
Plaut, Raphael, xviii–xix
Poland, 61, 63, 150, 152, 204–5, 229
Police
    and deportation of Jews, 65
    and factory raids, 125
    and hospital, 95
    and Lustig's Police Presidium job, 24, 114, 141, 219
    search for underground Jews by, 107

Police Presidium (Berlin), 24–25, 114, 141, 219
Police ward, 9, 42, 74, 95, 157, 163, 165–72, 212
Polish Jews, 35, 59, 113
Polizeistation (police ward), 9, 42, 74, 157, 163, 165–72, 212
Pregnant women, 70
Preuss, Annemarie, 24, 214–15
Prison ward. *See* Police ward
"Privileged Jew" rules, 53–57
Propaganda by Nazis, 52, 101, 178, 196, 198
Psychiatry, 88–89, 153–56, 236
Public transportation
    accidents involving, 103–5, 170
    hospital staff's use of, 97, 103–7
    prohibition against Jews' use of, 73, 77, 97, 110

Quarantine facility, 89–90

Rabbis, 33–34, 38–39, 59–61
Radios, ban on, 59–60, 100
Radlauer, Dr., 182
Rape, 199, 214
Raphael, Fräulein, 2, 5, 254n
Rassenschande (racial defilement), 52
Rath, Ernst vom, 35
Rathenowerstrasse stable, 124, 126, 128, 129, 135
Ravensbrück concentration camp, 5, 194
Red Army. *See* Soviets
Red Cross, 202, 233
Reich Citizenship Law, 50
Reichsbürger, 50
Reichssicherheitshauptamt (RSHA, Reich Security Main Office), xvii, 24, 40, 80, 90, 96, 141, 142, 143, 159, 178, 179, 181, 183, 198, 217–18, 237–40, 275n
Reichstag fire, 21

Reichsvereinigung
Baeck as president of, 38, 59–61, 80, 222
budget of, 181–82, 183
deportation of employees of, 77–81, 86, 144, 147
and deportation of Jews, 60–62, 64–67, 72, 77–81, 258n
and director of hospital, 218
dissolution of, in 1943, 80, 151, 178
and factory raids, 122–23
function of, 39–40, 80
and Gestapo, 39, 72
health and social welfare functions of, 174–75, 178–81, 184, 193
and *Heimeinverkaufsverträge*, 184
and insurance claims, 182–83
and intermarriage, 54
Lustig as head of, 2, 81, 144, 158, 178, 184, 209, 211–12, 261n
Lustig as head of health department, 11, 27, 43, 62, 80
Meyer's research on, xviii
offices of, in hospital, 158, 177, 180, 232
in postwar period, 209, 211–12
proposed name changes for, 179, 211
records of, xvi, xvii, 180, 263n
revival of, as *Rest-Reichsvereinigung* (1942–1945), 80, 177–84, 232
after Soviet liberation of Berlin, 204
and transfer of title of Berlin Jewish Hospital, 90, 182
See also Gemeinde (Jewish community)
Reichsvertretung der deutschen Juden (Central Representation of German Jews), 38–39, 60
Rischowsky, Felix, 102, 137–38, 196
Rischowsky, Günther, 102, 118, 137–38, 162, 193, 196
Romania, 168–69
Rosemarie H. *See* H., Rosemarie

Rosenberg, Frau, 175–76
Rosenberg, Herr, 175, 176
Rosenberg, Oskar, 87, 148, 206, 268–69n
Rosenstein, Paul, 82, 87
Rosenstrasse camp, 129–34, 137–38, 141, 146, 268n
Rosenthal, Harry Siegfried, 3–4, 208
Rotholz, Alexander, 267n
Rothschild family, 173
RSHA (*Reichssicherheitshauptamt*), xvii, 24, 40, 80, 90, 96, 141, 142, 143, 159, 178, 179, 181, 183, 198, 217–18, 237–40, 275n
Ruthen, Rudolf aus den, 126

Sachsenhausen concentration camp, 5, 42, 46, 106–7, 155, 166, 194, 209–10, 253n, 269n
Sammellager (temporary holding camp), 2, 7, 9–10, 28, 60, 65–67, 74, 76, 95, 99, 100, 107, 118, 147–50, 152, 155, 157, 161, 163, 166, 169, 190–91, 194, 195, 198, 212, 213, 225, 231, 233, 237, 257n, 265n, 267n, 268n
Scarlet fever, 89–90
Schachtel, Uri, 243
Schiffer, "Excellence," 173
Schönfeld, Dr., 79, 87, 214, 260–61n
Schools for Jewish children, 38, 149, 178
Schüfftan, Lotte, 93–94, 101, 102–3
Schuster, Paul, 82
Schwesternheim (nurses' residence), 7, 20, 69, 87, 96, 110, 245, 247
Segall, Dr., 206
Seligmann, Erich, 25, 220
Sexual liaisons
in hospital, xix, 27, 87, 98, 99–100, 113–17, 226
Lustig as sexual predator, 27, 98, 99–100, 114, 226

Shiff, Frau, 88–89
Shirer, William, 232
Siechenheim (nursing home), 151–53
Siedner-Cohn, Lili, 82
Siemens factory, 113, 120
Silberberg, Dr., 205
Social welfare, 20, 33–38, 174–75,
    178–81, 184, 193, 208, 243
Soviets
    approach to Berlin by, 195–98
    arrest of Stella Kübler by, 213
    arrival of, in Berlin, 198
    bivouacked on grounds of hospital,
        199
    and death of Lustig, 209–15
    liberation of hospital by, 1–13, 15,
        189, 253n
    occupation of Berlin by, 198–208
    rape by, 199, 214
    and Sachsenhausen concentration
        camp, 209–10
Speer, Albert, 121–22
Spitzel (informers), 107–8, 170, 190,
    194–95, 213, 231
SS
    and deportation of Jews, 67, 78–79,
        96, 119, 161
    and factory raids, 121, 125–26, 128,
        135, 136
    before fall of Berlin, 195, 196
    and *Frauenprotest*, 130–33
    and hospital, 95
    and hospital forced labor, 137–38
    and ill or injured Jews, 42
    and intermarriage regulations, 57–
        58, 235
    Leibstandarte division of, 125
    records of, 275n
    and Soviet occupation of Berlin,
        200–202
Staatsangehöriger, 50
Stalin, Joseph, 212, 213
Stalingrad, battle of, 100, 133

Stettiner, Fräulein, 205
St. Hedwig's Cathedral, 130
Stoltzfus, Nathan, 52
Strauss, Hermann, 83–84, 87, 205,
    234, 260–61n, 262n
Stürzbecher, Manfred, xvi
Suicides by Jews, 69, 73–76, 79, 84–
    87, 119, 142, 176, 205, 225, 260n,
    262n, 273n
Surgical department, 42, 45, 71–72,
    82, 170, 185, 219, 272–73n
Sweden, 244–45, 249
Synagogues
    in Berlin, 33, 59, 65, 66
    of hospital, 20, 110–13, 204–5, 218

Theresienstadt ghetto, 63, 79, 80, 83,
    89, 100, 128, 134, 148–52, 168,
    171, 183, 184, 188, 194, 205, 208,
    221, 233, 245, 247, 255n, 262n,
    265–66n, 268n
Tuberculosis, 117, 171, 204
Tuchmann, Dr., 224–25
Typhoid, 204, 208

Unemployment of Jews. *See* Employ-
    ment/unemployment of Jews
United States, 229–30, 232
Urban Krankenhaus, 89–90

Vorstand (governing body of
    Gemeinde), 80, 218

Wagner, Ruth Ellen, 159–62
Wagner, Thorsten, 272–73n
Water supply, 196–97, 201
Wehrmacht Reserve Field Hospital
    (*Lazarett*), 7, 91–92, 100, 182,
        188, 196, 198, 201–4, 240, 274n
Weimar Republic, 47, 63
Weissensee cemetery, 4, 19, 178, 181,
    197, 232, 254n
Welfare programs. *See* Social welfare

Westheimer, Erna, 6
Wills, Leslie, 244
Winau, Rolf, xv
Windmüller, Dr., 163
Winterfeld, Dr., 244
Wöhrn, Fritz
  arrests of hospital staff by, 159–63
  and deportation of patients and
    staff, 142, 222–24
  inspections of hospital by, 96, 159–
    65, 175, 193, 222–24, 237
  interrogation of Frau Rosenberg by,
    175
  Lustig's instructions from, 220, 240
  and Lustig's Police Presidium posi-
    tion, 24
  war crimes trial of, 28, 210, 215,
    276n
Wolff, Theodor, 167
Wolfsohn, Dr., 206
World War I, 21, 23, 25, 47, 51, 196,
  197
Wyden, Peter, 107, 210

Yellow stars for Jews, 32–36, 54, 56,
  94, 95, 97, 101–3, 105, 107, 120,
  122, 159–60, 162, 173, 202, 221
Yom Kippur, 59–60, 66

Zionists, 37, 222
Zwilsky, Ehrich (Erich)
  on anti-Semitism in postwar Ger-
    many, 206–7
  defense of hospital staff by, 227–28
  and deportations of hospital staff,
    143–45
  employment history of, 81–82, 147
  on hospital needs in postwar period,
    208
  Lustig's protection of, from depor-
    tation, 147, 148, 151, 158
  positive comments on, 98
  as postwar administrator of hospital,
    209, 247, 248–49
  on postwar conditions in Berlin,
    207
  postwar life of, 248–49
  as *Reichsvereinigung* administrator,
    81
  residence of, at hospital, 186
  and Soviet liberation of hospital, 12,
    199
Zwilsky, Klaus, xi, xii, 12, 113, 148,
  193, 197–99, 248–49
Zwilsky, Ruth, 12, 113, 148, 149, 186,
  199, 247, 249

MIST IN THE TAGUS

Mist
in the Tagus

opkinson, Henry T.

By TOM HOPKINSON

BOSTON · · · 1947

LITTLE, BROWN AND COMPANY

CONTENTS

I   FIRST NIGHT IN MARINHA   3

II   THE LADY FROM THE AGENCY   13

III   THE FIRST FREE MORNING   28

IV   MORNING IN THE WATER   42

V   MEETING WITH A RESCUER   52

VI   ON THE FISHING BEACH   67

VII   A FISH FOR LUNCH   84

VIII   THE VISIT TO VALLADO   99

IX   ON THE CASTLE WALLS   113

X   THE JOURNEY BACK   129

XI   FADOS SINGERS   140

XII   A WALK TO THE CHAPEL   154

XIII   THE VIEW FROM THE POINT   166

XIV   AN EVENING VISIT   180

XV   THE FRANTIC SEARCH   198

XVI   SURVEY OF THE BATTLEFIELD   211

XVII   THE WANDERER'S RETURN   222

XVIII   "TAGUS, FAREWELL . . ."   239

MIST IN THE TAGUS

There is in this country, and particularly about the valley of the Tagus, a mist which rises suddenly. When the mist is risen, one cannot tell whether the passers-by are men or women, or creatures of some other species.

— Old Guidebook to Portugal

I

FIRST NIGHT IN MARINHA

THE square in the village of Marinha glowed with a reflected light, and panted in an expanding heat. The rays of the sun, after beating for sixteen hours down onto the cobbled square, had lifted off, and shot now against the towering cliff beneath which the village sheltered. In the clear light of evening every detail of the cliff stood out as though it had just been constructed — the streaky yellow of its crumbling surface; the flowering weeds and cactus clinging to every ledge; the framework and mechanism of the lift which slid between iron guides from the village no one left to the cliff top no one visited, with the tiny sailors' chapel jutting classically above the brow. All these, like an enormous backcloth, faced the light, and rained down a powerful reflection into the square below.

Though the sun's rays threw no heat, there was little coolness yet for Marinha. Into the air of coming night the painted fronts of shops and small hotels, the cobblestones, stalls, and pavements, were shedding off almost visibly the warmth stored up during the day. In the hot air of their oven square the Marinha people baked like biscuits, crowded together as at a public killing.

Midweek activity was at its height. Today was Tuesday. Tomorrow the square would become a fish market. Anyone wanting to sell *espadrilles* or shawls of chemical brilliance to the fishermen's wives, harsh metallic sweets to the swarms of children, colored photographs of the lighthouse to the visitors, must get the business done tonight, or wait till Friday. A swaying mass filled the whole center of the square, which was raised some six inches above the surrounding pavements: the hot air rang with a continuous general din, a furious chatter of bargain, purchase, refusal, browbeating, accusation, cries of greeting, rebuke, and the wails of children.

Seen from above by the visitors — shopkeepers and small business people from Lisbon or Oporto, perched along the balconies of the coarsely painted hotels or pensions which lay around the square — the crowd was a honeycomb kaleidoscope, a hundred knots of women circling round seated heaps of clothing, the owners of goods for sale and their excited customers. From time to time as those above looked down, a whole fragment of the crowd would stumble and break away from the raised platform, edge along, and dive in again wherever opening allowed.

The twelve or fifteen feet of space between square and balcony corresponded to another and wider distance between the occupants of each. Those seated on the balconies enjoyed an elevation, partly of height and remoteness from the bustle, partly of superiority to the fishing people who lacked the dignity and the resources to perch on the balcony of the Hotel Granja or Avenida and listen to the blare of the Lisbon radio. To those above there was something reassuring in the sight beneath, the milling crowds of women and girls in black headdresses, close-fitting cotton bodices and an infinity of skirts and petticoats, barefooted and with insect-bitten legs, who argued, harangued, and recognized each other in total disregard of the audience above their heads. Beside the women, but remote from them, silent and abstracted, stood a scattering of old men, with a fringe of boys too small even to pick fish out of the nets, but each observing, down to the very infants, the dignified aloofness proper to a man.

Though the life of the square appeared so self-absorbed, in the minds of those present was a distraction and expectancy, so that even while the women bargained for an unspeakable piece of household furniture — nothing but the tawdriest and shoddiest ever found its way to Marinha — they would send a

glance towards the upper corner, between the Bank
of the Holy Spirit and the café of Senhor Branca the
brothel keeper, where the only road out of the village
wound up from sea level, over the pass beyond the
mountain bowl in which Marinha and the woods and
farmland behind it were enclosed.

Down this road, twice a day, came, and before
long would come again, the yellow omnibus which
joined Marinha and its people to the town of Vallado,
to the network of main roads, to Lisbon, to the great
Atlantic and South American steamship routes, to the
wide world their ancestors had discovered four and
a half centuries ago.

A lull in the screams of bargaining, a turning of
baked faces towards the descending road, a compres-
sion of bargainers to clear a few square yards, and
the bus had swayed and creaked to stop. Those
nearest surged in towards it — runners from hotels,
official porters to carry the luggage of visitors, un-
official porters to carry the luggage of visitors, beggars looking for money, women for the excitement of
recognizing an acquaintance. The driver, proud as
if he controlled a battleship, jerked on the hand brake,
flung the door wide, and forced his way — in white
cloth cap and gray cotton jacket — through into the
office with a bunch of papers. His passengers began
slowly to climb down, the young ones stepping
straight, the older women turning about, clenching

their belongings against the brass handrails, and lowering themselves, stern foremost, into the crowd.

All were soon swallowed up in jokes and handclasps, and now, last of all, as though she had been waiting on purpose for the crowd to clear, there jumped down out of the bus a girl. She was dressed in a white frock and a short scarlet jacket. Her round soft hat, pulled over thick black hair which brushed her shoulders, gave her a schoolgirl air, though there was none of the angularity of a schoolgirl in her figure. Her age could have been from nineteen to twenty-three. She was English, and was making no pretense about it.

"No, thank you. I can manage quite well for myself," she said in her own language to the leavings of porters, hotel touts, pimps, and beggars who pressed round her. "No, thank you. Please leave it alone." Seizing back her suitcase, she set off with it down the square as firmly as if she knew where she was going.

Caroline Page had found an unlucky evening to arrive for her fortnight's holiday in Marinha. It was now the middle of the holiday season. She had reached here on a Tuesday, when the rush of visitors from Lisbon was already settled in. From one hotel to another she passed, carrying a large suitcase, a roll of magazines, and a dark blue coat. She made her inquiries in French, and most of the proprietors spoke French in answer, but the English-French and the

Portuguese-French did not mix. Those who said
"No!" she understood. But when they said more and
tried to help her, she found the instructions hard to
follow. Besides, most of the pensions were on the
square, where the crowd was still milling as if at a
religious festival, and her conversations were continually interrupted by the visitors who were already established pushing their way past her home to dinner.

Once, while she was waiting on a landing for the
proprietor, the door of a room opened. A young man
gaped at her in surprise, and then invited her to step
inside. Twice from doorways in the street figures
reached out hands to take her case. Once her roll of
magazines slipped out from beneath her arm, and she
had to gather them up in the dust from a crowd of
hurrying feet. Conscious that night was closing in,
she pressed on from one full hotel to another. The
less she knew where she was going, the more assured
and determined she struggled to appear.

The last pension at which Caroline tried for a
night's rest was the Pension Douro. It seemed indeed
to be the last one she could try. It was the end house
in a row overlooking the sea, and its wall was built
flat up against the face of the yellow cliff. There was
its name in colored glass above the door, but inside
was no office or waiting room, nothing but a staircase, leading she could not see where. The stairs were
of pitch pine with an encrusted handrail and plaster

banisters. They were covered with thin linoleum in a blue and purple pattern. A paper in the favorite mud-red and orange taste, heavily embossed, enflamed the walls. At the head of the stairs sat a life-size shepherd boy of porcelain playing a flute. The back of his head had been removed to accommodate umbrellas and the fishing nets of children. On the landing where he sat was a kitchen dresser. On it were two bathing dresses, a rubber bathing cap, a pair of baby's drawers, a wine bottle, and a plate containing two sardines in oil and a half-sucked orange.

Caroline had already turned to go when a door along the landing opened, a small bright-faced waiter appeared in an evening coat and white flannel trousers: "The Señorita for dinner, yes," he declared in English, and within two minutes Caroline was sitting by herself at a table in a corner of the Pension Douro's dining room, as secure for the moment as a Portuguese.

In spite of bluebottles and radio, the food was good, the attendance quick and friendly. Here, if only she could, thought Caroline, she would stay. She passed the waiter a large tip to secure his favor, and asked to see the Senhora.

The Senhora was an iron-bound barrel, filled to capacity. From her face and through every movement gloomed a violent, domineering nature. A brass-bedstead, linen-cupboard Mussolini, her very servility was threatening. She listened to Caroline as if giving her a chance to incriminate herself, then declared, with finality, that she had no room left, and would have no room empty till the autumn.

"But my telegram," pleaded Caroline. " You must have had my telegram from Lisbon — asking you to reply if you had nowhere to put me up."

But the Senhora's porter had already informed the Senhora that the young English lady had tried half the hotels in the place before coming here. Regrettably no telegram had been received. Turning to go, Caroline tried a second, larger, lie.

"My newspaper in London," she said, "will be surprised to learn that I am compelled to leave Marinha without describing its attractions for them. No doubt there are other places in Portugal which will prove more hospitable" — and she beckoned the waiter for her coat and case.

The Senhora hesitated. "It is too late," she declared. "You cannot leave Marinha tonight. There are no buses."

"Then I shall have to tell the people of London," Caroline replied, quick to see her bluff was working, "that in Marinha the visitor must sleep on the seashore," and she started for the stairs. To part with one English visitor, a being of that curious race who never check through the bills presented to them, would be painful to the Senhora. To cut off a possible flow of such visitors direct from their wealthy capital would be insanity. "Stop!" she exclaimed dramatically. "To sleep on the seashore would be for a woman a dangerous experience. I shall take it upon myself to solve this difficulty for you." She turned to the eager waiter.

"Pedro, prepare the small bedchamber for the lady! There is," she explained to Caroline, "a small chamber for boxes on the stairs — it is scarcely more than a cupboard. My husband sleeps there when he is at home. It is at least better than the seashore, and your countrymen will see that in Marinha we understand how to inconvenience ourselves for the sake of our guests. Unfortunately, owing to the extra work, it will be necessary to charge as for a full-sized room."

Within three or four minutes Caroline found herself installed, with much ceremony and less convenience, in the smallest room she had ever seen. It was part of a landing, boxed off with lath partitions. Everyone going up or downstairs seemed to be coming, seemed actually to be inside it, with her. Its single window opened, not over the sea, but onto the kitchen entrance and the dustbins. No one, however, could see in; it was a place where she could unpack her suitcase, and could sleep. Above all she had an unchallengeable right to be here.

As she shook out and hung up her crumpled clothes

before, as she intended, taking a last walk in the evening, Caroline addressed herself, as she was accustomed to do in all times of crisis or relief:

"You're a silly girl, Caroline. You ought to be very thankful. It's true the Senhora is a poisoner. It is her habit to make visitors ill, and then tell them they must leave immediately. But at least you're here in a room, by yourself. By yourself. . . ."

Caroline sat down on the bed. She was surprised to see her own hands trembling. She was annoyed to find that she had no longer the energy to go downstairs, to meet the new faces out of doors, to resist any longer the public gaze. She decided to get into bed, but to say some very strong things to herself about this weakness before she settled down to sleep.

She had hardly got into bed, however, before she was past saying anything to anyone, and the sound of the shopkeepers pounding up the stairs after their last drinks in the square crashed round and above her head unnoticed.

II

THE LADY FROM THE AGENCY

IT was caprice that had brought Caroline Page to Marinha for her summer holiday, but it was one of those caprices which, as soon as they come into the mind, are accepted, and hold good against all arguments and difficulties. She had heard of the village by chance, at once resolved to go there, and would listen to no alternative. To friends who asked why she chose this particular place, she could only answer that she wanted "to get away." When they asked what she wanted to get away from, she said "from everything." By this most of them understood her to mean her job, the city where she lived and worked, the boardinghouse in which she lodged. To few of them did it occur that in "everything" she might include themselves. One or two may have reflected that she might possibly mean herself, or herself as well as other things.

Ever since she could remember clearly Caroline had earned her own living. That did not mean that she had been earning her own living very long, at most not more than four or five years. But in her mind her life was divided into two periods.

The period since she had left home, changed her own name for another, and started providing for herself, deserved to be remembered day by day as it had happened. Good or bad, each day was hers and separate. It had been, as she considered it, "real life."

The other period of her life was simply the whole of her childhood and youth up to the time when she left home — all of which had faded into a vague indistinguishable mass about as present to her as the eighteenth century.

The dividing point in her life, the leaving home, had been no sudden decision on Caroline's part. Indeed it had not been a decision at all. The intention had been with her ever since she could remember, far back into the mythological period following infancy. There had never, she believed, been a time when she had not intended to leave home, and the strength of her intention was proved by the fact that through a large part of her childhood Caroline reckoned time, not *from* her birth at all but *towards* the expected day, so that in her own mind she was not so much thirteen years old as twelve months nearer. It was proved above all by her ability to wait, to hold on, to avoid making a false start.

Once she did leave, she would leave for good. There was to be no being brought back with ignominy. No asking pardon. No making terms. Once she had cast off, she would be free, and if she starved she would starve quietly in her own way. Therefore it had always been clear to Caroline that she must not leave home until she was able to support herself. It was no use waiting until she actually had a job; that was too much to hope for. If she were to start asking round her home — and where else could she ask? — word would soon get back to her family. She must wait until she was of an age to be able to walk into a factory or office without seeming ridiculous by her childish appearance, and demand or beg a chance to show what she could do. She must wait, she decided, at least until she was sixteen. If, at that age, her face and figure would make her pass for eighteen, she would go. If not, she would condemn herself — by her own impartial judgment, given in front of the mirror, in the clothes she would wear in asking for employment — to a further twelve months' waiting.

On her sixteenth birthday Caroline decided in her own favor. She might go. She had in her money box, and in the Post Office Savings Bank, a total of £7 14s. 3d. This she withdrew. She would have had more money, but it was the custom in her family to give presents on birthdays and at Christmas. Caroline had a father, a mother, and a brother, besides an aunt who stayed regularly in the house. Dutifully, while under her parents' roof, she conformed to their present-giving custom and made inroads on her savings to the extent of at least two and sixpence on each occasion.

In going, Caroline took with her everything useful which she could fairly call her own — that is to say, her clothes; various possessions, such as a handbag and a blotting pad which she considered her share of advantage out of the present-giving; a silver mug, and a knife, fork, and spoon which had been given to her on her baptism. These last had been packed away in a cupboard of her mother's ever since she could remember. However, she got them out without hesitation. They were hers. They had been presented to her. They had her name carved on them.

On the other hand she left behind two objects she particularly wanted — a watch and a fountain pen. The watch was a spare watch of her mother's which had been lent her "for the time being." The fountain pen had been lying about the house for a year, until no one knew whose it was. Her father, in a moment of liberality, had told her she "might as well use it until someone else wanted it." In neither of these cases did it seem to Caroline that her right to the object had been established.

She left home on a Saturday afternoon. Her parents had gone to London for the day, and her brother had taken himself to a cinema. It was the day after her birthday. Caroline had all her belongings ready packed. They filled two suitcases and a brown paper parcel. At the last minute she took off her coat and wrapped the parcel in it. She had an idea that to be seen carrying a paper parcel might cause her to be noticed, and so make it easier for her to be traced.

She took the train for London — her family lived some twenty-five miles outside — changed halfway at a crowded junction, bought a fresh ticket, and set out for Northampton. She chose Northampton because she had not the slightest connection with the town. She had never been there. She had no friends there, and it did not seem the sort of place to which a person leaving home was likely to go out of excitement, or led by a romantic dream. Besides, she had heard that shoe factories were doing well, and she thought she might have a chance of being taken on.

At the junction where she changed trains she posted a letter to her parents. She had written the letter in varying words a hundred times during the past four years.

Dear Mother and Daddy:
I expect you have known for some time that I am not very happy at home. Lots of people, I expect, feel the same way, and I should not mind this, only I do not feel

[17]

myself useful either. In fact I feel rather in the way. You don't get anything from my being here, and it costs you a certain amount for food, clothes, school, and cetera.

I have taken the things which are mine, and I have got some money which I have saved up, so please do not worry any more about me. It won't be any good trying to find me and bring me back. So please do not do so. I have changed my name, and am going to a quite different part of the country. If anyone wants to know where I am you can tell them I have got a job. By then most likely it will be true.

She signed it with the name which she had in that moment given up, and had now almost forgotten, *Hazel*. "It's a soppy name," she said to herself as she wrote it down, "and I shall manage much better without it. Good-by, Hazel. That's the last I shall ever see of you."

She chose the name Caroline because she had read in an English literature book about "the Caroline poets." Having literary dreams herself, it seemed a well-omened name. Besides it had a pretty sound. "Page" she liked because it was short and simple. "Miss Page" could be shouted through an office or factory without one's having to blush for belonging to it. It was easily remembered. It went with Caroline. It had subtler, more romantic associations — connected with girls in disguise, and belonging to the same period as the "Caroline" poets, which made the practical reasons for choosing it more palatable. Caro-

line Page she had been ever since. She was Caroline
Page on her passport, and it did not occur to her
twice a year that she was going about the world under an alias.

The first job Miss Page secured had been in Northampton, in a shoe factory — as a packer at 23s. 6d. a
week. She had taken a room for 12s., and on the other
11s. 6d. she fed, clothed, bathed, enriched her mind,
and entertained herself. She ought, in addition, to
have made provision for ill-health, holidays, dependent relatives, and old age, but decided to neglect these
precautions for a year or two.

She was fortunate in her landlady. Either out of
kindness or forgetfulness a gas ring had been left in
her room. On this Caroline cooked her breakfast and
supper, and by this she warmed herself as she read
books borrowed from the public library. There was
not a great deal of cooking for her to do. A threepenny
tin of Woolworth's sardines was a treat only possible
twice a week. She lived perpetually short of food,
usually hungry, and almost always cold. But young
people, and particularly girls, can stand a lot of star-
vation. Indeed, during the period between the two
wars, a large part of our industrial machine would
certainly have come to a standstill had they lacked
this power.

After packing boots for five months, Caroline got a
job as salesgirl in a department store. Her pay was

now 27s. 6d. a week, and she imagined she had gained a step. It looked, at first sight, like sardines every night. But the store had an elaborate system of fines and deductions which took a shilling or two from most girls, most weeks. She was expected to pay 6d. a week to what was called a "Welfare Club," and another 6d. to a "Sports Club." She had to dress rather better in the store than in the factory, and was in the end, so far as money went, no better off.

In other ways she was worse off. She had a bullying shopwalker instead of a forewoman, and the girls in the store were much less friendly than the factory girls, who accepted every newcomer as an equal and an addition to the interest of life, disliking only those few who insisted on dislike.

The shopgirls, in contrast, were continually struggling to catch somebody's eye, to be promoted, to get themselves transferred to another department where there was said to be less work, or might be more commission, or to become engaged and get out of it altogether. A double struggle — against the world and against one's fellow strugglers — was more than Caroline at seventeen was yet prepared for. She left the store and, having taught herself typewriting and shorthand, found a job in an accountant's office.

From Northampton Caroline came to London, accepting formal reconciliation with her family on the way; that is to say, she was not to come home for holidays unless asked, but might write each week and say how she was getting on. They did not contribute to her support, but both sides were expected to give Christmas presents and to remember birthdays. From a typist at £2 a week, she had progressed to a secretary at £3 10s. From a secretary in a big advertising agency, she had managed to get herself transferred to the copywriting staff at £5, with the right to a fortnight's paid holiday a year.

And here at last Caroline was approaching her ambition — to live by her own writing. But at this point certain new problems had arisen for her, partly of life, and partly of her work. She had not, for example, imagined herself as using whatever talent as a writer she possessed to persuade mothers to bring their children up on what were euphemistically called "health" salts. And when she raised the question of whether this was really the best way to start the children off in life, it did not seem to her a sufficient answer to be told that the agency had a doctor of its own, who was willing to support the firm's advertisements with his fully qualified medical opinion.

When a car her firm had undertaken to sell proved unsatisfactory and wore out too fast, it did not seem to her that the best solution was to change the "appeal" of the advertisements, and start advertising its "long life."

She got tired of going round to see titled ladies, of-

fering them £50 a head to praise a brand of cigarette they disliked, or to be photographed in support
of a face cream they never used.

Caroline was as tough as most of her companions,
and had no wish to quarrel with a way of living to
which she had climbed so painfully, but she knew at
the back of her mind that she could not go on like
this for long. She had too definite a picture of herself, and too much respect for the calling of a writer,
to continue in that trade.

In the matter of her feelings Caroline had much
more than reached a turning point. She had come to a
full stop. For more than two years she had been engaged in a love affair with a married man, a musician
by the name of Hilary Skene. It was not quite the
first. Far back in her Northampton days Caroline had
a brief, confused, and almost meaningless love affair
with a grown-up boy in her department store. There
had been little attraction, and still less of love. Curiosity, and the fear of being afraid, which still governed many of her actions, had been the chief induce-
ments on her side. On his, a youth's ambitions to
begin his score. That had been all until two years ago,
at a party given by a friend, Caroline had met Hilary.

Hilary Skene was short and dark. He had rough,
bushy eyebrows. His eyes wore an offhand, humorous
stare. He was sensitive, amused, indulgent. He dressed
casually, but with care. He was friendly without be-

ing effusive, and his coolness had an effect of depth.
At first indeed he seemed to have every quality Caroline could want, and some advantages which she felt
that she particularly lacked. He had read a great
deal; he knew the names, and had seen some of the
works, of many painters. He was a good enough violinist to be sure of his place in a well-known symphony orchestra.

Caroline had met nobody like him, and for a time
he entirely carried her away. She lived, dreamed,
breathed in Hilary, killing time without interest between one meeting and the next.

Such intervals, whether for a few hours or a week
— they were never longer — were like the journey to
a point one longs to reach, not boring only because
of the knowledge that one has left, and will arrive.
So Caroline traveled through life in a doze of love,
which did not prevent her from doing her work and
seeing her friends, but refused more than passing
interest to anything which did not lead to Hilary.

And yet there was one great difference between
Caroline's and a full love affair. She could, and did,
give herself up entirely to the thought of him and her;
but in fact they had never more than the shortest
spells of time together — and this devoted life of the
imagination was lived by her alone. Hilary was married. He had never disguised the fact; indeed it was
his habit to make much of it, to treat it flamboyantly,

as though it made him doubly interesting, and his way of life twice as amusing, that there should be a wife and family in the background.

Caroline had never cared for this arrangement, but she accepted it. It had, as it were, been in the agreement from the beginning. What she was not prepared for was what had been happening to her in the last six months. This was nothing less than the gradual turning of her, by Hilary, into a kind of second wife, one who was on the spot for his convenience in town, as his real wife was for his convenience in the country. It had begun with Hilary's asking her to do odd jobs for him, which she might manage more conveniently from the office than he from the bed-sitting-room which was all he had in London. She typed letters for him, made telephone calls — not without some awkwardness as to why she should be speaking on his behalf. She met him at the station when he was going down to the country, and carried back to his room whatever he did not mean to take with him in the train.

After a while, Hilary became more exacting. At the start he had been grateful for any evening she could spare, and would rush from a rehearsal to spend half an hour with her at lunch. Now he was annoyed if she were not free at whatever time happened to suit him. If they could not meet with complete convenience, he preferred not to meet at all. He spoke vaguely of people he had to go and meet "on business" — though till now he had always told her the least detail of everything affecting his career.

She could not help noticing, too, that about money his attitude had altered. He failed to find half crowns in his pocket, where apparently they should have been, and allowed her to pay for taxis through their unexpected absence. His face would brighten when she said she was taking him to dinner, not he her; and that charming taste in presents, once freely shown, was now successfully held in check. It was Caroline who gave things to him.

She was, of course, perfectly well aware of what was happening, but Hilary had come so to overshadow her whole life that she could not face even the idea of being without him. The alternative, of knowingly sinking to become his slave, would require only to be stated for her to refuse with rage. Pride would in the end prove stronger than love or habit, but she could not yet risk letting them come into conflict.

And then the moment she was half waiting for had come. She saw Hilary — thick eyebrows, humorous offhand glance, rough tweeds, and casual but flattering attention — with the girl who had been their hostess at the party where she met him first. That one look told her all she needed, as one look continually does. When next she saw Hilary, she made a scene.

Caroline was not afraid of scenes. She told him he must choose between the two of them. Hilary immediately and gracefully chose her — and as he did so Caroline saw in a flash that this was not what she wanted. She was through. She had had two years of intelligence and charm, and if that was all charm and intelligence amounted to, she'd look elsewhere. Hilary was a musician without music in his soul; a philosopher not in search of truth; a lover unconsumed by passion. They had lived together for two years, and what had she done to him? In what imaginable way had his life been affected? He had caught a few late trains, and told a few extra lies. He had missed a single rehearsal for her, and they had enjoyed a number of meals and entertainments together. They had loved each other, and she felt, as she looked at him, as little affected by it as by the rain which fell on her last winter. It had happened. It was over. It did not matter any more. She would go to Portugal.

In spite of her department manager, who told her plainly that it was inconvenient — hinting also at possible gains if she worked through to the autumn without break — Caroline had insisted on taking her holiday when she wanted. She had excused herself from the various small parties, made up at the boarding-house or office, which were going off together to Scotland, Cornwall, or the Channel Islands, and were sure she would particularly enjoy being with them.

Pressed as to her plans, she replied that she was going to Portugal. Yes: she was going by herself. No: she knew no one in that country. She knew no one else who was going to be there at the same time. She knew no one who had ever been there. Had she made herself quite clear? She just happened to want to go to Portugal, and she just happened to want to go alone; thanks very much for asking all the same.

She had worked out the route in a travel agency, bought the ticket at a reduced rate through the firm, drawn out what money she had saved throughout the year — and here she was.

III

THE FIRST FREE MORNING

HAVING dressed slowly and carefully in the first and freshest of her holiday clothes, Caroline came down to breakfast and sat at the table which had been hers the evening before. The morning was brilliant, the room already hot. An agreeable problem lay before her among the rolls and coffee, a problem delightful to all who work in offices and factories, giving pleasure merely by the fact that it is set, apart from any thought of how it shall be solved, the problem of "what to do with today?" The problem required no attention. It simply lay before her among the cups and plates.

Though Caroline had not come down early, she had almost finished her meal before the window table, the best table in the room, began to fill. It had been empty the evening before. Families who tried to sit there had been driven away, and the table remained unoccupied all evening — a privilege for which the

Senhora would certainly not charge less than the full price. Even from the empty table Caroline had derived the feeling that the owners would not care: she imagined them as quite capable of ordering dinner in two hotels and not eating it in either. But now the owners of the best table were coming down and taking what was theirs. She ordered more coffee and sat back to look at them.

There were four altogether when their party seemed to be complete. They were all young, lively, and self-absorbed — so self-absorbed that Caroline thought it safe to watch and listen almost openly. They spoke English, though not so well as to prove it their own language.

Their talk was gossip. It was entirely concerned with people, and very few people at that. It was mildly malicious and noticeably snobbish. It had certain recurrent themes: the stupidity and commonness of the people on the beaches; the interest and importance of various people known to them and to the fashion magazines, people whom they had been seeing earlier in the year in Paris or London, or whom they would see later in the year in Cannes or Scotland. The family of one young man was referred to constantly, and the career — obviously in the future — of the other.

Caroline began to rough out in her mind an imagined existence for them all. A difficulty was that, though they seemed to be together, they did not fit into any common level of life; and if they just happened to be here by chance, how was it that they formed such a seemingly united group? Could one of them be so silly as he appeared? And if he was, did not the others notice it? Was one as conventional as she seemed, and if so how was she found amongst this free-and-easy party? To these and other questions Caroline sought answers in their conversation; but she was seeking them, it appeared, too openly, for after a few minutes something she could not catch was said, and then one of the party, a young man, got up and came over to her table. Caroline had a moment of horror that he was going to ask her not to listen with so much interest to their conversation. If he did, she knew quite well, there was no possible answer she could make. Instead, he introduced himself by the name of Paul Caird, and asked if Caroline would like to come and join them at their table.

"The Senhora told us last night that you were English. We would have asked you to come and have a drink with us, but it was too late. We think you had already gone to bed. I am English, too, you see, so naturally it is pleasant to be friendly. Are you by yourself? Yes. And you have not been here before? No. Well then, if you are staying in Marinha some time it is possible my friends and I can be of service to you. We shall all be most happy if we can. Bathing,

for example, is impossible here, unless you are provided with a bathing tent. So late in the season there
are no more to be hired. All these terrible people come
and hire them all. You will have seen all the terrible
people on the shore. Frightful! Unspeakable! So hor-
rid! They take all the tents. Fortunately we have a
large one, which we reserve from year to year."

He smiled at her in the most genial manner,
smoothed back his beautifully combed golden hair,
adjusted his scarf, and held out his hand. "You would
like to come and meet my friends," he said.

There were a number of things in this speech which
Caroline found surprising — apart from its length. She
had never been abroad before, but she had always
understood that the very last idea held by English
people who did go was that it was "pleasant to be
friendly." Even the fact that one was English was supposed to be shamefacedly concealed. This young man
had announced it in his first four sentences — in spite
of which he seemed only partly familiar with the language. He had most of the words, but flung them out
anyhow, for listeners to attach whatever meaning
they might fancy. "Frightful! Unspeakable! So hor-
rid!" And then the bathing tent. She was by no means
sure she would have found it impossible to bathe
without a tent, and there seemed something comic in
the claim to own a large one. However, she was grateful to anyone who knew the village and, perhaps, the

language, and she could see that in dealings with the
Senhora a block of four long-term residents might be
better allies than a nonexistent newspaper in London.

It was an oddly attractive group into which Paul
Caird now introduced her. Paul himself was a young
man made for display, with his fine gold hair waving
back from a smoothly sunburned forehead; with his
even, almost delicate features; with his scarlet-and-
yellow silk handkerchief, knotted with painstaking
carelessness inside a pale blue shirt. Though he was
obviously vain, there appeared to be a simplicity in
his vanity, a contented acceptance of himself which
was as good as charm.

Hélène Vorsich, to whom Paul introduced her first,
was a tall, imposing, fair-haired girl. She held out her
hand with a smile which continued after she had returned to the contemplation of her shapely sunburned
legs. She had the figure of a mannequin and a face
which gave, at first sight, a suggestion of classic
beauty, but failed, looked at more closely, to live up
to so much promise.

She had the broad forehead, even rounded brows,
shaped eyes, straight nose, and molded lips. It was a
face made for sculpture and the diadem. It was a face
that should have conveyed serenity simply by being
seen, but an absence of grandeur discounted the fine
elements. In the broad forehead was a furrow, not
burned there by feeling, incised by anxiety from

within, the anxiety of trifles. The mouth was too narrow; its down-turned corners gave an air of petulance. Such serenity as remained was hard to distinguish from complacency.

To the second of the two girls Caroline was about to speak, but found she was being introduced instead to the other young man. He was dark — dark-haired, brown-skinned, black-eyed — with a sleek international air, but a friendly smile in spite of it. He was wearing a dark blue shirt, a well-cut coat of a biscuit color, and perfectly creased white flannels. He had the kind of elegance that made his well-cut clothes inevitable, as if he had grown up inside them, but invested with an air of extra smartness anything old or untidy — such as the battered soft hat hooked onto his chair — which he cared to use. His name was given her as Maxim Darré, and "He comes of an exceedingly good French family," explained Paul in a quite audible voice as soon as the conversation became general. "He is spending a month with us before joining his parents in Biarritz."

"Joining his parents," Caroline thought, as she watched and listened, might give the key to Maxim. It would serve to account for his movements during life, and could be used later on as an obituary. He had the rather tamed air which many well-born young Frenchmen wear. They know the world. They amuse themselves about in it. But behind them looms always the shadow of the family, and, at the first tug on the string, back to those arms they fly. There was a friendly desire to please in his face and manner, but something deeply conventional as well. Caroline felt she was being accepted — but only because certain accidents of manner and appearance, some born with her, but more which she had knowingly put on, brought her within his idea of what a girl should be with whom a young Frenchman of good family could sit over a breakfast table by the shores of the Atlantic.

Talking easily about her journey, about the people she had met on the boat, about the lack of any reason for her coming here — giving what was expected in return for what she could pick up — Caroline surveyed the fourth member of the party. She watched her the most closely and she liked her best. "And this is Bettina," said after she had shaken hands with his other friends, seemed to be all the introduction Paul thought necessary. Bettina was clearly of different social standing from the others, and it appeared that this fact — to them at any rate — was important. It did not exclude her, but it set her slightly on one side. It came out too that she was not staying at the pension, but living in the town.

Bettina was small, with a girl's figure, but the hands and feet of a big boy. She had soft gold hair cut short, eyes of a cornflower blue, and a wide but shallow forehead — "a brain one way and not the other," Caroline considered. Over and about her hung an unmistakable air of sensuality. It was in her lolling attitude, legs crossed, hands in pocket, ankle swung. It was in the common scent she used, chosen obviously for its commonness. It was in her mouth, which was small but extremely mobile. The mold of its curves was continually changing. In repose, which they seldom were, her lips were always just apart, as though giving access to her mouth, as though revealing just more than they should. She had the air of knowing that they did, and meaning them to go on doing so. A light down covered her upper lip. It was a disfigurement. So was the mole near the corner of her mouth, out of which grew three or four conspicuous white hairs. They were a disfigurement, but she wore them like a banner: "Why should I bother over a little thing like that?" Her whole appearance and attitude were lightened by a kind of mockery: "Yes. Here I am. Exactly as you see me. More so, if anything." . . . She was like an immoral novel saved from being tedious by its wit.

Her dress showed the same blend of humor with palpable seduction. She wore close-fitting white shorts, a soft white frilly shirt — which, loose and frilly as it was, did little to hide her two small breasts — white socks, sandals, and a beret. The sandals looked expensive. Beret and socks could have come from a market stall. It was clear that she collected her wardrobe as and where she fancied. She would have no meanness about what was costly, and no prejudice against what was cheap. She dangled smoked glasses from a finger, and a portfolio of drawings leaned against her chair.

"Have you been here long?" Caroline asked, realizing suddenly that the others had stopped talking, and she was still looking at Bettina. Bettina civilly sat up and turned towards her to reply, but while she was preparing another stepped down before her.

"Paul is English," began Hélène, in a dry practical voice. "He is from the University of Oxford, from the College of St. John's. He is here for his vacation. He has been in Portugal one month. We stay at Marinha four weeks. Then we travel to Coimbra. Of course Paul has come to Portugal many times before. He speaks Portuguese."

"Really," said Caroline, looking at Paul with interest. "That must make it much more amusing for you all."

"And French, and Spanish, and Italian, and German," Paul announced. "Give me some more coffee, please, Hélène. And tell the waiter to bring us some fresh rolls. These were made yesterday. They are frightful. Abominable. Beastly. I can't think how the Senhora put them out."

"Not German, Paul dear," said Bettina. "Say Eskimo or Babylonian, if you like. None of us will know. But

[36]

not German, do not say you can speak German. Not when I am here."

"Paul speaks any language," declared Hélène, helping him to coffee.

"And he speaks them all equally well," Bettina answered smiling.

"And you?" asked Caroline, sharing the point of the last remark with Bettina, but speaking to Hélène. "Do you speak all languages as well as one another?"

"Hélène lives in Paris," answered Paul for her. "She is a dress designer. Wonderful, most beautiful clothes she designs. Very good. You will see. You will adore them. She is a great success." Hélène smiled complacently down at her sunburned legs. "She is really wonderful," Paul repeated; "you will be delighted." He took a lump of sugar and put it in his mouth. "She has made clothes for the ballet," he said. "She could have been a stage designer — or an artist."

"Were you always in Paris?" Caroline asked.

"No, I come from the Savoy," Hélène replied. "I am in Paris for three years. Paul and I met last year. We come here this year for our holiday. Paul came to Paris to fetch me, and we drove down here by car." They smiled at each other. "We met many of our friends, some very well-known people, on the way."

"And now you are going to ask me to give evidence," suggested Maxim. He spoke charmingly, recognized every social situation so easily that Caroline hoped for a moment he was going to be amusing. All he said, however, was: "I am French. My family live in the Dordogne. They have a business in Lille, and in a year or two I will have to go into the business. Till then I travel and amuse myself — as I am doing now."

"What . . . ?" began Caroline. She was going to ask what the business was, but stopped herself, seeming to have heard somewhere that French people do not ask each other what work they do, but wait till they are told.

"What sort of business?" broke in Bettina. "Maxim's family make knives and forks, don't they, Maxim? Maxim need never be without a knife or fork. It is a great comfort to him — to us all on his behalf. Well, sometimes we think they make spoons as well. At least they have made one spoon, a very charming little silver spoon for Maxim. He has it with him now. If you look closely, you will be sure to see it."

"And Bettina," said Maxim, leaning forward as if to flick her in return. Then he paused. He knew so well what each occasion required, lacked only the ability to produce the phrase he needed: he was like a general who knows all the moves, and has none of the resources. He fell back on a simple statement. "Bettina is an artist," he said. "She comes from Germany and lives in Paris. That is where she met Hélène. Bettina is a friend of Hélène — and of us all. That is, if I can call us friends," he ended rather lamely.

"No," said Bettina promptly, and left the word lying before them for a moment, so that they could apply it in any way they pleased. "No, I am not an artist. Picasso is an artist. I make drawings."

"An artist *is* a person who makes drawings," said Paul, a little crossly, either resenting a distinction he found hard to follow, or disliking having to think what someone meant when on his holiday.

"No," answered Bettina. "An artist is a person who lives for art. It can be bad art, but, such as it is, it is his life. Art is not my life. Leo is an artist. Art is Leo's life. He lives for poetry."

Maxim turned to her. "Leo is a friend of ours." He caught Hélène's eye. "Leo is somebody we know. He lives in Marinha. He is a young German exile who writes poetry."

"Leo lives for a good many other things besides poetry," said Paul.

"Not at all," Bettina declared. "Everything for which Leo lives becomes poetry for him."

"And Robert?" demanded Hélène. She pronounced the name in the Continental way, emphasizing the first syllable. "Is Robert an artist because he lives for Leo?"

Bettina turned to Caroline. "What do *you* think an artist is?" she asked.

"An artist is a person who does something so well that it gives pleasure to others to see or hear him doing it. You can be an artist in eating *foie gras,* if you like."

"Then Paul is our best artist," declared Bettina. "Paul is an artist in hair combing, an artist in scarf tying, and an artist in shirt choosing."

"Bettina also is an artist in shirt choosing," remarked Caroline at the frilly blouse.

"That is not artistry," said Bettina. "That is the exposition of the obvious."

Paul was becoming restless. The fact that the conversation was often concerned with him did not compensate for his finding it rather difficult to follow. His restlessness quickly reached Hélène.

"We should go down to the shore and bathe," she said, in the tone of a mother whose children's convenience comes first.

"Yes," said Paul, getting to his feet. "Soon. Before all the people come. Later in the morning," he told Caroline, "the shore becomes horrible. Unbearable. *Foul!* So many people. Such frightful people. You cannot imagine." He spoke with extreme emphasis, but his look bore no relation to his words. He was at the moment turning over chocolates with his finger to find one he had not yet bitten into.

They all got up. Bettina more slowly than the rest.

"What about Quinta?" Maxim asked. "Do you not

want to wait for him? If you like I will wait here with you."

"Oh no," said Bettina, uncrossing her legs and reaching for her sketches. "Quinta will find his way all right. He will guess which way we have gone. Quinta is sure to follow."

As the two of them walked down to the shore behind the others, Caroline observed Bettina with delight. There was scarcely a man who failed to turn and stare at her, shopkeepers, fishermen, the postman, the few elegants — all alike. All became men at sight of her. All felt themselves entitled, catching her personality at a glance, to a prolonged and greedy stare. And, if their eyes met one another's, a half-smile passed between them. At her passing, social distinctions were abolished. Fisherman smiled at fisherman. But shopkeeper smiled at fisherman too. Even a government official would share a glance of amused recognition with a passer-by.

Bettina was perfectly aware of the effect she had, and perfectly unmoved. Wrapped in her own kind of *savoir-faire* — not quite the brazenness of the whore, nor yet the imperviousness of good breeding — aware of herself and of other people, contented and quite unconcerned, she strode on a plane of her own between the two.

IV

MORNING IN THE WATER

THE first day slipped easily past. Caroline was not so much accepted as absorbed into the party. She spent the morning bathing from their tent. She went for a drive with them in the evening in Paul's car. At their insistence the Senhora found — apparently without difficulty — a much better room into which her things were moved by the delighted waiter, who seemed to feel personally responsible for Caroline's enjoyment of her holiday. She was lent a scarf by Hélène, which she rightly considered a surprising mark of favor, and she met Bettina's Senhor Quinta.

Quinta proved to be a Portuguese businessman. Whatever Caroline had expected of the man who was "sure to follow" Bettina, it was certainly not this. He was neither rich nor old, not young, nor gay, nor handsome. He was short, baldish, middle-aged, a salesman of agricultural machinery in a country where a barge of melons is unloaded by fourteen men walking all day in an endless circle between barge and quay, carrying each a single melon. It was true that he was not needy, not without influence, and "sure to follow." He had apparently been following all summer. The quest, Caroline thought, was not unrewarded, but it could scarcely be sheer enjoyment, all the same. He had a wistful sentimental air, and Bettina did not look like a person with a high tolerance of bores.

On the second morning of Caroline's stay, at about eleven o'clock, following what was clearly the holiday routine, Paul got up from the breakfast table and led his party of five down to the "large" tent. The girls undressed first, and then lay on the sand in their bathing dresses while they waited for the men. Caroline had a dark blue and white bathing dress. It was very plain, and she had had to borrow £4 to pay for it. She was glad she had. Hélène admired it with a professional eye, and the men by looking twice at her as she lay on their rug.

Hélène was magnificent inside a green and red beach suit in which it would be impossible to enter the water. She lolled in it on the beach like a goddess on Olympus. She looked like Hera at the moment when, inflamed by the coming of Aphrodite, Zeus regarded her and reflected that the desire now possessing him was greater than he had ever felt, either as a shower of gold, in disguise as a mortal seducer, or even for

[43]

that reluctant maiden whom he had been obliged to transform into a cow.

Bettina, Caroline thought, did not look well in a bathing dress. Her frame was too slight for her hands and feet. Her long stride was awkward, and she had no shoulders. It was clear that her odd costume of every day was more carefully thought out than first appeared. Caroline, rolling over onto the warm sand, knew just what Bettina would wear in Paris. A tight-fitting dark skirt, or kilt, another of her frilly blouses, flat-heeled shoes, and a blue or scarlet beret. She had another thought — that Bettina probably looked much better dressed than she did naked.

Bathing, for the party to which Caroline was now attached, had nothing to do with swimming. It meant lying on rugs and towels until the Lisbon shop people began to fill the beach, commenting scorn-fully on their manners and costumes, then down for a scamper along the water's edge, a lot of shouting and laughter to show superiority to the public, and back to their tent to change. Maxim, who wore a bathing suit embroidered with a scarlet dolphin and the name of a smart Riviera swimming club, would make half a dozen tentative strokes. Paul splashed along the seaweed like a child. Hélène and Bettina seldom wet so much as their feet and ankles.

To Caroline, brought up with an older brother, with the shades of an English High School round her

shoulders, this did not seem the right way to behave
— particularly in a foreign place, and for someone who
took so much pride in being British as did Paul.

Caroline's schooling had stopped early, at the
period where one Englishman is equal to five of any
other nation. Even if she did not literally accept this
now, she certainly recognized it as the duty of all
English people to show themselves superior, to give a
lead to every Continental, in matters of sport or daring. She was slightly but definitely ashamed of Paul
for so little upholding national prestige. She intended
to make up for it in person. Without noticing the
shouts of the others, she ran down to the sea, took a
plunge through the biggest wave that came, and
struck out for a raft with diving boards floating some
quarter mile out from shore.

To her surprise the water was extremely cold. At
Marinha the full weight and depth of the Atlantic
drives sheer up against a wall of sand as steep-to as
a roof. It is the only considerable bay in fifty miles of
rock-bound coast. No stretch of golden sand here
warms the waves as they lap softly in. The tide has
the normal rise and fall of the Atlantic, but at top-
most flow the water comes a bare twenty yards
farther up the shore than it does at lowest ebb. The
fish caught half-a-mile to sea are not the flounderers
and skulkers of the coasts, but the bold-swimming
and cruising fish of the high seas.

The water struck chill. It was rougher than it had looked. Caroline soon saw that she could not play her way óut to the raft. She settled down to swim. She swam as strongly as she could for several minutes, then looked up, expecting to see the raft floating almost to her hand. It was not at hand at all. It was a good hundred yards away. It was more — it was a hundred and fifty yards away. Caroline turned on her back, drew up her legs, and looked towards the shore. The shore was now a good deal farther than the raft. It was easier, she saw, to go on, and, as she rolled over in the water and struck out again, she began to issue orders to herself: "Take it easy, now. Don't hurry. Keep a good long stroke. Kick out with your legs. It isn't far. You've swum much farther at school. Don't get excited. A hundred good long strokes — and you'll be there."

Forty strokes, fifty, seventy: Caroline was getting tired. Her arms were growing heavier. Her breath grew short, and when, in gasping for air, she drew in a mouthful of sea water, it cost her another effort not to choke. She kept on for the hundred strokes, finished them, tiring fast, added ten more — and looked up.

Yes, the raft was closer now. It bobbed there in the sunlight, no more than forty yards away. She would make it, Caroline could see, but without anything to spare. As to how she would get back to land she refused to think. Not much could happen to her on a raft in any case. The thing now was to reach it. All this time Caroline was swimming, not strongly, feebly, but progressing, her eyes on the spot she had to reach. She had sunk from a side stroke to a quiet breast stroke, unable any more to lift her arms out of the water. Twenty more strokes, and she'd be safe.

But now at this moment as she watched and swam, something unexpected, something impossible, was happening. The raft, the whole structure, was tipped madly down towards her. The top, the diving boards, came swooping forward, as if the whole thing were being caught up from below and overset. She could see the matting where one stood to dive. She could see the only person on the raft, a man, clinging close round the central pole to hold himself on. She looked straight down onto the top of his gold head, as if she were a bird. She imagined she did not know what. Something — a gigantic fish, a submarine — was rising from the bottom, coming up immediately below the raft, turning it over in the sea. Now it was going to sink. The raft she was swimming to was going to sink.

And then, almost within the second, everything reversed. The raft was flung violently back away from her. The top dipped over and swung off, like one of those toys with weighted bases. The boatlike belly of the thing, the seaweed-covered keel, was jerked fiercely up towards and at her, exposed as it had never been since it was made and launched. Caroline saw, she heard, the working of the great chain which locked it down fast to the sea bed . . . and at this she realized what was happening.

A succession of heavy rollers, the wake perhaps of a liner passing four miles out, had come sounding down at speed upon the shore. The coast was straight. The bay of Marinha was unprotected: here were no long stone quays or harbor works, no far-protecting arms thrust out to break the inrush of the seas. The happenings of the ocean could continue unchecked up to the very beach of Marinha, and they would continue unchecked right over her.

As the first wave began to swell beneath her, Caroline struck out. She was swung straight up onto the crest. She enjoyed a moment's relief, to find herself above it and not underneath, and then the backwash took her. Down the long slide of the wave's back she was dragged, no more able to move than if her arms were tied; unable even to raise her face out of the boil of waters.

A second time, and this time in despair, she was flung high up on a crest. The strength left to her was no use against such force as this. Shaking her hair and the salt out of her eyes, she took a last look round. The raft, bowing its head furiously at her, was no more than fifteen yards away. Around the central pole the same almost naked man was clinging still.

Across the breaker their eyes met. Caroline could not cry out. She could not speak or move. Down, down the full length of a waterfall she was being dragged once more with buried face. She was afloat, but had ceased to struggle. Down into the trough; then up again. And there on the peak, as she hung between two worlds, she saw that the raft was empty. The man, she imagined, had been swept away.

"Hold to the rope," a voice was saying in her ear. "Hold the rope tight. I could be able to climb up and pull you too. Do not let go. That is the last of the big waves. I pull you: you come up out of the water. So!"

"His name," said Paul, choosing the half-dozen largest prawns out of the dish and passing the rest across the table to Hélène, "is Robert Kranz." He pronounced Robert in the German way, with the first syllable strong as if in "rowboat." "He comes, I think, from Hamburg. He is a doctor. He left Germany three years ago because of the Nazis. He has been living in Marinha for six months. Before that he was for a year in Paris."

"Does he live by himself?" asked Caroline, making the question as casual as she could.

"No." There was a pause. "He lives with Leo."

"Oh, yes. And Leo is your friend?"

"Well, yes. That is so. Leo is our friend."

Again there was a pause. It was not so much that

[49]

the four exchanged glances at the name of Leo, but that she felt them deliberately refrain from doing so. They ate determinedly into the prawns, sardines, and olives, and did not look up.

Well, thought Caroline, I can fail to notice an atmosphere as well as anyone.

"What does Leo do?" she asked.

"He is a poet." It was Bettina speaking. "He is a very good poet, and a very unusual person. He is German, too, like Robert — but he comes from the south, from Franconia. He left Germany to avoid military service; and Robert left because Leo did. You will go to see them?" she inquired.

"I have been asked to," Caroline answered. Then, thinking her words did not show warmth enough, she added quickly: "And of course I want to go."

"Leo is away now," said Bettina, who seemed to know more about the affairs of the household than the rest. "But it is possible he may be coming back this evening. He has told certain people that he would, but with Leo it is never sure. Anyway, Robert will be glad to see you. You know where they live?"

"4, Rua dos Pescadores."

"Yes," said Bettina. "You should go and see them. You will be interested, and it will be a pleasure for Robert."

"Are you really going?" Paul inquired, laying

down the carcass of a prawn. "Then tell Robert . . ."
There was a pause.

"Tell Robert," put in Maxim, "that we are all very
grateful to him for having saved you from the sea."

Caroline smiled her thanks, but she would have
preferred to hear Paul finish his sentence. As he began
to speak Hélène had looked across at him, and a faint
shadow of alarm, the only feeling besides self-satisfaction which her face had so far shown, had passed
across it. Paul must have seen it too. It was no doubt
that which persuaded him to let Maxim finish his
sentence.

They had been eating their hors d'œuvres in the
lounge. At a sign from Hélène they rose to go into
the dining room. Maxim, having opened the door,
hung back a moment to come in by Caroline's side.

"We are all grateful," he said to her alone, "but I
am most particularly grateful."

Caroline smiled politely. She liked the compliment
better in its original form.

V

MEETING WITH A RESCUER

IT was dark when Caroline came down the steps of her hotel and turned along the edge of the bay to find the Rua dos Pescadores. It would be farther than she expected, Bettina had warned her, and she would pass three brightly lit fishermen's cafés on the way.

As Caroline walked along — rather fast to escape being spoken to, but cautiously to avoid the many figures rolled in cloaks or rags which lay against the whitewashed walls of the small houses — she was, as often, talking to herself. She was talking about the meeting that was going to take place. She was belittling it to herself beforehand.

By many of her friends the tone of Caroline's mind was described as cynical. She was "cynical" to the office when she criticized the claims her firm was so willing to make on behalf of any sufficiently wealthy patent medicine. She had been "cynical" to Hilary when she doubted whether there could be point in continuing an affair by which he obviously set so little store. Her father found her "cynical" when she decided to spend Christmas alone in London, rather than write and ask if she might be permitted to come home. She had been "cynical" for preferring Portugal on her own to going off with a crowd of friends to Jersey.

The truth was that Caroline possessed, as she had already learned, a sanguine and romantic temperament. It was backed by a readiness to recognize — and sometimes to accept — the consequences of her own acts, and held in check by a deliberate skepticism, the product of a mind already rational though not always cool, liable to lapses, baseless prejudices, exaggerated loyalties, but accustomed at least to studying the motives on which other people act, and to examining with some degree of impartiality into her own. Past self-deceptions had taught her the need to prepare her own attitude of mind towards occasions which she found in any way exciting or unusual: if it is impossible altogether to avoid being taken in by others, at least one should not be taken in by oneself.

She had been pulled out of the sea and saved from drowning by a man, young, unknown, and possessing — she seemed to remember from a short conversation on the beach after her recovery — a strong, though odd, attraction.

The young man was known, and his history was familiar, to the four people who had happened to befriend her. They regarded him, for some reason, with hostility, or at least suspicion. Their suspicion was in inverse ratio to her own liking for them and her respect for their powers of judgment. Bettina, that is, the one of the party she liked best and thought likeliest to form a sound opinion, was the most friendly to him. She seemed to be still on terms of intimacy and to know what was happening in the house. Maxim appeared to be neutral. Paul and Hélène, she thought, shared a common hostility, though they did not, it seemed, share it equally. Hélène had checked Paul when he was about to give her a message of some kind for Robert.

It would be in keeping with Paul's good-natured indolence to be casual in hostility, as in friendship. Hélène, Caroline considered, would be far more capable of a maintained and acted-out dislike. It was therefore probably Hélène who was keeping Paul up to the mark in the present quarrel, whatever it might be, and preventing his lapsing into easy relations, which on his own he would naturally have done.

As for her own feelings about Robert, there were many things pulling in his direction. Not only had he saved her life, he appeared himself under an interesting and romantic guise — the exile for friendship's sake. So far as she had heard, it had been open to him to remain in Germany. He had left his home for Leo. Then, they had met in a strange country, with all the freedom and interest that meant for her. Caroline had come here precisely in order to get away from the people and events of every day; eager for change, eager for new ideas, new experiences, new human contacts — anything that would help her to solve, or to escape, the problems she had left behind.

When she heard the others speaking dubiously, showing, as she thought, a critical attitude towards her rescuer, she felt inside herself the strongest impulse to come out openly on his behalf. Already she believed that she knew Robert better than they did. She felt committed to his side in whatever struggle or opposition might be going on.

It was to counteract the effect of all these feelings, which together exercised such a pull over her fancy, that Caroline had set herself as she walked along the shore.

"You know nothing at all about him, Caroline," she began. "He pulled you out of the water, and that's all. Anyone might do that. Almost anyone would have done it. He didn't risk anything, or not much. There you were, washing about like a dead fish, and he just pulled you in. He hardly had to leave the raft to do it. You'd have done the same for him, and even if he

[55]

had saved your life by risking his, that still doesn't make him any different as a person. He may be boring. Like most foreigners, he's probably conceited. All that about being anti-Nazi sounds very well, but by now it has come to mean less than nothing. Anyone who leaves Germany for *any* reason naturally gives out abroad that he left because he's anti-Nazi. It's the obvious way to sympathy. The whole population of Germany, outside their own country, would be anti-Nazi, whatever they might be at home. . . . He's a doctor? Well, what does that mean? It may mean anything. Coming from Germany it may mean nothing. They have doctors of everything over there — doctors of literature, doctors of engineering; doctors of advertising, for all I know. So what does it add up to, taking in all you know? Nothing. Nothing either way. Nothing *against* him, of course; but next to nothing in his favor either. . . . Be friendly when you get there. Be grateful. Try to make it a pleasant evening. Hope to enjoy yourself, if you like — but nothing more. Above all, Caroline, indulge no foolish notions." And, having found a phrase which pleased and amused her, Caroline said it over and over to herself, as, having passed the third brightly lit café, she began to search about for the Rua dos Pescadores. "Indulge no foolish notions, Caroline, my dear. Indulge no foolish notions. . . ."

It was a narrow street, with houses whitewashed

and flat-roofed like the houses of Morocco. A naked electric bulb, stark on an iron arm, showed the street's winding course but not the flaws and holes in its broken surface. The evening was warm. Many doors were open. Caroline glanced inside each one as she passed.

In one a barefoot woman, with skirts in geological layers and headdress like a funeral horse, was washing clothes. Two small children, naked below the waist, slept upon stools, their sideways heads laid flat upon the table as for execution. Through the slow air dazed bluebottles flew heavily, occasionally striking walls or lamp, and falling stunned.

In another, which appeared to contain no furniture of any sort and to be floored with six inches of powdery sand, four heaps of rags — which Caroline had learned to recognize as old women — squatted around a perforated biscuit tin, in which half a dozen fir cones smoldered. Laid over the fir cones a few sardines were blackening slowly into a meal.

Caroline had reached the end of the street without finding number 4. There was 1, 2, 3, and there were higher numbers, but there was no 4. She hammered on number 3, and, when an upstairs face leaned out almost on a level with her own, she said the name "Senhor Robert Kranz?" making as much of a question of it as she could.

The man pointed through a gate, facing the end

of the street, leading into what seemed to be either a farmyard or a garage, and made signs that she should go through. Then he pointed to the left, and made signs that she should go up. Caroline thanked him and went through the gate. On her left a small flight of open steps led up onto a low veranda, the roof apparently of a downstairs room to which no upstairs had been built.

With her foot on the lowest step, she hesitated for no reason. A shaft of light shone out suddenly and touched her as she stood there in the dark. She looked along the shaft. It was the beam from a paraffin lamp, and it led into a tiny outhouse on the far side of the yard. The lamp stood on a table. At the table a shrunken boy of about ten was folding sweets into bright yellow papers. The table where he sat was half covered with the sweets he had folded. The other half held an immense pile, upon which his work had scarcely made an inroad.

Caroline ran up the steps and knocked on a rough door divided into two halves as if giving entrance to a stable. There were sounds inside. The door did not open, but a rather troubled, sunburned face peered round the upper half. Caroline pushed her own face forward into the light.

"Ah, it is you," said a relieved voice. "Please to come inside."

Robert led Caroline into a low room, whitewashed,

with boarded floor. A table, some chairs, a bookcase of planks, and a chest of drawers were ranged down the right side of the room. On the left was a large recess. A slab of stone, supported on bricks to some three feet from the ground, made a table on which were a couple of paraffin stoves and a portable tin oven. Outside and above, running the whole length of the recess, was a single shelf, acting as larder, mantelpiece, and sideboard. At the point where the recess ended, a flight of wooden steps ran down into the darkness.

There were several books open face downwards about the room, some piles of unwashed dishes around the stove, a bowl of dead flowers on the mantelpiece.

"Please to sit down," said Robert, dusting a chair for her with his beret. He appeared pleased to see her, but had evidently made no special preparation. "I am afraid we are not very tidy. But Leo, he do all the tidying, and Leo is away. Leo will be sorry he is not here when you have come."

Caroline sat down. She had ceased to feel shy or embarrassed as soon as she came into the room, for Robert was obviously so much shyer than herself. His shyness took the form of thinking the room untidy, as indeed it was. He moved about it, flipping things with his beret, chivvying the dust off one onto another. He pushed a number of dishes out of sight, and threw the dead flowers down the stairs into the darkness.

"It feels nice in here," said Caroline, settling into the dusted chair. "Have you lived here long?"

"Leo and I, we have been here two months. We come here from a house farther down the road. We come because we have great trouble about a cock."

"A cock?"

"Yes. That is right, is it not? The masculine of hen. He sing all morning, from very early, from when it is first day. The cock belong to one of the fishermen. Leo and I, we think it could be that we buy the cock. We ask the fisherman. He say 'fifty escudos'! We say 'five escudos.' We wish to buy him, of course, to twist the neck. The fisherman will not sell. He continue to ask fifty escudos for a cock worth ten escudos. So we move. We come here. But here it is no better. Here is still noise every morning."

Robert's face went quite dark as he talked of the troubles he and Leo suffered.

"But what's wrong here? It seems to me the quietest place I was ever in."

"In the mornings," said Robert, "is terrible distraction. For myself I do not mind, but for Leo it is too much. The other morning there is talking of fishermen in the yard outside. It continue till two o'clock. We shout at them, but they go on. At three o'clock the man come and see to his horses down below." He

pointed down the stairway. "That is a stable. We say
to him: 'Go away. Can you not see to your horses some
other time?' He make no answer. At four o'clock the
fishermen all come out of the houses and go down to
the boats. At seven the man come again to fetch his
horses. Then we sleep until two in the afternoon."

"Couldn't you live the other way round?" suggested
Caroline. "Sleep in the day and talk all night."

"But Leo like the fishing beach," said Robert. "We
go there to watch the fishermen. Sometimes we stay
there the whole day watching. You will see. When
you go there, you will understand."

"Do you speak Portuguese?"

"I a little only, but Leo speak very well." His face
went dark again. "It is a pity Leo is not here to see
you. He is going off last Wednesday on the bus to
Estoril. There is so much noise — he cannot sleep.
Here is no one for him to talk to. He need a change,
so he go to Estoril."

As he talked, Robert had got up and begun to
prepare coffee. He talked in an urgent, explosive way,
as if, once started on any subject, he could talk for
days. Only he seemed to be afraid that he would
bore his guest, and to suppose that, because she was
a woman, no subject could interest her for more than
half a dozen sentences.

Caroline picked up a book that was lying on the
table. It was written in German, filled with diagrams,

and illustrated with numbers of photographs and drawings of human eyes — full face, side view, in cross-section, plain and colored. Penciled notes were written against many.

"You are looking at my book? That is because I am a doctor. They tell you I am a doctor? They tell you all about me at the hotel where you stay? They are friends of yours? You like them? You like Paul — and what is the other one's name — Maxim?"

"Yes," said Caroline, wishing to smooth down his easily aroused suspicions. "They told me that you were a doctor, and that you are German. They say that you do some work among the people here, but you cannot do much because the Portuguese doctors are afraid you will take away their trade. So you only look after the ones who cannot pay."

"They tell you about Leo, too. What do they say? What do they say of him?"

"They told me that he is a poet, and left Germany so as not to be a soldier. They say you left the country so as to be with him."

"Is that all? Do they not tell you more? Do they not say unpleasant things about him or me? Do they not say we have quarreled with them? What else do they say? Are they perhaps friends of yours?"

"No," said Caroline gently. "They aren't my friends. They have been very kind to me. I don't know any of them well. I like Bettina."

"Bettina is a friend of ours," declared Robert de-cidedly, as though the world were divided into camps, and she at least was in the right one. "Maxim is not anything. He cannot be a friend of anyone, or not a friend, because he is not anything himself; so we say no more about Maxim. About Paul I do not speak, because I do not feel good towards him."

"And Hélène?"

"Hélène is like Maxim. She is a nothing. She is a woman-nothing, like Maxim is a man-nothing. But they say that she is good for Paul. It could be. That is Paul's first love affair with a woman. Perhaps it is this which is good for him, and not Hélène."

"I'm not sure that Hélène is nothing," Caroline re-marked, passing over Robert's odd description of the relationship, which she put down to his imperfect English. "One may not like her, but I don't think she is just nothing. At any rate she's beautiful."

"A woman cannot be beautiful unless she has a face. Hélène is not a person, so she cannot have a face. Just a front part to her head. . . . Yes, I see what you are thinking," went on Robert, after a second's pause. "I see. You are wondering if you have a face yourself. You are a woman, so you start soon to think about yourself — not about the idea, and not about other people. About yourself."

"Yes," said Caroline. "I *was* thinking about my face."

For a second Robert lost his worried look and smiled quite naturally at her, quite naturally and kindly. There appeared, beneath the worry and suspicion, to be a warm nature, not averse to pleasure or amusement. "Well then," he said, "you *have* a face. You know very well you have a face. You know just what it is like. There is a face there, and there is somebody behind. It is a face, at first sight, like a pretty doll. That is how you look when I see you in the water with your hair all floating out. But you are not a pretty doll. Not at all. You have a face like that because it is useful to you. You made your face like that to suit your purposes. Is it true what I am saying?"

Caroline considered. In face of his suspicion and reserve she felt the need for openness. She wanted to tell the truth — even about trifles, even against herself. "Yes. I suppose it is. I did make my own face in a kind of way."

"And you made many other things about yourself as well — your manners, your way of speaking, this . . . this *smart* look you have. It is not part of you, like it is part of Hélène. It isn't *part* of Hélène at all. It's all of her there is. But with you it isn't even part. It's just something you learned. Something you taught yourself. Didn't you teach yourself all this?"

"Yes." It gave Caroline a positive sense of luxury to give herself away.

"Why did you teach yourself these things?"

"Because when I ran away from home I had to make myself into someone. So I made myself into the person that seemed to me most likely to get on."

"And you *have* got on since you ran away? Yes? You are successful? But underneath you are somebody quite different."

"What I am underneath is just what I don't know. I came here partly to find out."

"Well, you will not find out from Paul and Maxim and Hélène. . . . I am afraid the coffee is not very good," he went on suddenly; "that is because the ants are got into it."

"Ants?"

"Yes. We have here in this house many ants. They get into all our things. We eat, both of us, many ants a day. We wear ants in all our clothes. Now you have one or two ants to drink. We think it is on account of the stables. Look!"

He pointed to the floor. It was true enough. Across the boards were marching, not a handful, but a whole long column, a division or army corps, of ants, in extended battle order. They came up out of the wall on the far side of the room, passed along its whole length in an endless chain, paused at a point almost beneath the further wall where the darkness of the ant column swelled out into a pool, and then marched back again — a double line, perpetually coming and going within

[65]

a few inches of each other, without contact or inter-
ference.

"That is because Leo drop the honey," Robert explained. "They come to carry it away."

"But can't you stop them?"

"No. We do not wish to prevent them. Soon the
honey will be gone, and the ants will walk somewhere
else. What? You are already wishing to go. It is early.
Midnight is nothing here. I will be reading several
hours before I go to sleep. I have liked your coming.
You will come again. I am so sorry Leo is not here. It
would have been much nicer for you if Leo had been
here. You would have enjoyed it much more if only
he was here. And Leo — he will be very cross he did
not see you. He will be cross with me that you came
when he is not here. Walk quickly home. There is a
moon. You will be quite all right. The fishermen will
not speak to you. I must remain here in case Leo will
come back. . . . Otherwise I walk back with you.
Leo will be so sorry to have missed you. You must
come again. Good-by."

He opened the two halves of his door and bowed
her out, smiling at her, but glancing rapidly into the
darkness too. Before she was down the stairs, Caroline
could hear the bolts rattle back into position.

VI

ON THE FISHING BEACH

CAROLINE made an excuse the next morning to avoid the regular beach parade. Paul was preparing to look surprised at her defection, but Hélène intervened.

"Caroline must do what she wants," she said. "After all, she has only two weeks' holiday."

"Perhaps we should allow our guest to be drowned only once each week," put in Bettina, adding quietly to Caroline, "I should go along to the other beach if I were you — the beach of the fishermen." It was exactly what Caroline meant to do, and she was prepared to believe that Bettina knew her intention, and recognized the cause. Even Hélène, it seemed, had some of that woman's *esprit de corps* which consists in apprehending the vaguest, most distant suspicion of a love affair, and doing whatever can easily be done to urge it on.

The beach of Marinha, like the future life, is

divided into two distinct regions, and between them, though almost adjoining, is little communication. The holiday makers, with their rugs, novels, colored umbrellas, tents, rubber mattresses, and beach suits, clutter the northern half of the bay, under shadow of the imposing cliff crowned by the little church. To the south — where the land falls away and the beach is backed by nothing but sand hills and the few scattered fishermen's huts which prolong the town when streets have ended — runs the territory of the fishermen. No boundary line is visible between the two, but a stretch of sand two or three hundred yards long separates them. On this stretch are neither bathing tents nor fishing boats. It is a no-man's land in the social war, used chiefly by the fish-sorting factories for throwing away offal, poured red out of wooden tubs by bare-armed women, and as sleeping quarters by the fishing people, many of whom, having let their houses to the holiday makers, simply roll up in their cloaks and scoop down in the sand. In one corner is a playground where children from Lisbon, brought out under a government scheme, shout behind wooden railings under the care of nuns.

Immediately beyond this no-man's land lies the first of the fishermen's boats, which stretch on in a straggly line for more than a mile along the shore wherever they happen to be drawn up. This strip, a mile or a mile and a half in length by two hundred yards in depth, is alive with movement, noise, and color, from the first light of morning till the fall of dark. On and from this sliver of land the male population of Marinha — barring only a half-dozen priests, a score of police and government officials, a few soldiers, shopkeepers and doctors — carry on a ceaseless warfare with the sea, from the age of twelve until the day of death; they have carried it on, with much the same equipment, for perhaps a thousand years; and, as if sea were not enemy enough, they carry it on under conditions of grinding poverty, with gear in almost every respect unequal to its task.

That obsession with sea which holds so many English people was in Caroline extremely strong. She had chosen this country partly for the long sea voyage she had to make to reach it. She had chosen this village because of a phrase that she had heard. Someone, in describing Marinha to her, had said that to stay here was "like living in the water." She had been deceived into spending two days on the bathing beach, but she saw now she must make up for the time wasted. This morning Caroline had dressed with special care. She had made a fuss because her white shoes were not properly cleaned. But she had hardly leaned over the first fishing boat to look inside before she herself and everything to do with her were forgotten. There spread over her that glow of concentration which comes when senses and mind work so together that identity is no longer present, self-consciousness disappears, and the whole being becomes nothing but an observing and recording apparatus.

Softly but rapidly, little noticed in spite of her scarlet jacket and white skirt, she slipped about among the boats, the nets, the fishermen, the heaps of offal, the fish auctions, the fighting children, the great stretches of split and drying fish, attracting no attention from others because she had no attention for herself — and indeed there was plenty to occupy her eyes.

Up from the sea was blowing a fine mist. Above the mist was a strong sun, strong enough to throw shadows on the ground, to make a radiance in the upper air, but not strong enough to strike directly through and let a clear sky down upon the earth. The mist and the sea breeze made fishing weather, and the whole area of the beach was alive from end to end. Near by, on a tiny strip of gleaming sand polished by waves, a boat was being got ready for the sea. She was the true type of fishing boat of Marinha. Her keel was flat, so she sat squarely on the sand. She was short in length and broad in beam — more than one third as broad as she was long. Her stern was cut square, topsides and stern rose at a slight angle to her keel, so that she looked, stern on, like a wooden box with the sides forced outwards. But by far the most notable thing about her was her prow. Like the edge of a halberd, like the front of an old-fashioned skate, like the curve of a scimitar it rose up, turning back slightly as it soared. On a boat whose gunwales rose four feet from the keel, the curved tip of her prow would soar up seven feet high, and painted on the side to make it more conspicuous would be a mark, a flat white circle or an eye.

Caroline went up to the boat and looked inside. To anyone who had ever known a boat, the inside of this one was a nightmare. The frame of her was magnificent — timbers of great thickness socketed together — but her tackle was like the gear of a child's raft, homemade for sailing in a quarry pit. The oars were young pine trees with slats off packing cases nailed to the ends for blades. The mast was a rough pole with the bark still peeling. The sail had been torn, and patched, and torn again. The rigging seemed to be anything — rope, string, wire, or rag. The anchor was a large stone wound about with a rusty and jagged wire cable.

Five men were stowing an immensely long net into the boat. They wore a costume Caroline had never seen before, never in life, and never in photographs or paintings. In style every man was dressed alike, but in color no two wore the same — except as to their heads. For on the head of every man was a thick black woolen cap shaped like an angler's landing net, hanging halfway down the back and ending in a black woolen tassel. It was long enough to thrust the whole head into on a stormy night, and still leave enough over to wrap round the neck and make a muffler. On their bodies they wore what looked at first sight like pajama suits, except that top and bottom halves never matched. Above was a shirt, of curiously elaborate cut, adorned with pleats and ornamented with pearl buttons. Below was something between long pants and knee breeches, rolled up nearly to the knee. Both garments were made of the thickest kind of flannel, and both were in check designs, like Scotch plaids but in far greater variety. Some were crossed in scarlet, black, blue, white, and yellow, others were mauve, white, gray, and cream. All colors had faded. Every garment had been torn. Patches had been chosen not for their likeness, but their difference, so that the clothing of some of the men showed such confusion and variety of check that it was now impossible even to guess which material had been original.

No man wore shoes. Not one had ever worn them. Their faces, chests, and arms were burned to a thick cocoa-brown. It was not the clear color to which the idle tan themselves, but the color of a muddy tropic river. The skin off them would have bound a book. It would almost have made bark for a tree. Their faces were neither bearded nor clean-shaven, but bristly like the backs of pigs. Their looks were free, but without interest, as of men who feel themselves as good as anyone, but no longer expect the chance to show it. Their feet were like the feet of animals, powerful, insensitive, the toes separate and turning up. "They could tread on a fishhook and not notice it," thought Caroline.

Drawn by a noise of blows and shouting, she moved on. There, before her on the shore, a fragment of the unceasing drama of Marinha was being fought. To the men of Marinha it was nothing. It was nothing to anyone there but Caroline. It was nothing but a fishing boat coming in.

The fishing beach had been chosen for the comparative mildness of its slope, yet if you had run down the shore and jumped ten feet out into the water you would have come down well out of your depth, and if a fishing boat had gone down twenty yards out, as happens three or four times in a decade, the top of her mast would not have shown above the waves. A hundred yards out, it was on many days impossible to anchor with any gear ever seen in that village. The waves that hit the shore of Marinha were nothing but the full waves of the Atlantic, unmitigated from the sides by points of land, or from below by sandbanks. Just as they were far out upon the ocean, so they came pounding in. Fifty yards out, or less, their base began to be cut away from under them by the rising sea bed. As they neared the beach, they

[73]

stumbled and fell forward. As they hit land, they exploded — and through this roaring, boiling surf every boat which left Marinha put out, and every boat which came in had to be handled.

There was a boat coming in now, as Caroline was watching, a boat rather bigger than the one she had examined, perhaps twenty-five feet long, carrying a crew of eight or nine. Shouting to the shore for preparations to be made, the men held her off just beyond the limits of the surf, paddling with their oars and backing water. Then, when a bigger breaker than before was sighted, they struck out for land to get her running. As the wave began to lift her, they struck harder, two men to an oar, one pulling, the other facing him and thrusting. On the breaker's top the boat hung for a second, and then, as the men struck and shouted, she took speed and came racing inland upon its back. Perched high in the stern a small figure like a monkey was trailing something — a grapnel — behind him in the water to hold her straight. On she drove. The swelling wave beneath lifted her stern high in the air, till Caroline found herself looking right down onto the floorboards. Higher the boat came and faster — until at last, when it seemed she was certain to be flung bodily over, that long curved prow came to her aid: it pressed down on the water, holding her, and then, as she touched sand, took her weight. It held her running like a skid. The boat shuddered, rocked, ground forward a few yards up the beach, and then fell back. As she crashed, her crew with a shout leaped out of her. They had now a matter of seconds to get her clear of the next breaker which could suck her back.

Backing down towards her through the sand grunted and slid a team of oxen, dun-colored, black-muzzled, heavy-horned. Men with long sticks that reached right across the oxen's backs were handling them. As the boat came riding in, they drove them backwards even farther, till the breaker that floated the boat in swirled around their hocks. They sweated and jibbed, flashed frightened glances, but obeyed the rod. As the boat touched shore, one of the men seized the big hook in which the oxen's harness ended, smashing it through a strong iron ring in the boat's stem. Then the sticks cracked. Then ox drivers and fishermen yelled together. Then boys and men ran logs in under the boat's keel. The oxen's strong quarters rippled in the light. They slipped; they gave; they pulled again; their harness jangled, their long horns rattled on each other with a noise like a stick on palings; and so, in short bursts of only a few yards' pulling, the boat was run up the beach to safety.

The fishermen, suddenly gone slack, turned to un-

load the gear and slouch off to the fish weighing. The
oxen were allowed a minute's breath, then driven off
to wait for the next boat.

One look was not enough for Caroline. She must
see this battle a hundred times. She must watch until
she saw exactly what they did and why they did it.
She must watch until she could even have taken part
in it herself. She clambered over the gunwale of an
idle boat, pulled herself high up into the swordlike
prow, and hung there, forgotten by herself and unnoticed by anyone.

The mist from the sea came driving in, the sun laid
a hot hand over everything. High up on the shore
black heaps of rags squatted in the fish-drying sectors,
long stretches of sand covered with straw upon which
women endlessly laid small fish which other women
had gutted, then endlessly turned the small fish over
to dry out the other side. And all around and beneath Caroline, so close that she could have jumped
down onto the oxen's backs, the fight went on. The
boats put out. The boats came home. The men sprang
yelling out of them. The oxen strained. For half a
minute raged the fury and activity of war, then all
went dead. The battle here was over. It had broken
out already far beyond. It would flare up again beneath her before long.

For half the morning Caroline clung there. She
had come here in the first place to see Robert, but

when Robert actually found her in her perch, it took
her a second or two to realize who he was.

"Now I see why you live here!" she shouted, her
face dripping from the salty mist, her eyebrows encrusted with the salt. "Now I see why you can't
ever go."

"You are excited? You enjoy it?"

Caroline could not answer. She waved an arm
vaguely, half smiled: "I never saw such things before."

"I have come this morning to take pictures," Robert
de-'ared. "You would like to have some pictures —
no?" He pointed a small box camera vaguely at what
was going on.

"You don't take pictures like that, do you?" Caroline asked, coming back now to herself. She had had
to learn something about photography in her advertising work.

"Very good pictures. They are all good pictures
that I take. But" — he looked abstractedly at the
front — "I think there is some sand or some mist has
got inside the lens. Leo thinks it is sand has got inside. I think that it is mist."

Caroline scrambled out of her perch, and together
they began to walk along the beach. When they came
to obstacles, when they stepped over or under one
of the long ropes leading to the nets which were
being endlessly hauled up the beach by lines of boys

and women, Robert held out his hand to help her. His hand was sunburned, warm and steady. It took hold of hers firmly and naturally. He wore a white silk shirt, blue canvas trousers, and a beret set ab-solutely square on top of his gold hair. She was aware that he had tidied himself up in expectation of seeing her.

"You should stay here forever," said Caroline again. "You should never leave this place. It suits you."

"It does not suit me if we cannot stay," said Robert, his face clouding. "We have now a permit renewed for six months. We have used four months. Maybe it will be renewed again. Maybe it will not be re-newed."

"And if it isn't?"

He looked up, showing brilliant, but troubled eyes. "We intend in that case to go to French West Africa. We go to one of the plantations. I work as a doctor. Leo becomes a merchant." He propounded this stag-gering plan as if he were suggesting a visit to the market.

"But can you get there? How will you live? *Can* Leo be a merchant?"

"Leo can be anything. I am a doctor. In the planta-tions they need doctors."

"But do you think you will like West Africa?"

Caroline struggled to fit Robert and her picture of

Leo into what little she knew about African plantations.

"It is easy to see you are English. You think one goes anywhere and chooses what one does. Listen to me. Here is how things are for us. I leave Germany three years ago. Leo has left the year before. If we go back, the police seize us for avoiding service in the army. The Germans are in Austria. We cannot go there. The Germans are in Czechoslovakia as well. Italy is now the same as Germany. Already in Italy there is Germans everywhere. Jugoslavia is difficult. We think it too close to Germany and Italy. We never make politics, Leo and I, so we do not think the Russians take us in. Leo has a feeling that he does not like America — and perhaps we cannot get there either, even if we want. There is Greece; there is Spain; there is Portugal. There is the northern countries — but we like the sun. Besides, I was nearly kidnaped out of Holland, so I do not wish to go back there."

"How was that?"

"It happen when I am living in Paris. My father write to me. He ask me to come home and talk things over with the family, to see if we cannot agree. He promise I shall be safe. I say No: I will not come back to Germany. So my father ask me to meet him in Holland near the frontier. I go, but I remain suspicious. From the window I watch my father come to the hotel. Behind him at the end of the street a car is waiting. I look through my glasses, and I can see there are four men inside. Then I know why my father want me to come home. They are four Gestapo men. I walk out from the back of the hotel and on the table in my room I leave a note for my father. With the note I leave twelve marks — it is all the money I have. I write in the note that the money I leave is for my father to buy drinks for the Gestapo men when they find their time is wasted. . . . So now you see why I do not go back to Holland."

"What about France — or Britain?"

"In France," Robert replied quietly, "we make some very bad experiences, Leo and I. We think France is not in a good state. We are not happy there. In Britain we have no friends to ask us. . . . It is true that we think once we have some English friends. But we find since a short time we have not."

"So for the time being you must stay in Portugal."

"We stay in Portugal, and we hope there will come no trouble which make it necessary for us to go away." He smiled at two boys of fourteen or fifteen sitting in the shade of one of the boats. "They are two friends of Leo's," he explained. The boys did not smile back, however. They looked at one another embarrassed, almost as if ashamed, then looked away.

"Why do you think there might be trouble?" Caroline asked, to cover up the moment's awkwardness.

"I do not think there is trouble, or there isn't. I think only it *could* be that there is trouble. In a strange country, trouble can happen very easily. Here is Leo. He go now to Estoril. He go to Estoril because he is unhappy. He is bored. He is tired — and he has a quarrel with some friends of his. I say to him, 'Leo. You must go away. If you go, you feel better when you come back.' I have two thousand escudos, twenty pounds, which we have saved. So I give him the money. When it is spent, he come back, he settle down. Everything is then all right."

"But it could be," said Caroline, slipping unawares into Robert's way of talking, "it could be that in Estoril Leo gets into some difficulty, or stays longer than he expected. And then the twenty pounds is gone, and . . ."

". . . And what?" asked Robert.

"And you could still have to leave the country," Caroline suggested. She knew it was tactless, but could not resist pressing a stage further.

"It could be so," Robert agreed. "But the poor fishermen, you know, cannot eat chicken every day. It might be very good for them, and they might like it very much. But they have no money, so they just eat fish."

There was a pause, then: "Does it always happen like this?" Caroline asked.

"Like which?"

"Do *you* have to make all the plans for both? Do you always have to worry — for him as well as you?" She looked up at Robert. His eyes, a darker blue than any she had ever seen, grew darker still when he was worried or annoyed.

"You do not understand," he said, sharply. "For Leo somebody must worry, because he do not know how to worry for himself. For me he can worry. For the fishermen he can worry. When he come here, he worry about you. But for himself Leo cannot worry."

Caroline remained unsatisfied. She had more to say and had never been afraid of snubs; besides, in this case she felt sure she had justice on her side. The truth really ought to be pointed out to Robert. Robert, however, did not wait for the truth to be pointed out to him.

"Today," he said, "I think you do not swim. I ask you to come back to my house and have lunch with me. We go now to where the fish is sold. We choose a fish for lunch. You must be careful here in buying fish; always be careful."

"I should have thought all fish here was fresh. Or are there some kinds which are harmful?"

"Oh, it is not *that* you must be careful of. All the fish is fresh. Only you must be careful not to pay them what they ask. For a nice fish they ask you three escudos. You say 'No! — one escudo.' Then you buy the fish for two escudos. That is how it is. You bargain so, and you can live here very cheap. You can live here, two persons such as Leo and me, for one hundred and fifty escudos — that is about one pound ten shillings — for one week. But to do that you must refuse each time to pay the people what they ask. You always say less, and sometimes, if they do not agree, you take the fish, put down what money you have said — and go away. Leo and I, we do that many times."

Caroline looked up to answer, but Robert was not there. He had dropped back and was standing in a doorway; to her surprise, he was fumbling in his pocket.

"Never give," he had already warned her. "Give nothing to anyone at all. They are all beggars here. Everyone want something. The beggars want money. The fishermen do not want money, but they want cigarettes. The police and soldiers want a drink. Give to one, and more and still more come. They come out of all the houses to be given something. Everybody come. So, therefore, never give."

As he joined her again Robert looked awkward, as if he read what she was thinking. "That was a blind man," he explained. "Leo and I, we always give money to persons that are blind."

VII

A FISH FOR LUNCH

THROUGH all the crosscurrents of movement on the fishermen's beach at Marinha there flows one that is constant. It is the movement from the section of the beach where the fishing boats land their catches, up to a particular corner, the upper corner of the northern end, that is the spot nearest to the market square and to the beach where the visitors bask and flounder. It is here that, in the presence of two soldiers and a government official, all fish caught are weighed and the amounts due handed over.

A space about ten yards long by five yards wide is left clear on the fine powdery sand. In the center is the weighing machine with its long beam and shallow scale. Beside it stands the government official dressed in black, with pencil poised against his notebook. Close to him press two or three black-suited men with narrow faces, buyers for the fish-canning factory or the big fish firms of Lisbon — men who are never short of cigarettes, know how to use the telephone, and can write long messages on paper. Around stand the fishermen, bare-chested, with their skins like leather, their hair full of fish scales, and their powerful flat feet with the toes separate like those of birds. All wear their long black woolen caps.

On the outskirts gather half a dozen boys with what look like headless pigs painted in bright colors hanging down their backs. Headless pigs are just what they are, for the hides have been stripped off, sewn up, and tarred down along the seams. Still keeping their pig-shape they are used as floats, a couple at either end of the huge dragnets; so giving rise to a saying that has spread the name of Marinha through Portugal, that "the pigs of Marinha can swim."

Up to one side of the small clearing comes an irregular procession padding the sand, skirting the drawn-up fishing boats, elbowing its way through the women sorting fish. Over his shoulder the first man drops a small shark, about his own size. Behind him struggle two more. Across their shoulders a stiff pole bends under the weight of a great dark green triangle trailing two feet of its bony tail along the sand — a ray caught far out in the ocean. Behind come three or four pirates with what look like swords of soft metal twisted round their arms. They take off the swords, curled so for convenience in carrying, and straighten them out exactly as if they were strips of pliant metal.

They are not swords, but swordfish — *peche espada* — having the silver glow, brilliant but not sparkling, of the best women's evening shoes. Gold follows silver — a couple of men with boxes on their heads. From above each box edge show, evenly ranked and neatly bended over — for there is a way of arrangement proper to each kind — the transparent golden tails of a handsome orange fish, like a great goldfish in color but about the size and plumpness of fat perch. These are set down in their boxes beside the long straight silver blades, and farther back range the boxes of those that make less show, flatfish, conger, sardines, and the rest.

The sale begins. It is usually a matter of the black-coated men making an offer, and the fishermen nodding with no enthusiasm in acceptance. Occasionally there is complaint, and an adjustment. The selling here is wholesale; fish for the town is sold up in the market, or from baskets by women in the streets. But every fisherman, apart from what goes to the sales, carries home a basket for himself and will sell something on his way — particularly if a cigarette goes with the bargain.

"Who are the ones with the new clothes?" asked Caroline, pointing to half a dozen of the fishermen splendid in tartans, blue, yellow, gray, and scarlet, every mixture of tone and shade, but all conspicuously new. "Are they the owners? Do they come from one rich family?"

"They are the crew of the big ship — the *Holy Ghost*," Robert answered. "Last year it is the little ships that make the catches. This year the fish swims farther out. It is the *Holy Ghost* alone which catches much. Now," he went on earnestly, taking her arm, "you see what I say to you about this beach and the other. This is the beach of the living persons. The other is the beach of the dead. That is the beach where you go every morning for the swimming — the dead beach. You swim among the dead people. Down here is the live persons carrying fishes on their shoulders and selling it for the dead persons to eat."

Caroline looked at Robert.

"How do you know which are which? Aren't there *any* living on the other beach, or any dead ones here?"

"It is very easy to know one kind from the other," Robert answered, "because they all has the word on their faces, written in letters, DEAD. The shopkeepers and the visitors on that other beach is all dead because they have no feeling that they are alive. They do not know what life is. It goes past them, and they know nothing — even that they have not got it. It is like the wind which you cannot see blowing. They know what food is, yes, but what life is they do not know. On this beach they know what life is, because they know what death is. They meet him every morning on the sea. They fight him on the sea and they come home — still alive. So they have the faces of living men. The only ones on this beach that has not the faces of living men is the ones that come down here from the town, the soldiers and police, the government officials and the agents of the fish factories. They think they are finer than the fishermen, because they wear black clothes and do not go to sea. But the fishermen are alive, and they are dead. The fishermen is stupid, cruel sometimes, perhaps greedy, but they walk like living men upon the shore. The home of the shopkeepers is in the tombs, in the tombs in the cemeteries, with big pieces of marble on their chests. That is where they will all one day go, and all their life is only waiting — what you call 'killing time' — until they go there. And they bear as children other dead persons who will also make their life homes in the tombs."

"And do any of the fishermen not come home after their battles on the sea?" Caroline asked, looking about her at the faces, tough, sullen, and grasping, but hardly one without the dignity of manhood.

"Last year," said Robert, "there is a boat. She is called the *Blessed Virgin Mary* or *Lord Jesus Christ, our Saviour*. I forget. Perhaps she is just *St. Peter, our Patron*. It is a rough day, not very rough, but rather rough, and the boat is coming in. She is not very big, and not a little boat. She is one of the medium-sized boats, and she is coming in. When she is only forty or fifty meters out from shore, she is catched by a big wave, perhaps the man in the stern do not see it coming. She is catched and knocked sideways — the boats, you know, must never be sideways to the sea. In a second she turn over. All twelve men is in the sea."

"But can't they swim — such a little way out? What happened?" Caroline seemed actually to be looking down into one of the boats she had watched only an hour or two ago.

"They *would* be all right," said Robert. "They would be able to swim themselves to shore. Only the net go over them. Their own net is thrown over them out of the boat. Now in all the countries in the world the fishermen has knives — in case the net is thrown over them, so they can cut their way out. Or in case the sail cover them in the water, they can slash it through. In Germany every fisherman carry a long knife. In Norway all the fishermen has knives. The fishing men of Brittany has knives too. Certainly the Englishmen has knives. Only in this country the fishermen carry no good knives, for they have not enough money to buy good knives with. . . . And so they drown, all twelve of the fishermen of Marinha, out there not far from the shore where the people are bathing and playing about, because they have no money to buy knives to cut themselves out of the net."

Caroline said nothing. She looked at Robert, but he did not look back. He was looking in an abstracted way at the faces of the fishermen, and, as she watched, she became aware of something — the fishermen did not look back. Some of them looked closely at her. One or two of the younger ones smiled at her. But not one, as far as she could see, looked at Robert. They did not seem to be hostile. When they both wanted to watch the selling, room was made for them, but not one of the men caught Robert's eye, or appeared to notice him, even when his voice was raised in talk. It was as though, for them, he did not exist. She believed Robert was aware of this. She was sure it was something she should not refer to, any more than one would speak of the danger to a companion on a climb. She simply noticed it, with discomfort. After half an hour of watching, they turned away, went up into the town, bought one of the handsome gold-colored fish from an old woman, and entered the Rua dos Pescadores.

"And this," said Robert, pointing to a villa on the corner of the street, a villa in the favorite taste of muddy orange and dull red, three times the size and twice the height of any of the whitewashed fishermen's houses, "is the house of Senhor Branca."

"Then Senhor Branca must be a very important

man to have enough money to build a villa regardless of taste?" said Caroline, anxious to dispel the gloom cast by the fishermen. "This is the ugliest thing I have seen in the whole of Portugal. It makes me long to see its owner."

"Senhor Branca is one of the great men of Marinha," Robert told her with visible enjoyment. "Senhor Branca have two trades which make him very much respected and grow rich. In the daytime he sit in the chemist shop beneath his villa and sell cartouches to the fishermen. Cartouches is explosive cartridges which kills the fish and brings them floating dead onto the water. It is against the law to do this, so Senhor Branca is able to charge very much for the cartouches. In the evening he sit in his café. His café is at the corner of the square where you come in a few days ago on the bus. In the café is some girls, the daughters of two fishermen who lose their boat. He sells these girls to the visitors, to the business people, the officers, the doctors, the government officials. Only to the other fishermen he does not sell them, for the other fishermen do not go to his café. To sell the girls is against the law, so Senhor Branca can charge much for the girls, and that way he make money too. In a small time he will become so rich, he give up the girls and sell only the cartouches. Then he give up the cartouches, and have only a company to make cartouches — and not sell them himself, which is dangerous. He is then an honored man in Marinha."

"And what does he do then?" asked Caroline, turning to look up into Robert's sunburned face. "Retire to Lisbon, or go round the world like the great discoverers of the past?"

"No! Then he build a church — a church like his own house, but not so big. Or it could be that he build a fountain, a pool or fountain where the asses drink, so that he can write his name on it in big letters — 'Given by the liberality of Senhor Branca' — and with his own name he puts God's, for Senhor Branca is a religious man. Senhor Branca and God have their names side by side in the same size of letters. 'Given by the Liberality of Senhor Branca and the Grace of God the Father.' Something like that he will put on his fountain. And the asses will read it as they drink, and be grateful to this God and this Senhor Branca who give them the cold water."

Caroline laughed in his face out of delight, not at what he said, but at his pleasure in saying it. "Tell me more," she said. "More about Senhor Branca, and more about all the other people in the town."

Robert had gone over to the fireplace and was preparing the fish. "I tell you more," he said, "when this fish is ready. There are lots of other people in the town, but I'm afraid they will not all give you so much happiness as this Senhor Branca."

In everything he says, thought Caroline, a doubleness is present. He goes a little one way, then he quickly comes back and goes the other. He makes you laugh, and then warns you that there are other people much worse off. Sadness, even a sort of heaviness, is on top. Underneath are the gaiety and life, It is from these that his sharp perceptions come, not from the other.

She watched his smile. When most people smile, their faces change. When Robert smiles, she thought, he is transformed. Where other faces crease with laughing, his is smoothed out. He loses all traces of worry and preoccupation. He has the look of a small boy who runs along the road ahead and looks back smiling, conscious of a trick he has prepared to play. When he smiles, Robert forgets; he forgets, thought Caroline, the permits that expire, he forgets the passports to other countries that will never let him in, he forgets the twenty pounds that have gone to Estoril, he forgets Leo. . . . That, it came over her in a flash, that carefree look, that sense of ease and freedom, is what happens to Robert when for a moment he forgets Leo.

And now she had no difficulty in explaining his divided nature. To her mind it was all perfectly clear. Robert himself was simple, gay, and lively — but with something much more uncommon, a discernment almost uncanny as to people and their motives, an angry contempt for the life of money and convention. Over this unusual but uncomplicated nature, Robert was obliged, by his anxiety for Leo, to draw a cloak of mistrust and hesitation. Like a mother with a son who has gone wrong, he had acquired a habit of not trusting to the future, since he never knew in what situation he would find himself tomorrow.

Bettina had talked as if Leo were some rare spirit, whom it was perfectly natural for Robert to cherish, even at a sacrifice. To Caroline it was plain that the finer was being sacrificed to the less fine: the rare spirit dwelt in Robert, whom it would rather become Leo to tend and care for, if he were good for anything at all.

They sat for a long time over the fish, the cheese and coffee. Robert told her about the people of Marinha. She listened eagerly. At last he began to talk of his profession, of the medical work he did among the fishermen.

She had started him off by a question. It appeared that the book with the colored plates of eyes, which she had seen on her first visit, was not simply a textbook, it was the exposition of a theory, a theory of diagnosis through the eye. Through an examination of the iris it was possible to estimate the physical condition of the patient who had come for consultation. That was the theory. Did Robert believe in it? No. He did not believe it, and he did not disbelieve it.

The book had suggestions in it that were a help, above all in dealing with the fishermen, whose language he could not speak, and who were, in addition, completely ignorant of the simplest medical facts, and therefore could not say what was the matter. Almost, he said, they still believed that every ailment was caused by the devil, who was pinching or had laid a curse on the infected part. When a "hotness in the belly" was the most accurate description of a sickness they could give, it helped to be able to learn something from their looks.

What success had he had? Caroline inquired. Not very much. Since his patients had all to be non-paying, they were drawn from the very poorest. They did not take advice at all until their condition was acute; then they went usually to one of the other doctors first, and only reached him after they had been despaired of, and had spent any money they might have for medicines. It was, in any case, scarcely possible to get them to follow a routine. If they did not feel better after one pill or a single bottle, they decided the doctor was no good and gave him up.

He had one patient, a consumptive far gone in the disease, down on the shore. Caroline had no doubt seen him lying in among the boats with a big umbrella over his bed. This man Robert had so far prevailed on that he was willing to try and follow his advice. He had got him to eat tomatoes. None of the fishermen had ever eaten a tomato. They ate only fish and bread, a little meat very rarely on a Saint's Day or a feast. They drank wine and smoked cigarettes. They made almost no use of vegetables, and the idea of eating vegetables raw seemed to them madness — suitable only for a goat or ass.

The consumptive man had been persuaded at last to eat tomatoes, because he had heard that the shopkeepers staying in the pensions ate them. But so far Robert had not been able to persuade him to eat lettuce. He would like to persuade him to eat lettuce, because then some of the others for whom there was still hope might begin to eat lettuce too. But he thought the man would die before they got so far, and his death would probably be ascribed to the tomatoes. There was consumption among all the fishermen because of the way they lived, and the things they ate and did not eat. Consumption, and many other diseases too.

Could the consumption be got rid of? Yes, it could. But it would require that all the families should have more money, and that they should be taught sensible ways of living. It was therefore not likely to be brought about.

Besides, the people resented being taught. Why was that? How did they resent it? What did they do? And here Robert touched upon a circumstance which seemed to Caroline of particular interest, apart from the general interest she was already feeling in all that concerned Robert and his way of life.

The consumptive man, it seemed, had a young brother. When Robert went to sit and talk to the consumptive, which he did several times a week, Leo would sit and talk to this brother — a fisherboy of about fifteen years of age, and very good-looking. They were "great friends," said Robert. Once or twice the boy came to see them at their house.

One evening after they had paid their visit and were leaving: "We see outside the house a crowd of men. They are fishermen, come up from the shore. They are very angry, and some of them have sticks. They say to us, 'What are you doing there?' I answer them, 'I have been seeing to the sick man. I am a doctor, should I not see one who is sick?' They say their business is not with me. I do not know what they mean, and they come closer with their sticks. Then Leo, who is afraid of nothing, runs up to the first man. He seizes from him his stick. He stand there before them all and he call out, 'Come here any one of you who please, and I will fight him with this stick!' But no one come. So Leo still stand there, and he shake his stick at all the crowd. His beret has fallen off, and his hair, which is long and golden, is blowing back. 'Come on,' he say, 'and fight me now. Or else each man, go away home.' So then, while they are talking, we walk quietly backwards up the road. I pick up

Leo's beret. I make him cover up his head. We slip into one house and pass out of it at the back, and we come home.

"I say then to Leo: 'It is best for you to go away. You go away for a few days, they forget everything. Then later you come back. It is all well again.'"

"But why did the men come after you at all?" asked Caroline, bewildered.

"They do not like me teaching this sick man to eat new things."

"Then why should it be Leo, and not you, whom the men threaten?"

"Come on," said Robert, getting up and reaching for his beret. Clearly he had said more than he intended, and regretted having said so much. "Your friends is waiting for you. I come back with you to your hotel. It is great pleasure to me to have been seeing you. You will come again soon, I expect?"

Caroline smiled. "I expect so too, Robert," she said.

As they went out of the door Robert turned back, letting her go first. He was a moment longer than she expected, and Caroline looked round to see if he was coming. He was securing the door with a large padlock, newly fitted.

VIII

THE VISIT TO VALLADO

EVER since her introduction to their party, Paul, Hélène, and Maxim had been talking of the visit to Vallado. It was clearly a necessity for Paul always to have a treat of some kind a short way ahead, in order to prevent his becoming too bored in the present. Hélène, Maxim, and Bettina all humored him in this and, when he became irritable, would remind him of the coming treat and soothe him with the prospect. They had been soothing him over the past few days with the prospect of Vallado, and today, Saturday, the prospect was to be a view. The car, hired from Senhor Branca, the cartouche seller and café owner, was at the door. Maxim and Bettina were already inside when Caroline came down. Maxim had been installed beside the driver. Bettina was in the back.

Caroline, invited by Paul and Hélène as their guest, got in and sat on one of the tip-up seats with her back to the bonnet. Bettina slipped across and took the

[99]

other one beside her. She was wearing a close-fitting, dark blue shirt with an open collar. She had a work-man's handkerchief of scarlet and white cotton round her neck, a white sun hat like a child's, and her usual spotless shorts. They seemed even shorter than usual as she put her legs up on the hot seat, waiting for Paul and Hélène, and twisted her ankles admiringly in the hot sun. "Don't forget to bring a rug," she called out to Hélène as she came downstairs, "we shall want it on the way back." Hélène held up the rug she was al-ready carrying. "I'm sorry Paul is late," she said, add-ing without any touch of sarcasm: "He is finding it difficult to choose the scarf which suits him best."

Paul came down at last, wearing another of his luxurious silk handkerchiefs knotted with elaborate carelessness over a linen shirt. He looked twice at his party, once to see that their appearance did him credit, and once to catch the reflection of his own ap-pearance from them, and got in.

"This is not a very smart car," he said apologetically to Caroline. "It is not our own. We have left ours in Lisbon. Something had gone wrong with the steer-ing. It was all right while we were going straight, but when we went round corners it seemed sometimes to make movements on its own. We thought we ought to have it seen to."

The car drove across the square, turned past the café of its owner, and began to climb up out of the bowl of Marinha, through the short belt of cultivated land, towards the dusty uplands of Portugal. Caroline found herself looking down onto the fishing-beach where the thousand-year battle with the sea was going on, searching out the elaborate villa that marked the end of the Rua dos Pescadores, traveling up it to find the small courtyard of number 4. Her eyes picked up the villa and the road, but which of the maze of small rectangles was Robert's she could not make out.

She had been aware, even before she experienced it, of the double or treble mixture of feelings that came to her now — a regret that for one afternoon she could not possibly see Robert; the contentment of knowing that he would certainly be there when she got back; the excitement of going to a new place in the company of people who knew him and would be sure to talk of him — with, added to all, the strangeness of feeling each one of these things so sharply. Bettina, alone of those present, might partly be aware, Caroline thought, of what she was feeling and the cause of it.

The car had come out now onto the upland road. Trees lined the way. Cottages, built of cement blocks with roofs of red tiles, were the only houses. Many seemed to contain not more than one room each. The windows were shuttered, but unglazed for economy. On the thin cement walls of the gardens rows of

ripening melons balanced. When, on a straight stretch
of road, another car appeared, the two would rush
towards each other hooting furiously, trailing each its
own dust cloud after it. Still hooting, they would
pass, and the last hoots would not die away until
long after the other was out of sight. Occasionally a
cart drawn by bullocks came towards them. The
driver of their car would hoot, whether it was in the
way or not, secure that the oxcart could not hoot
back. To the drivers use of the horn was clearly the
main enjoyment of a car.

Paul smoked incessantly. Hélène, out of good nature, smoked more than she wanted because Paul
never smoked without offering one to her. He offered
cigarettes also to Maxim and to Caroline, sometimes
to Bettina, never to the driver.

"You think I smoke too much?" he inquired of Caroline. "I smoke only about fifty cigarettes a day. Before I knew Hélène I smoked much more — often I
smoked a hundred cigarettes a day. I think Hélène
is curing me. Robert says she is not curing me. Robert says I smoke just as much as ever. He says I am
disgusting in the amount I smoke, and he will not
come near me until I smoke less."

He spoke quite naturally, with no shame or false
modesty, recording what seemed to him a serious
difference of opinion on a matter of general interest.
He was visibly waiting for Caroline's reply. Did she

think he smoked too much, or didn't she? At the mention of Robert's name Caroline felt that Hélène was watching her, and that Bettina was deliberately not doing so.

"I think they are both right," Caroline replied. "I am sure Hélène has done you good. But I think she has not yet completely cured you." The answer appeared to please Hélène.

"The patient has been cured," remarked Bettina, "but he is still a victim of the disease. The doctor has manifested his skill. The disease has shown its determination. They are worthy opponents, and the struggle between them may easily go on for many years. I have one of those wars myself — between my conscience and my nature. It has gone on for so long now, I don't think I could do without it."

"In that war," said Caroline, "I am on the side of your nature."

Maxim turned round from in front.

"We are coming to a belt of castles," he announced. "When the Portuguese were driving out the Moors, they built a line of castles at each key point as they advanced. Then at the end of another campaign, when they had gained more ground, they built more castles." He pointed to a gray stone keep on a hillside rising from the pinewoods. "That is one of the castles built to keep back the Moors when the country was being set free."

"Isn't it about time it was set free again?" asked Bettina.

"The land of Portugal," declared Paul, "is free already. It has a government of progressive conservatism, based on the religious feelings of the people, whose first concern is to safeguard the inheritance of the past. Until this enlightened government came in there was a good deal of . . ." he searched for a word. . . "a great deal of . . ."

"Strife," suggested Caroline, not because she knew anything about the subject, but because it seemed the sort of word Paul was looking for.

"You are right," declared Paul, leaning forward to look approvingly at Caroline, "there was a great deal of strife. Now there is no strife any more. I have to know about these things," he explained amiably as he leaned back. "It is part of my training for the Diplomatic Service, which I intend to enter."

"No more strife among the people," observed Bettina, "and very few watermelons."

Did she wish Robert was here? Caroline was wondering. Did she want him sitting here beside her in the car? To some extent, she felt, she was already seeing with his eyes. The cement boxes with their scraps of cultivated earth were not just elements in a landscape. They were symbols of the life that went on inside them, products of a system and a plan, which one might accept easily as Paul, critically as Bettina, or against which one might struggle as did Robert. How often in Robert's case was the struggle needless and mistaken! If he were here, he would be struggling now, arguing, growing angry, trying to make Paul smoke less and Hélène think more; trying to make Maxim recognize the existence of other worlds than the best circles; trying to codify Bettina's generous inclinations into a way of life — which would then be unnatural to her simply because it had been codified; trying to bring lucidity into minds whose natural element was an amiable confusion; making himself hot, and exhausting his own spirit. Caroline saw Robert always with a slight frown, which came from his inability to make other people see. She loved him for trying — but what is the inability to make other people see, except one's own inability to accept other people as they are?

The car took a sudden swerve. Caroline and Bettina were flung against each other. Paul, leaning forward from the back to comb his hair in the driving mirror, had slipped and knocked the driver's arm.

The road into Vallado swung over a bridge and straight up to the foot of a tall cliff, out of which soared the castle they had come to visit. The car slowed and stopped. A mahogany-faced peasant was working by the roadside.

"Hi," called out Maxim, beckoning with his long

cigarette holder. He continued to call out until the man came over. Maxim asked him the road, repeated the instructions to the driver, and sat back, knocking the ash off his cigarette. He gave nothing to the peasant, and no word of thanks. He just sat back, knocked off his ash, and the car drove on.

In the little town they stopped.

"You will want to have some tea," Paul declared.

"It's only half-past three," said Caroline doubtfully, looking at Bettina. "Shouldn't we go up to the castle first, and have tea afterwards?"

"There is a kind of cake in a shop here which you will very much like," Paul explained. "When we came here before I have eaten seven of them. I brought four more home for Bettina. Bettina ate them all. You like them very much, Bettina, don't you?"

"Yes, Paul dear," said Bettina.

"Then we all want to have tea now," declared Paul, satisfied.

The radio was whining in the café. It seemed to keep the flies moving in the windows when by nature they would have been asleep, or dead. On the wall was notice of a fête that took place six months ago. Against the counter stood a big basket of fresh-looking loaves with a flea-bitten cat asleep amongst them. Paul ordered coffee and some cakes. When the cakes were brought he picked out one with an apricot on top that made it look like a poached egg, and ordered a whole plate of cakes like that one. These, Caroline supposed, were the cakes she was going particularly to like. By the time they came, Paul had bitten into the first. "Good God!" he cried out suddenly. "Hélène! Maxim! Help!"

"What is it?" they asked, thinking he had been stung.

"The cakes!" Paul cried. "Can't you see? They are absolutely deadly. They must have been made last week. No! Take them away! Take them all away!" He flapped his hands at the proprietress. "Horrible! Filthy! Monstrous!" He leaned confidingly over to Caroline. "Don't eat any of those beastly cakes; they're poisoned."

"Caroline and I promise not to eat any poisoned cakes," Bettina said. "We're going to walk up to the castle, and you will come on after in the car." She took out her purse, offering to pay her share.

"No, that's all right, Bettina," Paul declared. "You're having tea with us today." Bettina put her purse away. Caroline accepted her position as guest and said nothing. She admired Bettina's attitude about money; it was clear and consistent. She had shown it several times already. When Quinta was there — or presumably any other temporary protector — he was to pay everything for her. She made no move to pay, herself, and if he had not paid for her she would undoubtedly have told him to.

When she was on her own with friends, as now, she never failed to offer her share of all expenses. There was no fumbling, or pretending she had not brought enough, or offers to borrow and pay back later. She always brought out the money due, and offered it. If it was accepted, she handed it over and forgot about it. If it was refused sincerely, she put the money back. With Bettina you could always know just where you were.

They started off up the hill.

"You must not be cross with Paul," began Bettina. "Above all you must not dislike him."

"On the contrary," said Caroline, "I am already fond of Paul."

"I am glad," said Bettina. "But almost all of us have begun by disliking him. Of course he is all the things people say he is, but at least he does not pretend. He can't understand why everyone doesn't do just what he does — take whatever it is they want, eat as much as they please, enjoy anything they fancy. Most people who live like that are discontented. But Paul is not discontented. He nearly always enjoys the things he gets — and then, you know, as soon as he has got something, and before he has grown tired of it, he wants something new. That keeps him interested. At the most, sometimes he is peevish. And when he makes himself ill, he is tiresome for a day or two.

Then he gets well again, he can once more eat and smoke too much, and he is happy."

"And Hélène is good for him?" Caroline asked.

"It is good for Paul to be with a woman," Bettina answered, "and there are not many women who would take so much trouble with him as Hélène."

Out of two questions she wished to ask, Caroline chose one: "Why does Hélène take trouble?"

"For the same reasons you and I do things — some good, and some not so good. Hélène loves to manage and control. In her shop she controls her staff by giving orders, and she manages her customers by humoring them. With Paul she is partly a mother humoring her child, and partly a *vendeuse* humoring her customer. Just occasionally, too, she gives orders. Hélène has the neat mind of a Frenchwoman, and Paul fits easily into it. She knows she will always be the master. Then she is ambitious, and Paul for her is a good marriage. She is very much concerned about his family. She knows she will not be accepted yet, but she thinks in a year or two she can manage to be accepted. I think so too. She means Paul to be occupied — but she sees clearly that he will never do real work of any kind. She plans for him to get a small job in the Diplomatic Service, and she thinks that with money and his family she can do the rest. But above all it is necessary for him to get a post of the right kind, and if she cannot get him into the British Diplomatic Service, they will take up another nationality. Paul's family is of all nationalities. It will not be difficult for him to become Portuguese or Brazilian, or Swiss."

"So you really like Hélène?"

"Yes," Bettina answered. "I like Hélène. If she is successful, she will give me up, or you, if you are not successful. But if we come to the back door she will always see that we do not want. She has a sense of propriety, which is next best to a warm heart. It will be proper for you and me to come to the back door, and not speak to Hélène in the street, when she is successful. And it will be proper for her to give us five hundred francs each and an old dress if we are in trouble. If we are in hospital, she will come and visit us. If we are in prison, somebody else will come on her behalf. She will not abandon us, and she will not compromise herself. Hélène and I understand each other very well. By the way, she likes you, too."

"And Maxim?"

Bettina hesitated. "Haven't you found out all about Maxim for yourself?"

"Nothing at all."

"All right, my dear," she said, "but remember you started asking questions and not me." She looked at Caroline, who nodded, shaking a wave of black hair out of her eyes. In the sun Caroline's hair took on new life, a vivid life of its own, separate as that of a plant or tree. It glistened and shone like water, black or gleaming in the sunshine, almost dark blue in the shadows. Bettina, who took an impartial pleasure in the good looks of other women, rested her eyes with satisfaction on Caroline's rich black hair, as Caroline nodded for her to go on.

"I do not like Maxim," Bettina said. "I don't think I shall ever like him. When he came here first, he wanted me to be his mistress. I was not interested in him, but I might some day have been. I had just left a friend of mine in Paris. I could not then be interested in anyone. Maxim did not care to wait. He offered me money to sleep with him without waiting. So then I told him some things which he had not heard before. . . . If I let someone sleep with me they can give me money or not, as they like. It makes no difference. But to offer money when I do not want him — that is the act of a man without feeling. Anyone — Quinta even — would not think of such a thing. Even so I could perhaps forgive Maxim — not so as to be lovers, but so that we could be friends — only now he is angry with me because of the way I spoke to him then. He is so small, and so important. He cannot forget and make it up, so he prefers to go on being angry. Underneath all that charm, he has a little, selfish heart — but why should I bother telling you all this? I saw you watching him today when the peasant came to the car to tell us which road to take. You keep your doll's face very still and pretty, but it shows more than you think."

"Doll's face? Who told you it was a doll's face?"

"Nobody told me," answered Bettina, patting Caroline's smooth cheek. "I can see things of that sort for myself."

They were passing a military barracks. Some ten or twelve soldiers, country boys in greenish uniforms with dirty boots, were shuffling about at drill in a sergeant's charge. Suddenly through an archway behind them came an officer. Tightly packed into a smart uniform and leggings, with close-cropped hair, and a monocle stuck into a bald and shiny face, he cantered a glossy little mare across the square. The mare, both spurred on and reined in, rose and fell like a yacht in a cross sea with a short uneasy motion, the lieutenant, who knew how to ride, clenched firmly to the saddle. Catching sight of Caroline and Bettina, he shouted something at the sergeant in a manner both offhand and peremptory, disregarded the man's salute, and disappeared towards the town.

The same thought crossed both their minds. They were too well aware of what the other was thinking to need to say it. They turned to each other and laughed instead. . . . "But at least," said Caroline, "our man has better manners."

X

ON THE CASTLE WALLS

THE two girls passed through the gateway and walked up the road which circled the hillside to the castle on the top. To their right, on the outside of the curve, the road was fortified with battlements which rose, every hundred yards or so, into a tower from which they could look out over the country. The castle and the fortifications were being restored — excellently, as all reconstruction and preservation work is done in Portugal, the land that lives by looking backwards. Huge blocks of stone, partly shaped, lay by the roadside. A number of men were moving stones on hand trolleys. A winch and some wooden scaffolding seemed to be all the machinery and gear they used.

"There's something I want to ask you, Bettina," Caroline began. "You needn't tell me anything you don't want. I know I sometimes ask people things I shouldn't: I suppose it's because I wasn't very well brought up."

"I wasn't brought up at all," Bettina answered. "Perhaps that's why I liked you as soon as I saw you — we're creatures with something in common. Though — "

Fearing Bettina might be going to speak against herself, Caroline quickly took her arm. "Shall I ask you straight out what I want to know, or work round to it in a way which you will see through from the start?"

"You mean you'd like me to tell you what I know about Robert Kranz?"

"And about Leo," added Caroline. "It's not only that you seem to know more about them than the others, but you seem to have a different feeling towards them, too. A better feeling, or at any rate less confused."

"My feelings about them are often quite confused enough," Bettina answered. "It wouldn't be easy to have simple and direct feelings towards either of those two."

They were standing in an embrasure facing out over the corkwoods. Caroline felt Bettina's look upon her, but she did not turn her head. She just looked out over the dark green woodlands. "Tell me as much as you can," she said; "begin at the very beginning."

"The beginning," said Bettina, "was a long time

back. Robert and Leo have known each other for
eight years, that is from before the time of the Nazis'
coming to power. They were then both living in Berlin, both very young men living on their own. Leo was
eighteen, and Robert about two years older. Leo was
a poet who wrote for certain magazines, and had a
small allowance from his family to live on. Robert was
training to become a doctor. They happened to take
rooms in the same apartment house. Leo had the
room just over Robert's. They did not know each
other, but Robert had very often seen Leo going out
in the morning to buy food, or coming home from a
party late at night. Robert had seen Leo, and he
wanted very much to meet him. He had come to
think a great deal about Leo, though still he did not
know him. He was always wondering about Leo and
his life. He used to imagine himself as knowing Leo,
and was always thinking of ways of speaking to him
and becoming one of his friends, but somehow it
never happened.

"One evening," went on Bettina, "Robert was sitting in his room. He was sitting late at his table working. It was after midnight, and the house was dark.
As he sat in his room he could hear voices overhead.
At first they were the voices of people arguing. Then
there was shouting and a quarrel. Then it seemed
that there was even the sound of crying — and at last
someone, a man, ran down the stairs and rushed out

of the house. After that for a long time it was quiet
again. Robert had worked during the arguing, and
he even worked during the quarrel, but now it was
quiet he could not work. He could only walk about
the room, and he kept on looking at the ceiling as if
he expected to see something there. Overhead there
was for a long time no sound. Robert still walked, and
he still kept looking at the ceiling.

"He was not wondering, he says, whether he should
go up, or not go up. He was not thinking about going
up at all. He was simply walking about his room and
looking at the ceiling; and then suddenly, for no
reason, he rushed out of his room, ran upstairs, and
burst open Leo's door. Leo was lying on the carpet
by the fireside. He had cut open the veins in his wrists
with a razor blade, and he was now part way to being
dead.

"Robert at once took charge. He bound up Leo's
veins. He rushed all through the house. He snatched
the hot-water bottles away from all the sleepers. He
took the brandy from a man who was drinking himself stupid. There was no wood for a fire, so he broke
up furniture and burned it. He even sent a blind man
— who was the only person sober with his clothes on
— to fetch the best doctor in Berlin.

"It was the time of his own examinations as a doctor, but Robert did not go for the examinations. For
three weeks he did nothing but take care of Leo. He

borrowed money from all his friends to buy things for him, and he lost a year before he could qualify as a doctor.

"Perhaps you know what happened after that. Later on, after the Nazis came to power, Leo became liable for military service. His family said that he should serve. They would give him no more money if he did not go into the army like the others. Robert said that to go into the army would kill Leo — he was not obliged himself to serve in the army because of the special work he was doing as a doctor. So Robert smuggled Leo out of the country, and arranged for him to go and live in Paris. For a year he sent money to him in Paris, and then he himself came to Paris for a conference about medicine. He had meant to go back to Germany, but when he came to Paris and saw Leo there, he did not go back. After a time he could not go back even if he wanted. By staying out of the country he had become liable to be sent to a concentration camp."

They had turned and were walking up the hill.

"In Paris . . ."

"I know," said Caroline. " 'In Paris, Leo and I, we make some rather bad experiences.' . . ."

"Did he tell you what those experiences were?" Bettina asked.

Caroline shook her head.

"In Paris, while Robert was away, Leo had taken

up with some strange friends. I was one of them, so I know what they were like. We all drank, and most of us took drugs. There were some who were strong and could stand it. There were others who were always partly poisoned, until one day they were altogether poisoned and one did not see them any more. There was one man quite white like paper who never ate anything at all, except sometimes, perhaps once every two days, a small part of a lettuce. If he went to a party he would bring some drugs with him, and the inside of a lettuce in case he should wish to eat. They talked always about art, but what they did all the time was drink, and sometimes some of the stronger ones made love a little, and every now and then one of them would copy out a small poem. There was only one among them all who was an artist and did real work, and that was Leo. They took to Leo partly because of his looks, but chiefly because he worked. The work that Leo did was a distinction to them all. So they clung to him, took for themselves the credit for his work, and did everything they could to stop him working more.

"These were the friends of Leo when Robert came to Paris. He had not meant to stay in Paris, but when he saw how Leo was living on drugs and drink, and sometimes a little poetry and lettuce, he stayed on. He succeeded in becoming attached to a hospital for foreigners in Paris. He made enough for them both to live on, and he took care of Leo. I have at home a small book of poems which Leo finished at this time, and Robert managed to get printed for him."

"And the other bad experiences?"

"The other bad experiences began when they wanted to leave France. We all of us think all the time that war is coming. The question we ask every day is, 'Where shall we go and live so that we can escape?' Robert and Leo feel sure that France and Germany will be at war; therefore they do not want to stay in France, to be interned and later perhaps get caught up by the Germans. They do not like America, so they make plans to go to South America, to Chile. The Consul tells them that to go to Chile they need thirty thousand francs — so much for fares, so much to secure admission to the country, so much to the official who arranges everything for them. So they sell everything they have. They write to all their friends all over Europe. They promise this is the last time they will bother them, and they ask them to be generous and give everything they can afford. They send wires and cables, letters and cards. At last they get the thirty thousand francs. And then, when they are just about to go, the official who arranges things for them mentions that of course they will only be allowed to remain in Chile for six months. After that they must leave the country and come back."

"But how . . ." began Caroline. "You mean they

were swindled? Why couldn't they denounce the official? What did they do then?" She put her hand on Bettina's arm.

"They were distracted. They could not spend everything they had in the world in order to be in Chile for six months. So they give up all their plans. The ship bookings they can still cancel if they pay a forfeit, but they have lost in bribes four thousand francs, and they have bought many things for Chile which they do not want in Paris. Robert was furious; he was determined to bring a case against the official, but we all prevented him. If he had brought a case, the official might have been disgraced, but Robert and Leo would certainly have been turned out of France."

Caroline hesitated. "That is a strange story," she said, "about the official."

"It is all true," said Bettina. "I was there and saw what happened. I even read the letters: Leo showed them to me."

"No, I don't mean that," Caroline explained. "I mean something different. Do you suppose," she went on slowly, "it was just that the official did not happen to remember the regulation which only allowed them to stay six months in Chile?"

"Do you mean, do I think he meant all the time to swindle them? Yes, of course he did. That's what officials are like. That's how they make their money. And they enjoy doing such things as well."

"No. I mean something else. D'you think it possible the official first acted in good faith — and then . . ."

". . . and then found out that people coming to Chile could not stay more than six months? That would be absurd. These were his own country's regulations."

"And then found out that *these* people would not be allowed to stay more than six months," remarked Caroline, kicking at a stone as she strode slowly up the hill, taking long strides to match Bettina's.

Bettina gave her a quick glance. "I had not thought of that," she said. "But why should they want Leo to leave in any case?"

"It was only what you said about drugs that made me think of it," said Caroline. "But very likely it was just the natural wickedness of officials. Did Robert and Leo come straight here from Paris?"

"They came straight here, and they arrived a month or two after this time last year."

"I suppose it was you who told them about Marinha?"

Bettina was puzzled. "Yes. I had been here two years before."

"Did . . ." began Caroline, and stopped, suddenly feeling she was going too far. She was bewildered at her own perception: Bettina's story was to her, at this moment, like the part of a pattern from which one can easily guess the rest.

"Did what? Come on, out with it."

"Did you tell Hélène about Marinha as well?"

"What, so that she could bring her rich English friend? Perhaps I did. . . . Perhaps there's not very much I can tell you after all, my darling."

"There's something. Tell me why your plan didn't work."

"It did very nearly work. It was all fixed up. I didn't start with Paul, of course. I started with Hélène. At last I got her to agree that Paul should guarantee Leo, to secure his admission to England as a refugee, and he would find some friend of his to guarantee Robert. I promised her that they should be no burden. I swore the money would be found to keep them, if only Paul could get them into England. And I promised, on top of that, that they would not stay in the country. I promised that they should go on to a colony or somewhere. There was a big official from the Dominions Office staying in Estoril last year. He became friendly with me. He promised me — I made him swear on a Bible — that if they could both get to England, he would help them on. Only they must get to England first."

"Well, what happened then?"

"It wasn't so easy as we thought. The Home Office, or whatever they call it, made delays. I kept on writing to Paul from Paris. At last in the spring it seemed everything was fixed. Paul got a note in London that he could apply for Leo to be admitted. Once

Leo was in England, a friend of Paul's had promised to send in a guarantee for Robert. Paul came out here a month ago to fix things up with both of them. I thought then it was all going to come right."

"Well; what happened?"

"Until the last few weeks it seemed everything was fixed." Again she paused.

"Go on," said Caroline, "d'you think I'm going to be shocked, or something?"

"Maybe you will be shocked, my darling, when you've heard it all. But what happened was quite simple: Leo became very friendly with Paul — and Hélène did not like it."

"Why on earth should she mind that?" asked Caroline. "D'you mean she knew about the drugs — and was afraid Paul might go in for all that, too?" She paused, not getting a reply. "Anyway, Hélène couldn't keep two people here — in danger perhaps, or on the way to danger — just out of jealousy?"

"No, she couldn't. She might have liked to, but she wouldn't do it. It would not have been proper, and Hélène knows what is proper and what's not."

"So then . . . ?"

"Then, my darling child," said Bettina, "came the scandal of the fisherboys."

Caroline stopped where she was. "The scandal of the fisherboys," she repeated slowly. In a flash the story Robert had told came back into her mind. But though it clearly belonged, it did not make sense, and on all this her perception threw no light. "What scandal?" was all she could ask.

"Leo became friendly with a fisherboy. He was always asking him in, and going to see him at his house. He used to go about with him arm-in-arm. One day the fishermen went for Leo. They attacked him in the street."

Caroline struggled to get the picture clear: "But Robert thinks the trouble was because he told the boy's brother — the sick man from the shore — to eat tomatoes."

"Nonsense!" said Bettina bluntly. "Robert knows everything. How could he help knowing it? Isn't he about with Leo all day long?"

"Then couldn't he make Leo behave sensibly? I can't see why the fishermen should mind Leo going about with the boy — but I suppose he seems to them a foreigner, and different. Anyway you can't live in a place and keep on having rows. It isn't worth it."

"No," said Bettina. "It isn't." She spoke slowly, and Caroline could feel Bettina's look upon her. It seemed a questioning look.

"But there's one thing I don't follow in all this," Caroline declared. Bettina turned a half-frightened glance towards her. Caroline had no time to consider why Bettina should look frightened, before fear changed to relief at her own next question.

"Why should all this silly trouble about a fisherboy affect the guarantee for them both to come to England?"

"When the fishermen attacked Leo and Robert, the police were called out. Whenever police are called out they must make a report. We guessed they would make a report on this case, so we made an inquiry and found out what they had said. It was bad for Leo — and Robert."

"How did you . . ." Caroline had begun to ask, but changed it to: "Senhor Quinta found that out for you?"

"Yes," agreed Bettina. "He had many drinks with the Chief of Police, and he found it out for us."

"So then what?" Caroline demanded.

"So then, of course," Bettina continued, "Hélène heard of the report as well as we did. The report would go up to the Government, and it would be available to the British Home Office when they inquired about Leo before he finally came into England. It is also our experience that the police of different countries exchange all kinds of information." Caroline checked herself from looking up at this, and Bettina went on. "Hélène persuaded Paul that it would be harmful to his career to guarantee and bring into England someone against whom there were police reports. If anything bad should happen with Leo while he was in England the police would be certain to make inquiries. They would see that Paul had given a guarantee for Leo, and they would very soon find out that Paul had been here when Leo had this trouble. Paul would have concealed something which he should have told, and his connection with Leo would be suspect. Paul has not great gifts of mind, and certainly he would have no chance in the Diplomatic Service if he should start with any kind of scandal."

"So Hélène persuaded Paul? And Paul told Leo that he could not guarantee him after all? And there was trouble?"

"Yes. There was a big scene in the chief café. That is why we do not go there any more. It was not Leo who made the scene. When Paul said all this to Leo one evening after dinner, Leo just looked at Paul quite quietly for a minute, then he said: 'Are you wishing to betray me, Paul?' He did not speak to Hélène or to me. He didn't say any other words to anyone. He just sat on his chair, and looked out onto the square, and once he took off his beret and ran his hands through his long hair — Leo has long gold hair almost like a girl. . . . It was Robert who made all the row."

"What happened then?"

"Then? Nothing. Just a common row such as goes on any day. A row, of course, was what Hélène wanted. If there was a row, then there would be no more meetings with Leo and Robert. I was sitting there in the café, and all the time I smoked cigarettes and looked only at Hélène. When Leo said quietly: 'Are you wishing to betray me, Paul?' Hélène looked very pale. She looked even a little frightened. I thought to myself: 'She will try and make Paul leave Marinha tonight.' But when Robert began to talk loudly and abuse Paul and his friends, then she looked safe again and comfortable. That was what she had expected. Now everything would be all right."

"And Robert could not see that?"

"If you have a child, dear Caroline, and someone walking past gives it a kick, you do not think what will happen, you just attack the man who gives the kick."

"And Leo is Robert's child?"

"A child is one of the things Leo is to Robert."

"You mean . . ."

"I mean that there comes a time for the child to leave its parents. And it seems to me that time has come for Leo."

"Shall I tell you what it seems to me, Bettina? It seems to me quite time for the parent to leave this child. I have not met Leo. I don't know anything about him except that he is a poet and has long gold hair. From what I hear of him, he is not only a child, but a baby. He must be the most helpless and selfish person still outside a nursery. He has ruined Robert's career. He has taken him away from his own country. He has lived on his work, and prevented him getting on. He has taken all his affection, and neglected him for other people. In every trouble Leo has looked to him for safety and protection. Whenever anything needs doing, it is Robert who must do it. Robert worries for both of them, and works for both of them — and now Leo has taken the last twenty pounds and gone off to Estoril! And while Leo is behaving like this, everyone is all the time thinking about him, and worrying for him. 'What will become of Leo?' 'Where will Leo go?' 'Is Leo happy?' 'Has Leo any money?' — and nobody takes the least notice of Robert, who is really much the more unusual person of the two." Caroline was conscious even as she said them that the last words sounded stilted and unnatural. All words sound stilted that are said to conceal other words, which are felt but must not be said.

"Caroline," said Bettina, quietly and kindly, "can it be that you love Robert?"

Caroline paused. Then "Yes," she said, "I think I do. I'm not in love with him," she quickly added, "but I think I love him." Then, her perception coming back: "It doesn't at all matter my telling all this to you, Bettina."

"Of course it doesn't matter — but why?"

"Because I can see that you love Leo."

X

THE JOURNEY BACK

CAROLINE and Bettina sat, in their cool summer clothes, in the angle of one of the stone windows of the fortress. Below them fifty feet of castle wall fell away sheer. Below that again some five or six hundred feet of cactus and shrub-covered rock ran down, at the sharpest angle on which shrub can grow, to the swarm of red-roofed, lemon-washed houses divided by the river's stony course.

Halfway down and to the left rose up the tall stone arch by which they had entered, giving onto the square where the same handful of soldiers were still raising small explosions of dust in the movements of their drill. As they looked out over the town and river to the rolling corkwoods the two girls could see nothing on earth so high as they were. They seemed to themselves to be sitting in the sky, and both of them as they talked kept fingering the massive stonework of the window, and glancing back into the courtyard of the fortress only a few feet beneath, for reassurance.

"You've told me something," said Bettina, "so now I'll tell you something."

"If it's good advice," said Caroline, "you can save it for another day. I've given it myself, and it hasn't done any good."

"All the same," said Bettina, "I do give you a piece of good advice. Partly for your own sake, because I like you — but a lot more for my own. It's all very well having an accomplice, but she ought to know what she's in for." Bettina paused. "Well, no. You can't know that," she added, "and perhaps it's just as well, but you ought at least to be shown a warning notice."

"I'm not going to back out now."

"*Now* indeed! Why, you haven't yet touched the fringe of things, my dear. You could get out of it at this moment without a single mark. You haven't even begun to be contaminated."

"Well, you're in it far enough. Why shouldn't I be too?"

"It's different for me. This is a clear and limpid stream to some of the things I've been in. Besides, as you may have noticed, I've already provided myself with a way out."

"Quinta?"

"Exactly. When everything goes too far, when it

gets to the point where I can't do any more, or am too frightened, I *shall* get out. I shall put myself in safety."

"As a Portuguese citizen?"

"If necessary, as a Senhora," said Bettina. "But you, my dear Caroline, you will go in neck-and-crop, and once you're in you may not be able to get out. Perhaps you will even be too proud to try. If things go well, you and Robert may just possibly come out of it together — that is, if you're serious in loving Robert. If they go badly, you will be drowned in the mud with the others."

"How is it you're so certain you can keep out, and I can't?"

"Oh God!" exclaimed Bettina. "I've been in all this so long. I know why I'm in it, how far I'm in, where I'm trying to get to, and when to give up. You can't know how far you're in, because you don't really know yourself, and you can't get out when you want because you're already a little in love, and will be more. The farther you go, the more you're caught. That's why I say, Get out of it while you can. Go away. Stop your holiday; go home. Or leave Marinha and go to Coimbra, or to Lisbon. I'll help you pack and put you on the bus tonight. You were called back by telegram. I'll tell you some people in Lisbon who will be friends and show you round."

"That's very good of you, Bettina, and perhaps I

shall accept your offer after all. I could still go. But if I stay, and I know you want me to stay really" — she shot a quick glance at Bettina to assure herself that this was true — "there's one thing I need to know, and which nobody but you can tell me." She paused, and then came out boldly with it. "If I stay, is there any hope? Am I certain to fail before I start? You know, and I don't. Is there any chance at all?"

Bettina considered, drawing a grass between her teeth. "You mean is there a chance to make Robert break with Leo? Is there a chance to *save* Robert, that's what you mean, isn't it?"

Caroline nodded.

"Yes," said Bettina. "For Robert there is about one chance in five. For Leo there's no chance at all. Leo is not a man, and never was. I think he is something different from a man, a creature of some other kind. I think Leo is more than a man, and many people think that he is less. But underneath everything Robert is a man like other men. Only he is unlucky. He has become entangled with an angel, when he should have fallen in love with a woman. Ever since he knew Leo his life has been anxious and ashamed. Leo is not ashamed, for he knows that he is what he is. He did not make himself, and does not feel responsible or guilty. You cannot alter Leo, or make him into something different. There are only two

[132]

things to do with Leo — to care for him as something
rare, or to beat him down with sticks and kill him.
That's what the fishermen tried to do, and they were
right. That is what will be done one day with Leo.
For a woman to fall in love with Leo is an act of
madness. For a woman to love Robert is not madness.
It might be dangerous, but it is not mad."

Caroline said nothing. She seemed absorbed in
throwing a fragment of cement at a bird which was
breaking a snail to pieces on the wall below.

"Yes," went on Bettina, "it is still quite possible
that Robert can go on living and be happy; and you
may be the one person who can help him do it."

"What makes you think that?" asked Caroline, at
once put on her guard by flattery.

"Because you have courage, and you have the
power to love — I mean, to see what somebody is
like and love them for what they are, not for the
picture you make of them which happens to be con-
venient to you. And there is something odd about
you, Caroline. You're not the simple person that you
look. If you were, you'd be no good in this. Robert's
not everybody's husband, but you're not everybody's
wife, though you may look it. You think too much.
You will only be happy with someone who is also odd,
and who has a mind as strong as yours. Robert has a
very good understanding, also he has more patience.
But you have got something he has not — a faith of

some kind. Something which is more than his own understanding, and which you could pass on to him. There *is* a chance for you. Everything depends . . ."

"What does it depend on?"

"It depends first on whether Leo will stay away for a few days, and" — Bettina hesitated for a moment.

"Go on," said Caroline impatiently, "what do you take me for?"

"And secondly on you. . . . That is to say on your experience. It is really a question . . ." Bettina actually began to stammer.

"What is it, Bettina dear? Come on, out with it, for God's sake!" Caroline held Bettina's arm close to make up for the impatience she was showing.

"Well, if you want to know," Bettina said, "it's this. I don't know if you've had a lot of lovers, or two, or none. The point is that you can't expect to be happy with Robert very soon. He may be happy with you, but you won't be happy with him — and if you expect to be, you'll be disappointed and everything will break down. It's bound to be a long time before things come right. D'you understand? Or does it all sound Greek?"

Caroline pressed Bettina's hand. She was far from following what Bettina's warning meant, but she realized she was going to need patience. She felt herself possessed at this moment of all the patience in the world. She was grateful, too, to Bettina for trying to give her advice, though she was well aware that, placed as she was, Bettina could not be wholly on her side. She gave Bettina credit for doing the best for her, Caroline, that she could, subject to her constraining need to do her uttermost for Leo. The two girls pressed each other's hands, and smiled, allies — with reservations.

Down below them, hundreds of feet down, but so close that it seemed a good jump would land them both in the back seat, a tiny car was crawling over the dusty square towards the arch that gave access to the fortress. The little figures inside had caught sight of the two girls on the battlement and were making signals to them to come down.

"That's perfect," said Bettina, stretching her long slim legs and getting up. "That's Paul all through — to bring us out here to see the castle, spend the whole afternoon eating cakes he does not like, and not even bother to walk up here before he leaves. Now he will never want to visit Vallado again, because he's certain he has seen everything there is."

Slowly they walked down the hill. As they passed through the arch Paul was already shouting and waving his arms. They walked with increasing slowness to give time for the last things they had to say.

"And now," said Bettina, "I think there's just one thing I can do to help. It isn't much, but it's necessary. Leo will *not* be coming back for a few days."

"But how . . ." began Caroline and stopped herself. She had no time to ask needless questions when the question of all had not yet been put. She held Bettina with her hand.

"You can promise that," she said, "but can you promise something much harder?"

"What?"

"If Robert and Leo *should* separate, can you guarantee to get Leo on his own into a safe country?"

Bettina considered. "You mean," she said, "can I promise you that, if Robert comes to love you, you are not taking Leo's last comfort and protector from him?"

Caroline shook her head. "No!" she said. "If Robert should one day want to come with me, can I promise *him* that Leo is going to be safe alone?" She waited, lips parted, for Bettina to go on.

"No," said Bettina slowly. "Only Hélène can promise that. Ask her yourself; she likes you. You might manage it. Don't spare the flattery — she'll see through it, but enjoy it all the same."

"So, Paul!" she shouted gaily. "I see you have been buying sweets. They will make a charming present for Hélène, and you can eat them all yourself on the way home."

"Yes," said Paul contentedly, "I have been buying a great many different things. I have bought you and

[136]

Caroline each some biscuits. And Maxim has bought a pretty scarf."

"For a girl?" inquired Bettina.

"For his mother," Paul replied.

"That is a very charming idea — which no one but Maxim would have thought of," said Bettina.

Already the heat of the sun was lifting off the town. Maxim was placed again beside the driver. The other four packed into the main seat together. Paul, having combed his hair and adjusted his scarf, fitted the creases of his trousers to his knees and lit a cigarette, took Hélène's hand. Caroline wondered if she would care to have her hand taken after quite so much preparation. She and Bettina settled down together; one of Caroline's arms lay along Bettina's shoulders. She felt great warmth towards this girl whom she had never known until a week ago, and whom after a week's time, she was sure, she would never see again. She would have liked to tell her of her feelings, and promised herself that she would do so before her stay came to an end.

Through a confusion of thoughts — about how she was to make use of the "one chance in five" in the short time that was still left her; how Bettina was to make sure that Leo did not come back too soon; about the complications she had already entered and the far greater complications which might loom ahead — one thing remained as a continual puzzle. What was

Bettina's part in the whole story? Why was she so concerned about what became of Leo? She had admitted to "loving" him, but what love was that which spent all its time planning for the beloved to be somewhere else? Was it Leo's poetry she loved, or his mind? Had he placed her under some obligation in their Paris days? Who, in the world of which Bettina spoke, was "us," and who was "them"? How was Leo's safety to be assured? In the same way that high officials in the Dominions Office staying at Estoril were brought over to his side? And what was "our" experience of the police of different countries? Had the drug business been left behind entirely in Paris, or did it reach out, perhaps, as far as Marinha?

The evening grew colder. The girls drew a rug over their knees, padded coats and anything that gave warmth around their shoulders, snuggled down still more closely to each other. Maxim in front was lost in his own thoughts, which seemed to take the form often of no thought at all. Hélène had laid her head on Paul's shoulder, and was complaining that they were going to be late, that they had not told the Senhora, that she would be angry with them, as she had been last time.

"We will pay extra," said Paul, comfortably, "and perhaps we will give her one packet of those sweets which we do not like."

Now the light was fading out of the sky. It had left the road and the trees on either side. In the falling dew the dust swirled up more slowly, hanging like smoke of a train behind them. When at last they reached the hotel the first stars were out, and the riding lights were up on the few big fishing boats which lay off in the bay all night.

Caroline walked slowly to her room. On the dressing table was a note.

I think it might be that while you are here you will like to hear the singing of the *fados,* the Portuguese folksongs. Leo and I enjoy them very much. They are not to be heard in cafés, but only from some of the village singers which I know. If you will like to come and hear the singers I will arrange with them for tomorrow night. Do not please say anything about this to the others, because it could be that they will ask to come as well, and I am not at present friends with them on account of certain things. I hope you will like to come, and so please send a message to me in the morning.

Your friend, ROBERT.

Caroline sat down on her bed and got out her pen.

DEAR ROBERT [she wrote], I should like to come and hear the *fados* very much. I shall tell the others I am coming to see you, but shall not say anything about the singing. Thank you.

CAROLINE.

She was glad to have the note, which she had been expecting. She would have thought better of the omen if its ten lines had contained no name but hers and Robert's.

XI

FADOS SINGERS

ONCE again Caroline was walking along the road beside the shore, as she had walked on the first night of her visit. It was late. The *fados* singers were at work all day. They could not come to sing until it was dark; besides, the *fados* were intended to be heard at night. The party was to last from ten till three. "You can lie in bed until lunchtime tomorrow," Robert had told her. "Leo and I, that is what we always do when we hear *fados*."

Underneath her arms Caroline was carrying two parcels. In one she had two bottles of wine. The other held a special cheese, which Bettina had told her was the delicacy of Marinha. She wore a cool light-colored frock, no stockings, an old silk handkerchief of blue and gold over her black hair, and she had a coat around her shoulders in case it should be cold on the way back.

If romantic, Caroline was also extremely practical.

She had learned long ago that, in any interview of importance, matters never go the way one wants them to unless one is perfectly clear beforehand what that way is. It is only in an established relationship that lovers can meet with no intention but to be happy together, and this was still far from being established. Moreover, time was short. She could not afford that most delicious luxury, simply to follow an attraction and see where it leads. She hadn't got the time to spend herself, and, if she hoped to do anything for Robert, their friendship would need to ripen fast, to ripen out of friendship altogether.

Nor could she leave the direction of things in Robert's hands, knowing that his feelings must be far more uncertain and divided than her own. In the position they were in, each meeting had to be a landmark. There was no room for the casual or unimportant. An hour together in which they made no progress was a backward plunge: two such hours must spell the end of everything. Each conversation, almost each sentence, was significant.

Caroline was quite clear then that this evening had to mark a big step forward in her friendship — in her love — with Robert. She was clear that it would rest with her to make sure that it did. She had even appointed to herself a test which would show whether the evening marked real progress, or must be written off as no more than a social engagement, and her

[141]

growing feeling for Robert as just another of her self-illusions — the "foolish notions" she had been thinking of that evening as she first walked round to visit him. Her test was simple, a tidemark of fact against which she could check her direction without regard to the drifts of feeling. Would Robert go to meet the midnight bus from Estoril — which he had met, she knew, every night since Leo left? Or would he either forget it altogether, or stay talking to her and let Leo take care of himself? If he stayed, she had won at least one round in the struggle. If he went, she failed; and in view of the short time left her, probably for good.

Robert was delighted with her presents. He explained to her, what she knew already, that the cheese was a favored delicacy, and she showed herself delighted at the lucky chance which had led her to choose it. "The wine, too, will be a great enjoyment. I have here only two bottles, and it could be that the singers will be thirsty enough to drink one whole bottle each."

The room was tidier than when Caroline had been there last. One corner of the mantelpiece had become a bookshelf, instead of the books being strewn all round the room. The pots and pans had been cleared away, stowed downstairs in the stable, she imagined, and the room had visibly been swept and dusted. There was a check tablecloth with food of different kinds — sandwiches, slices of cold ham, cakes, cheese, the materials for making coffee, and the four bottles of wine. In her honor, apparently, a box of sweets had been bought, and a bunch of flowers secured from somewhere — perhaps by giving money to a bewildered fisherboy to go and find some. A shaded lamp stood on the table, and there were candles in the corners of the room. The night was warm, but a small fire of fir cones moldered in the grate.

Caroline stretched herself into a large chair. "There's only one thing I miss, Robert."

"What is that?"

"Your ants. Where have they gone?" The dark living trickle no longer flowed across the floor.

"The ants has eaten all the honey which Leo and I drop. Now they are gone to another house where someone else has dropped some honey. Later, when I drop some more honey, they come back."

Robert was moving about the room still putting the last touches. As he moved about, the light of the lamp and of the candles caught his fine gold hair. His eyes were dark, yet brilliant. He was using his beret as a duster, flicking over the chairs and table, and finally as a hearth brush to sweep up some fragments of fir cone that had fallen from the fire.

That was like Robert, Caroline considered. If she'd been giving the party for him, the room would have been ready at whatever moment he came in: from that second she'd have stopped her preparations, and thought no more about them, only about him. But he had set himself the task of putting the room tidy, and must go on with it till everything was perfect.

"It is because this is the first time," he said apologetically. "I have never before tried to make a room tidy like this one is to be. I begin early this morning. By ten everything is clean. Then suddenly I notice, *underneath* everything is not clean at all. The top of the table is not dusty, but underneath the table it is very dusty. So I dust all the underneaths. I sweep underneath carpets, and I even sweep down those stairs, where we throw everything away since first we come here. I do that because I notice some kind of smell. That take till two o'clock. Then I eat lunch. While I eat lunch I see that the fronts of all things are clean, and the underneaths of all things are clean, but at the back of things it is not clean."

"At the back of what things?"

"Pictures, the beds, the chairs, the heaps of fir cones for the fire — at the back of all these things, there is still great dust. So I clean all the backs. That takes still two hours. Then I find that with cleaning the underneaths and the backs I make so much dust that the tops is again dusty. So it is six before my room is clean. So then I have one drink, or two; and then I clean myself. And now I am glad to see you!" He drew his chair up in front of her. "I am glad to see you, Caroline, and I can tell you that I have been hearing things about you."

Caroline sat up. "From whom have you been hearing things?"

"Never mind from whom. The things I hear are good. You would be pleased if you had heard them."

"I certainly mean to hear them," Caroline declared. "But first I want to hear from whom they came."

"From Bettina."

"And what did she say?"

"She say only one thing, but you will see yourself that it is enough."

"Go on," urged Caroline, "you can see I'm mad with curiosity. I'd sooner Bettina said something nice about me than anyone — or almost anyone."

"Bettina say," declared Robert solemnly, "that she know me now for many years. In all those years she know me, the most useful thing I do is to swim out to the raft and be there when you are carried past. She say that for this one act she forgive me many stupid things. Bettina, you know, is a friend of mine, but she is often angry with me. We are often angry with each other. We do not see with the same eyes. We think each other has a good heart, but is not very sensible in the head. 'But at last, Robert,' Bettina say to me this morning, 'you have done something sensible. It has not hurt you. See now if you cannot go on, and do two or three other sensible things as well. Try and do just one sensible thing each week.' "

"Shall you act on her advice?" Caroline smiled with pleasure. Behind the smile her mind was working. Why had Bettina seen Robert? Was it connected with her plan to keep Leo away for a few days? Was this one remark all Bettina had said about her? What were the "two or three other sensible things" which Robert should do now?

There was a knock on the door. "It is the singers," Robert said, and added, "It will be kind if, before they go, you will say to them some nice words about their singing." Robert was not one to leave the formalities to chance.

The *fados* singers shook hands all round, were given cigarettes and wine, and arranged themselves with a good deal of care on a low sofa in face of Caroline and Robert. The table was pulled close in front of them, and the lamp pushed in the background. The candles in the dark corners were put out, except one which the singer made a sign of wanting to have left. It would give him something to fix his eyes on.

In the three faces was little striking at first sight. The singer was short and plump, with fair hair cork-screwing back from a face that seemed slightly offended, but broke into a charming smile when its owner discovered he was not. He looked like any second-class international tenor, and could have mixed unnoticed with the business people on the bathing beach.

The two musicians were of another type, apparent at once as Portuguese or Spanish. They had neither the vulgarity of the bourgeois nor the defiance of the fishermen. Young, but already worn, thin, dark-complexioned, with black and deep-sunk eyes, they looked as undernourished as their clothes were worn. By trade they were small shopkeepers. One of them, Robert explained, mended shoes, the other sold pans and hardware to the women.

Slowly the musicians drifted nearer to their music, plucking at the strings between drinks and puffs of their cigarettes. They watched one another as they plucked, as though for some signal they would recognize. On the right of the musicians sat the singer. In the center was the shoemaker. Across his knees and chest was a guitar. On the left, immediately in front of Caroline as she leaned back into a deep but crazy chair, was the man who sold pots and pans, paler under his dark skin even than the other. His shoulders hung forward till they seemed to meet. His movements were hesitant, like those of an animal with brutal owners. His instrument, which he called "guitarra," had a round-bellied soundboard and six double strings of wire. It looked like some kind of mandolin. As they picked at their instruments, the man in the center caught the eye of him on the left, and with a jerk of the shoulders they were off.

They played two or three melancholy and drifting songs, and then the singer took up the note. The songs were short. They succeeded each other w th little pause. Sometimes it was not at once clear whether a new song had begun, or a variation of th old. The songs had variety, but a common character prevailed. You did not need to speak Portuguese, Caroline thought, to know how this character should be interpreted: it was the quality of wistful longing, longing for what cannot be, and a plaintive grief over that which is. It was not entirely romantic. It was not at all debonair or gallant. It was often sentimental, and sometimes artificial, but above all it was human. The falseness was human falseness, human shallowness, entirely without pretense. It was based not on any dream of perfection, but on the world we know and the wish that it were just a little easier to live in, a little warmer; that rewards came more fairly and more easily; that love and longing should, as a law of nature, meet their satisfaction; that, having met it, they should not so quickly fade. The words, Robert told her in a pause, were invariably banal. A sailor complains that he must go overseas. A girl moans that the leaves are falling off the trees. When those same leaves were buds, her lover was beside her. Now the leaves are gone, and he is gone as well.

But if the words and sentiments were common-place, their effect on the singer was quite otherwise. When the little man sang, he passed away into his song. He closed his eyes. He summoned up all his life into his lungs and throat. The sweat poured off him. He sang partly as a man, and partly as a woman, using the voice and notes of each. He looked at no one, thought of nothing but the song, seeming to fear if he looked round that somebody would catch his eye and smile and kill the music. With straining muscles of the throat and forehead, with painful expansion and contraction of his chest, with pressure of his hands upon the insides of his two plump knees, he drew the song out of himself. The manner of his singing combined the soaring and dying fall of the flamenco with something of the turns and trills of the Italian.

In the pauses, always short, he would look fixedly in front of him, occasionally turn a nervous eye towards his listeners, not for any sign of approval — rather, Caroline thought, to reassure himself that no obvious and foolish thanks were being offered — and would then strike off into some other mournful but comforting appeal.

The man with the mandolin never took his eyes off the third player, except momentarily to look down at his fingers. He would see in a flash the chords he wanted, set his fingers to work, and fasten his eyes again on the guitarist. He was completely concentrated on the music, but he was not drowned in it. He noticed whenever Caroline raised her head and looked at Robert, and a shout from the street could penetrate his ears.

The third musician, the sad and sickly figure with the caved-in chest, passed into a fit of rapture as he played. He handled his instrument with a tender but ferocious brilliance, not as though he were repeating anything he had learned, rather as though he and his instrument were performing a new act of creation in a mutual frenzy, or as though when they reached together a high peak of excitement, music were engendered by them on the air, and flowed out through them into the room.

He clung to his instrument and swayed it with him like a nursling. His fingers attacked it with a controlled violence. He tore from it at every second exactly the shade of feeling he required, set that shade trembling on the air, set the eardrums of his listeners vibrating to the influence which flowed through himself, making his instrument throb and moan, sing and entreat, ring or clash with absolute assurance.

As he played, he rocked to and fro, not evenly but irregularly, often against the rhythm, and occasionally a loud groan or grunt would burst out of his lungs. No one took any notice of this, not the other players, nor either of his listeners. Once or twice he sounded his instrument in some way differently. His partner gave the faintest glance of surprise, and Caroline felt that this which he now did was something utterly new even to his partners. Together the three went into a kind of holy rage over their music which gave it a quality beyond and additional to all excellence of technique, which brought a pain into Caroline's throat, making it after a time not possible for her to catch the eye of anyone there, even if she had wanted to.

Reclined upon the chair, she gave herself up entirely to the music, ebbing and rising in her feelings as it rose and fell, only getting up to fill the wineglasses and pass the cigarettes whenever there was pause, moving unnoticed because unconscious of herself. Once, when the guitarist seemed almost to have played his breath away, ending the song with an extraordinary and long-sustained dash of resonance, then slipping forward against the table and giving out the deepest of his painful grunts, Caroline slid out of her chair and pressed both her hands over his as they lay on the table. The man looked up at her with a long look and, when she moved back into her chair, something happened which had not happened before. Robert of his own accord touched her. He put his hand onto her shoulder as he passed round her chair to make the coffee. He did not simply brush against her as if by accident. He laid his hand firmly

[151]

and deliberately on her shoulder. Caroline could feel its imprint for an hour.

It must have been two the next morning when the songs came to an end. For the last hour her chair and Robert's had been close together. Caroline felt an assurance that she was understood, that they understood each other. As they met over and through the music, so they met and understood one another upon other planes as well. Whenever she looked up at Robert his eyes were on her; often his face was dark and troubled, but as he caught her look his face would clear. He seemed to regard her not merely with pleasure but in an odd way with approval, and to derive confidence from her being there.

After the singing, coffee was made. The musicians ate and drank a little, smoked a last cigarette, then turned to pack up their instruments. Caroline could hear Robert speaking to the singer, the leader, persuading him to accept twenty escudos for the evening's pleasure. When the matter was settled and the three were lined up to go, Caroline spoke slowly and carefully a phrase she had prepared and learned in Portuguese: "I wish to thank you three gentlemen very much indeed for the beautiful music. It was worth coming this long journey from London in order to hear it."

In the doorway as she was leaving, Caroline hesitated. Down below in the courtyard the musicians

were waiting for her. They were going to play her
home through the streets along the seashore to her
hotel. The first notes of a lullaby burst gently like
bubbles onto the still air of night.

Robert took her hand, "Caroline!" She looked up
into his dark eyes. "I watch you this evening with
great happiness. You are now my dear friend." He
was holding her hand in both of his. She put the
other hand up to his face and drew it down and
kissed him.

"You are my love," she said.

As, borne on a tide of music, Caroline walked out
of the courtyard and started home down the Rua dos
Pescadores, two thoughts floated through her mind
like clouds that cross each other: that she was hap-
pier than she had ever been before, and that it was
strange Robert had not come out to see her home.

XII

A WALK TO THE CHAPEL

CAROLINE slept on next morning until late. There was no one in the breakfast room when she came down, which was just as she had hoped. Paul had already led his forces down onto the beach to occupy strategic positions before the despised visitors came down for their maneuvers. She had a book with her, but she did not read it. She was quiet and contented on the surface. Underneath was the tension that comes with any serious undertaking when one is part-way successful. It would feel worse to fail now than never to have started.

Halfway through the meal a note was brought her by the little smiling water, who seemed to take pleasure in his task. No sooner had she read it than she felt she had been expecting this all along, and was aware of what she would read before she opened it.

CAROLINE: Will you come for dinner with me here tomorrow evening? Please.

ROBERT.

It was the shortest note she had had from him, and the first that had not mentioned Leo. She wrote an even shorter reply.

DEAR ROBERT: With great pleasure.

CAROLINE.

Although she had seen little enough of his writing, she was so familiar with the way he made each letter that she found herself imitating his broad-looped *l*'s and overlarge *e*'s without intention. Until the note arrived Caroline had been wondering how to spend the day. Now her course was plain.

"Hélène," she said at lunchtime, "are you three doing anything this afternoon?"

"No," said Paul, looking up eagerly in hope of a new amusement. "We never have anything to do in the afternoons."

"Oh, this is nothing exciting, Paul," Caroline told him — "except for me. I want to go up to the chapel on the top of the cliff. We've lived almost underneath it for so long, I'd like just to see what it's like."

"We can go in the lift," Hélène suggested, looking across at Paul as though wondering whether her child's strength would be equal to a proposed expedition, "and there's a café on the top where we can sit.

I think you'd like it, Paul. You haven't been up there for a long time."

"Good," declared Paul, pleased to have the problem of the afternoon decided for him. "I shall enjoy that, Caroline. It's a very good idea. And Maxim will come too. Maxim likes going in cars and trains, and things of that sort, don't you, Maxim?"

The lift was simply a large iron cage sliding slowly up well-greased metal rods. Except for a goat track skirting the side of the cliff, it supplied the only means of communication between Marinha, the fishing port, and agricultural Marinha, a series of gardens and vineyards on the cliff top. It had been built about the year 1890, and rapidly impregnated by its passengers with a combined smell of goats and garlic. In the half-century that had passed, the smell had thickened and enriched to an extraordinary degree. Stepping into the lift was like falling down a drain, but stepping out on the cliff top was equally dramatic. Clear air, after the three-minute journey, seemed strange to the lungs, too thin and cold for sustenance — and if Paul and his party drew out their handkerchiefs as they got in, the sturdy agriculturalists sat down to fan themselves when they got out. The air on the cliff top, they explained to one another, was extremely "strong." It took much getting used to — and it was the custom to get used to the strong air in the café, tying one's animals to the balcony or the table legs, before going on past the little chapel to the small holdings and farms beyond.

The chapel proved to be no more than a single room of great antiquity, perched halfway between sea and sky in what, Caroline thought, must surely be one of the twenty most wonderful situations in the world. It was built of blocks of stone, and lined with plaster. There was an altar at one end, before which a silver lamp was burning. The plaster walls were decorated with frescoes — Christ walking on the water and the miraculous draught of fishes — which appeared to be of great age. The setting of the scenes was Marinha itself, its beach and cliff and chapel — but, on top of the old, later artists had made additions to bring the picture up to date, not with any irreverence, but as a child adds smoke to a picture of a railway engine, for reality. In this way the lift by which they came up had been drawn boldly in onto the cliff face, and the blood-and-orange villa of Senhor Branca painted up above the foreshore. In the middle of the square a bus, half the size of the square itself, was unloading its gigantic passengers.

Maxim at once took the subject in hand; he explained that in Marinha, with the old fishermen's dress and the ancient style of boat, many of the old art forms and methods lingered on. The peasants and fishermen felt no special reverence for the past, because the past had been exactly like the present. The only real difference was that the men of the past were now dead, and the men of today were alive. Like the Homeric heroes they felt, if anything, a rather patronizing sympathy with their predecessors — and, no doubt, had painted in the bus and lift to emphasize their own superiority of technical invention. In the same way, if one looked closely, one would probably find that engines and propellers had been added to the fishing boats in which the disciples were struggling to bring the miraculous draught to land.

"What other arts survive in Marinha?" asked Hélène. "This is the only sort we've ever seen."

"Dancing," said Maxim, "and the *fados*. Haven't you ever heard the *fados*?"

"Oh yes," answered Caroline unthinkingly. "I think they're marvelous. I could listen to the *fados* singers all night; but I never knew they were specially old."

"When did you hear the *fados*?" Maxim asked. "Perhaps in Lisbon on the way here?" Caroline could feel the others turn their eyes towards her.

"I heard them last night when I went to supper with Robert," she answered, but though she spoke out boldly she could feel at once that, in the others' eyes, her not having told them of the *fados* singing implied a secret bond with Robert. "There were some men there from the village — shopkeepers, Robert said they were, but they sang like angels."

The one-roomed chapel did not keep them long, and on leaving it Maxim, who always understood Hélène's wishes concerning Paul, led him away to the cliff-top café for a drink.

"I should like to walk on a bit," Hélène declared. "How do you feel, Caroline? There's a little light-house on the point. Shall we walk along and have a look at it?"

So it's not only I who want to have a talk with Hélène, Caroline considered: she has something of her own to say to me. That ought to make things move more easily. She replied that she'd be very glad of the chance to walk a little, and the two of them set off.

"I hope you're enjoying yourself at Marinha," Hélène began, when they had left the path and begun the scramble out towards the point. "Two weeks in a year is not a very long holiday. I know, being in busi-ness myself."

"It's the most unusual holiday I ever had," said Caroline, "and that's just what I came here for — to find something different." She was preparing to re-mark politely how much of the enjoyment she owed to having met their party, but Hélène was already speaking. "Well, you certainly began it in an unusual way."

"Yes. I don't want any more drowning — but that's the only unpleasant experience I've had."

"And that, at any rate, gave you some new friends."

Caroline paused. Hélène, it seemed, was determined to talk about Robert and Leo, and as she herself wanted to do the same, she decided to give the conversation a sharp shove.

"Yes," she said. "It did give me some friends, some others besides yourselves who have been so kind to me. But I think they — Robert at any rate — have the feeling that you are not very friendly to them. I think" — and here she knowingly stretched the truth a yard or two — "he would like to see more of you all, but feels he would not be welcome."

This, it appeared, gave Hélène the chance she wanted. "Leo and Robert," she remarked, "are very unusual and gifted people. Only, between ourselves, the fact is that they are not very good friends for Paul." She spoke firmly and graciously, like a Queen Mother explaining a point of precedence to a young princess. It was clear she had thought out exactly what she wished to say: she was making a statement for the Court Circular, and removing any misapprehension there might be in Caroline's mind as to her own position.

"It is not that we do not very much appreciate art," she went on, "or that we do not like the unconventional. But for Paul, his future career is so important, at this moment he cannot afford to take any risks. Later on, when he is established, it will be different. Then he will be above criticism, and we can suit ourselves on all such matters."

"You mean," suggested Caroline, "that there is some risk for Paul in being associated with Robert and Leo?" She spoke with a slightly incredulous inflection.

"No personal risk, of course," Hélène replied. "Paul is not like that" — once again Caroline was left with a sentence of which she could hardly make head or tail in the moment's consideration she was free to give it — "but risk to his career, certainly. Paul will not find it altogether easy to get started in the Diplomatic Service. He needs friends who can help him on, not ones who might pull him back."

Caroline's tone of voice had stung Hélène to speak more openly than she intended.

"You mean," suggested Caroline, uncertain how much knowledge to show or to conceal, "that if Leo" (she could not bring herself to use Robert's name in this connection) "were to get into some trouble over here, it could be considered a black mark against Paul simply that he happened to have met him."

They were scrambling up a steep pitch of track, and Hélène, who was leading, turned round to give her hand to Caroline. "No, not simply to have met him. But it would be a black mark against Paul if he had guaranteed him — you know, guaranteed that he was all right to come into England."

"Oh, I see . . . and if some trouble had happened over here, how would it be likely to get known in England?"

"Through the police record," Hélène explained. "The police make an entry in their records every time they come in official contact with a foreigner."

"Ah! the police record," said Caroline, as though hearing of such things for the first time. "In that case, of course, you're bound to take precautions. Paul's interests must come first, and it won't do for him to be mixed up with the police. All the same, you must find it awfully difficult."

"Find what difficult?"

"Knowing where to draw the line. I mean, we are all willing, I suppose, to take *some* risks to save a life. The problem is to know just what risks to take. It must be frightfully difficult when it isn't even your own career that's being risked." Caroline paused, and then unleashed the word which she had been saving as her most effective arrow: "There is, after all, a sort of *propriety* in all these things — so much concern for one's own affairs, so much regard for other people's dangers. To behave correctly one has somehow to reconcile the two — hasn't one? A government might be shocked because one had helped someone against whom something or other later became known. And private people, I suppose, might be just as shocked because one hadn't."

Hélène looked disconcerted. Caroline, frightened at her own daring, pressed on: "I suppose no one of us doubts that there's a war coming — and these stateless Germans are bound to be its first victims. If their own country doesn't catch up with them at once, they'll be handed over to gain favor with the Nazis, or at the very best shut away in prison to rot by governments who don't see why they should take risks on behalf of someone else's nationals. It's not really too much to say that for them to get taken in, or not taken, is a matter of life and death. Death tomorrow, if not quite death today."

And now Caroline — her senses at their keenest, watching Hélène's face in glances as they struggled along the narrow path — saw suddenly how to make matters go the way she wanted. She saw that Hélène's purpose in asking her for the walk had paralleled her own. It had been to state her own case, to prove how properly she had acted in the matter of Leo, fearing what Robert and Bettina might have said. She saw that her own implied criticisms — even the farthing's worth of threat in her reference to what private people might think — had had an effect on Hélène, but she realized also that it would not last. Left to herself, in a half hour's quiet thought, Hélène would discount all this as coming from Caroline's own aroused feelings towards Robert. Now was the moment to push on, to secure an undertaking. And the way to do it, as she now so suddenly and clearly saw, was to restore Hélène's complacency — having let fall her hint of threat, to drop all shadow of criticism and appeal for help.

"I've been thinking about all this," she said simply, "because I'm anxious to help Robert. I believe that if he stays in this country he's doomed. I *might* just be able to get him out, if I do everything I can when I get back. But you can imagine what people will think, when I start asking them to help a strange German doctor I met on holiday in Portugal. There'll be good laughs all round over that! I don't know about my 'career,' but something of mine will certainly have to be risked if I'm to help him."

"D'you mean," asked Hélène, "you'll try and get Robert into England on your own?"

"Yes."

"By himself, of course."

"Yes, by himself."

"Do you think you can manage it?"

"I shan't even try, if it means leaving Leo alone here. If it meant that, I should simply be wasting my time — because obviously Robert will never agree to come."

The two had reached the lighthouse wall. Beyond was a courtyard, and then the light itself. From close to it was no longer a lighthouse but a squat white tower, capped with swiveling reflectors like a great insect's head.

Hélène put both hands on the wall. "Robert isn't in the police record," she remarked, as though in self-defense.

This was the moment Caroline was waiting for, the moment to drop all disguise. "If Leo weren't in it either, or" — it was best to be perfectly explicit " — or, if his name should be in, but got taken out, will Paul still guarantee Leo? On condition that he goes on to a Dominion and does not stay in England?"

Hélène had been outmaneuvered, and her face showed that she knew it. She hesitated, then slowly and with visible reluctance, "In that case," she said, "I think Paul would guarantee Leo."

Caroline was remorseless. "You promise?" she demanded. "If the police record can be removed — and if it's certain that Leo will leave the country before long?"

"Yes," answered Hélène. "In that case, I promise."

In silence they walked back to join the others.

XIII

THE VIEW FROM THE POINT

CAROLINE was back once more at the lighthouse.
All the way down with Hélène she had been wondering what excuse she could find to stay on up here,
while realizing that in common politeness, on her own
expedition, she must return with the others to the
hotel. She had bought them a drink and something
called tea at the café, and then, when they reached
the lift, luck had stepped in to help her.

The day's work had just ended; there was a crowd
of workmen from an unfinished villa going down; the
lift was full, and the man in charge refused to take
them all. In a flash Caroline had slipped out. To say
she would walk down by the path could call up only
protests; and one of the others — Maxim, of course —
would insist on staying behind instead. Caroline declared she would have a drink, and wait for the lift
to come back. This they understood, and accepted.

She had turned and come back up to the lighthouse by herself.

Her immediate feeling was of triumph. The two conditions that had seemed necessary if she was to help Robert were now fulfilled. Bettina, in some way of her own, had seen to it that Leo should stay on for a few days in Estoril. She herself, to her own surprise, had gained a victory with Hélène: if Quinta could get the police record expunged, if Bettina had not lost her influence over high Dominion officials, Hélène was committed to trying to get Leo into England. And since Paul had already received a note from the Home Office giving him leave to apply for Leo's admission, it was now simply a case of writing a servile letter to explain why he had not made application sooner. Any good lie would do: once the decision to grant a permit had been reached, it would certainly not be revoked just because Paul was slow in acting on it. Meantime, if money was available, the police record could probably be expunged at once. It might be necessary, too, for Bettina to go to England to make sure the Dominions kept their word; but, taken all round, it was not too much to hope that Leo would be in England in a month or six weeks' time.

Caroline's mind raced on. The mere absence of Leo would itself be gain to Robert. The main thing, of course, was to get him into England, too, but in the meantime how much more peacefully he could live here on his own! What freedom from risk and worry without Leo! She saw Robert — in the weeks before arrangements could be made to get him in — working quietly among the fishing people; achieving success with his treatments, making cures, becoming popular; even the Lisbon Government, she imagined, coming to learn what he was doing, sending him a word of appreciation when he left. She saw herself, during these weeks or months, making preparations for him in London, but getting out here, somehow, anyhow, by plane to Lisbon — stealing a day or two from the office and making a week-end visit. She could feel the warmth of Robert's gratitude for his life restored and redirected, for all she had done for him already, and the much more she was going to do.

An excitement and elation filled her. She had been successful with Hélène, in a way she could never have expected and Bettina would find it difficult to believe. It was a sign of better fortune still to come. She had struggled through the painful period of her life, she had reached one of those happy spells when things of their own accord go right. Her coming to Portugal at all, her rescue from the sea by Robert, the crisis between Robert and Leo — which must have taken place almost the day before she got here — all these built up into a picture of events following a plan towards a predestined end, an end of happiness for Robert and herself.

Caroline passed the lighthouse. Here the track faded out, but a narrow goat path led on, turning back from the point to skirt the farther cliff, the one that must look over into the next bay, the bay that lay north from Marinha. It was a scramble here, but Caroline pushed on, using hands as well as feet, looking round every now and then to make sure she could get back, putting her hands down carefully because of the sharp cactus thorns. She felt, as she scrambled, a delight in her own sure-footedness which matched the clearness and assurance of her mind. She had only to look at a problem to see just what she had to do; she had only to look at the rock to see just where and how to put her foot; she knew at a glance which tufts would bear her weight, and which, while giving way, would hold just long enough for her to swing herself across.

With the sense of certainty went a sense of anticipation. Her eyes moved along the track, preparing for the moment when she would find herself overlooking a fresh view; meantime, her mind moved on to prepare itself for the coming struggle, the problem that still had to be solved.

Suddenly the goat track ended, so suddenly as to make Caroline catch her breath and press painfully close against the rock. What became of the last goat following it one could only guess, for between one stride and the next, the path had simply dropped away. Five yards before she was following a rough but visible route, and now, having rounded a bend, she took to air; she looked down onto a sea gull's back as it flew straight into the rock face below her. It was a rock face quite different from the one that looked out over the bay of Marinha; that one, facing south, basked all day in the sunshine; it was the color of something baked; lizards ran over it; a yellow weed, begotten of sunshine, lined all its cracks and crannies; long after the sun had set it was still hot to the touch. It seemed to have been handed down, a colossal relic of the Great Sun Age, the period of the classic love poets in whose works it never rains.

This face looked north; in color it was grayish black. Its base was black with spray, and tawny with a growth of seaweed hair. Sea birds, instead of sun-weed, beaded all its ledges. A few yards from Caroline a gull was sitting. She marked the yellow circle of his eye. She moved a hand; screaming his gull's alarm, he catapulted out on bent legs from the cliff face, and, as he soared far out into the middle air, seemed to draw off by unseen threads ten thousand other gulls, beginning with those nearest him, until at last the whole circle of the bay, the enclosed aerial bay which corresponded to the watery bay below, was filled with a frenzy of hoarse cries as the birds gyred and twisted, paying back in wasted energy of noise the effortlessness of their flight.

The gulls subsided into the shadowed rock. The waters of the bay rose and fell. Half a mile out to sea a fishing boat was beating up the coast. Caroline moved up the rock to a less precipitous corner, where she could lean back on her arms unaware of the hundreds of empty feet below. She was out of space for the moment, out of time as well. In the few days left her from her closing holiday it might be the last pause she would have. However matters went between her and Robert, she was unlikely before leaving to have time to herself. Tomorrow, she was convinced, the dinner with Robert tomorrow, must decide matters between them once for all. In the record of her life, tomorrow was the day of destiny. She had come up here for one purpose only, to prepare her attitude towards that coming day.

There are some men and women who, approaching a day which they believe charged with importance for their lives, prepare nothing, feeling perhaps that to make plans is to interfere with fate — and aware in any case that to make plans requires concentrated thought and the laborious weighing of possibilities against each other. Caroline was not frightened of the effort of thought, and she had learned long since that events are like children, they require a certain guidance from outside, if the blind element in them is not to outweigh the reasoning.

Again, there may be some women who, approaching the critical meeting with their lover, leave everything to him, having formed no picture, taken no decision as to how the meeting shall turn out. If such women there are, Caroline was not one; and she had had no difficulty in convincing herself that, whatever may be normal rules for love affairs, in this case it was necessary for her to see matters clearly and take decisions on her own. She had to know what she was about and where she was trying to get to, because if she didn't, nobody else would. In the situation in which Robert found himself, a situation of conflicting loyalties, with duty and affection dividing on both sides, he must be far less capable of choosing and keeping to a course than she was.

The fact before Caroline was simply this: if she hoped to secure enough influence over Robert to carry out a plan on his behalf, she had a couple of days in which to do it, and one evening and a night in which she could be reasonably sure of having him to herself. In four days' time she was due to leave. At any time after tomorrow Leo could be expected back: when he came, it was necessary that he should find Robert already committed to a plan which involved their separation. He himself had to prepare for a journey to England which would not be long delayed, and he must agree to Robert's following, as and when he could, with the help of a girl he had never seen or heard of, who detested him in advance, and whom he must almost certainly dislike.

Put bluntly, as Caroline was accustomed to put things to herself, she had no hope of getting Robert out of all this mess unless he were in love with her. In the short time that remained, that could scarcely be possible unless he were her lover.

But that, by itself, was very far from being all. It was not just a case of Robert wanting her, and her accepting his advances. She was required to take risk on a much greater scale: for the moment, indeed, she was required to take all the risk.

The last thing, it seemed to Caroline, Robert would be likely to do, with his painfully sharp sense of honor and the consciousness of his own confused and false position, would be willingly to involve herself with him. If sense of honor should not prevent him, pride certainly would. Touchy and exposed as he was, the only assurance Caroline could give him lay in making herself still more helpless. Her only hope of "saving" Robert was to let him feel, beyond doubt, that she loved him; not that she wanted him, or would like to marry him, or saw in him a refuge or a trophy for herself, but that she set his happiness above her own. He must be sure of all she could give him, without even the necessity or risk of asking for it. He must actually be convinced that, in accepting her love, he was as it were "doing her a favor," was consulting what had now become her interests more than his own.

She must be prepared to take the one course which as a woman she had been most taught to avoid — the abandoning, not merely of defenses, but of a cover for retreat. For if, beset as he was, the offer of her help should strangle or oppress him, he must be free — she told herself — to brush her aside, and not seriously disturb himself in doing so. All the sharp points of the situation must be facing towards her. If Bettina was right, if, at some deep level, Robert was humiliated and distorted by the circumstances of a life not natural to him — however willingly begun and however desperately clung to — then for a woman to betray herself, of her own accord to give up her reserve, to come out of her natural fortified position in order at any cost to reach him, that might be — it "could be" as Robert would say — the life line on which he, on which they both, would struggle to the shore. Caroline had satisfied herself there was no other.

It was this, this certainty that her reasoning was right, and her decision uninfluenced by wishes of her own, which reconciled her to the idea that she, by herself, was planning a future which concerned them both. She was taking decisions, she admitted, but only because she could see the course more clearly, and she absolved herself of all self-interest in what she planned.

It was with a mind almost at peace that Caroline began her scramble back. The heat of the day was over. From far out across the sea the fishing boats were beginning to draw in along the radii whose center was the bay of Marinha. Beneath its veil of mist the antlike activity of the fishing beach was at its height. The last swimmers had left the bathing shore; the first sleepers would soon be beginning to come down, replacing in the sun-warmed sand the lollers to whom they had let their houses.

When Caroline reached the chapel, the lift had not yet arri.ed. She turned towards the café. There, to her surprise, she saw Maxim seated. She would have hidden if she could, but there was nothing for it but to go on.

He rose, as she approached, with his usual politeness. Caroline had seen him until now always in company. She noticed a new assurance in his manner. "I came back to meet you," he declared. "I saw the others into the hotel, and then took the next lift up. I thought you might be glad of an escort. It is not always pleasant in the lift."

Caroline was relieved of any need to answer this by the waiter's coming up and Maxim's ordering their drinks.

[175]

"You were a very long time," he said. "I have been
sitting waiting for you almost two hours. At first I
expected to see you every minute. Afterwards I was
determined not to leave, in case anything had happened to you."

"I went round to the other side of the point, to the
bay with all the sea gulls."

"You should not have gone there by yourself.
Even among the village people it is considered
dangerous to walk there alone. If I had known you
wanted to see the bay I would gladly have come
with you."

"Thanks," said Caroline. "I just wanted to be by
myself and think a bit. Where I went there was no
danger at all."

As soon as she had said it, she felt guilty. It was
after all considerate of Maxim to wish to see her safely
down in the lift. However, the snub, if there was one,
passed over his head.

"I have been looking for a chance to talk to you
alone," Maxim was saying. "You must know that I
have watched you with the greatest interest ever
since you came. Somehow it has never been possible
to get you for a little while to myself. I am very fond
of Paul and Hélène, but one does not wish always to
be in the company of another couple — even if they
are people whom one likes. You see — I also can
appreciate solitude."

"I hope you enjoyed a little solitude while you were waiting." In the awkwardness of having to talk at all, everything Caroline said sounded wrong even as she said it. Now, where she meant to discourage, she was being pert. Maxim took this as invitation.

"But better than solitude," he declared, "is to be with another, when there is fellow feeling between the two. Are *you* not at all lonely here? Do you really prefer always to be on your own? I have been most attracted by what I have seen of you in your short stay. I should indeed be happy to become your escort. It is perhaps too early to speak of affection . . . but it may be before long, if you are unattached? We could at least make the holiday more entertaining for each other."

Caroline looked at Maxim, so good-looking, so well-turned-out, so full of his own kind of charm — so full he seemed to take pleasure in it himself. Wasn't he exactly what she had come here for — the very picture she had had in mind of the holiday episode that should banish Hilary? Banish Hilary? This would be Hilary all over again. She smiled at him, but it was a smile quite fatal to his cause.

"Thank you very much indeed, Maxim," she said. "I am flattered by your interest, but I am a solitary animal — and on this holiday at any rate I mean to stay one." Caroline intended to speak kindly, but experience was lacking. She spoke much too kindly —

[177]

with the kindness which showed she had not a trace
of interest in him. It was costing her, visibly, nothing
to refuse. She had not even to consider his offer and
put it from her with regret. For her, the offer and
himself were nothing.

Something in Maxim's face changed; behind the
charming man the face of a spiteful small boy could
suddenly be seen, the small boy who throws a stone
at the lighted window, and then runs. "If it's because
of Robert Kranz," he said, "I'm afraid you will find
that hopeless. No good. He's the other sort."

Caroline could by no means understand the words,
but she felt the brutality behind them. It fell on her
mind, disturbed and exposed with long self-question-
ing, like a heavy kick. It took her a moment to recover, then she leaned across: "There is after all one
favor I should like to ask. Will you wait for the next
lift, if I go down in this one?"

Though there was still pale sunshine on the cliff
top, at its foot, among the houses, twilight had come
down. Caroline, hurrying through the streets, was
reminded of her first evening, when she had found
every hotel in Marinha full and was expecting to sleep
out on the shore. At a crossroads, the last before the
hotel, she paused. Noise, shrill and unexpected, a
sound like children shouting, made her stop.

Across the road, at distance of a block or two away,
a rabble of boys was pouring, indistinct in the half-

darkness. She thought for a moment they made up a religious procession of some kind; torches were being waved, and there seemed to be the carrying of a figure upon shoulders — but there was something mocking and unruly about this procession which put the idea of religion out of mind. The boys were jeering. The figure was an insult; intended, probably, to be burned. They would burn it with hoots down on the shore. A torch flared up. Before the figure, rising and falling on the boys' shoulders, disappeared from sight, Caroline caught sight of its head. It was a dummy, crude as a Guy Fawkes. The face, from where she stared, lacked shape, but the head was covered with long yellow hair.

XIV

AN EVENING VISIT

TOWARDS eight o'clock next evening, Caroline was once more on her way round to the Rua dos Pescadores. She had passed the morning with her party on the bathing beach, joining in their meaningless and amiable chatter, arguing with Paul over the merits of different kinds of ice cream, speculating in apparent good nature with Maxim as to why Bettina and Quinta should have chosen this moment to leave for a few days at Estoril, and as to how soon they might be expected back. It was not, Caroline concluded, that Maxim, or anyone else, particularly missed Bettina. But they formed together such a cosy band of indolents the absence of one let in a cold draft on the rest.

After a slow and peaceful day, Caroline was feeling calm and possessed of all her faculties. She had done her thinking: her plan was the best one she

could make. So far things had gone right; to carry
through to final success might, or might not, be
in her power. She would never be better equipped
for success than she was at this moment.

Robert, it seemed, was not only expecting, but
listening for her. For the first time since she had come
up the whitewashed outside staircase, there was no
sliding of bolts following her knock. The door stood
half-open already, and it was pulled wide open from
inside as she came up the stairs. She had no time to
straighten her short lime-green dress, rearrange the
white jacket round her shoulders, or touch the vigorous mass of her black hair. She did not mind. All
these things and everything else about her was in
order, as she knew. She was not only in order. She
was looking this evening as beautiful as she would
ever look: it was quite natural for the door to open
of its own accord as she came up the stairs.

Robert might have been preparing all day for her
to come, so fresh was everything inside. The table was
laid, the food set out. There were flowers, and candles had been already lighted. Robert lifted her coat
off her shoulders and pulled up a chair for her. There
were no open books in the chair where she was to sit,
no flattened-out tube of toothpaste on the mantelpiece, no half saucepan of boiled potatoes on the
hearth.

"You've made your house look very tidy," Caroline

remarked. "I suppose you haven't thought of keeping it like this always?"

"No," said Robert. "It makes too much work for the memory, to remember where is the right place for each thing to go. Yesterday I sit down in the morning, and I think out — where is the right place for each thing to be? In the afternoon I put all the things in the right places. Then yesterday evening and today I use some of my things, and after each thing has been used I am obliged to think: 'Where is the right place to put it back?' After taking off my slippers I sit in that chair where you are now for some minutes, and I think — where ought my slippers to go now? In the end I can only think: the slippers should be on my feet. So I put them on again. There is nowhere else in a tidy room for a man's slippers to be."

"And when the room is in a mess . . . ?"

"When the room is in a mess, I simply look round it and see at once the thing I want. Then when I have finished with the thing, I leave it where it lies until I want it next. But I see you do not like things to be like that," Robert concluded with a delightful smile, "so now I have altered them. On your account, everything from now on will be in confusion, but at least it shall look tidy."

The meal was cold, and came out of the sea. Robert put plates of different things in front of her. As they ate and talked, the light faded away from beyond the open windows and the candles grew in strength. It seemed to Caroline that the world outside their room was fading and diminishing away, and that the whole of life for them had contracted by degrees into the candle pool.

"I hear you went up on the cliff top yesterday."

"You hear everything that happens in this village, Robert. Yes. I took Paul, Hélène, and Maxim for a great expedition. I wanted to see inside the little fishermen's chapel."

"How do you like the wall paintings, the apostles catching fish with Senhor Branca's cartouches?"

"I found them very touching. Maxim explained to us how they were done, and when we had finished listening he took Paul to eat five or six ices. Meantime Hélène and I went for a walk . . ." The sentence petered out because Caroline had not made up her mind whether to refer yet to the subject of her conversation with Hélène. Besides, she was expecting a sharp comment or two from Robert about Maxim's supposed knowledge or Paul's greed. She was relieved when they did not come. She did not want sharp comments on anyone this evening.

"Did you have a good talk with Hélène?"

With those words from Robert they were aware that the conversation strode a yard closer to each of them. Whatever Caroline might have spoken of to Hélène, it must certainly be something which concerned them both. The veil of speech was wearing thin; in a moment the reality of feeling might show through.

"I had the talk I wanted." Now that Caroline had reached the point where she could tell Robert of the arrangements made for Leo, she found herself sheering away. She did not want to mention Leo, and she did not want any gratitude from Robert. All that, if it was coming, could come later.

Robert was silent; he seemed to be considering. Then, when he spoke, it was to say something unexpected: "I believe, Caroline, you would like me to be friends with those people again — with Paul and Maxim and the rest. Am I right? Is that what you would like?"

"Of course I should like it," Caroline answered, happily regarding this as an effort towards pleasing her. "Why shouldn't you be friendly with them? You can't, of course, seriously be friends, because after all . . ." She hesitated for a word.

"Why because?" In a flash Robert's old suspicions had returned.

"Because they're too slight," Caroline answered promptly — loyalty to her acquaintances could go out of the window in comparison with Robert's feelings. "I like them, you know. They've been kind to me. But they don't go very far down into the water. For you, it would be a most unequal friendship."

Robert's brow cleared. "I thought you were going to say something different," he said. But the cloud had not entirely lifted, and Caroline's next words brought it back darker than before.

"How's your patient?" she asked. "You know the one I mean; he used to lie out under an umbrella on the shore."

"I don't know how he is," Robert answered, "I am at present not able to see him." He paused, looked up at her, and then continued with a visible effort to give her his confidence which Caroline actually felt as something painful underneath her heart: "His family and the other fishermen do not permit me to go there. It is on account of the trouble there was over the sick man's brother. I had not been there for some days, and yesterday I thought I should go to see how the sick man is getting on. . . ." He hesitated. . . . "There were some boys there when I went, and there happened an unpleasant incident. I do not go there again at present."

As Robert talked, a scene was passing before Caroline's eyes, visible just over Robert's shoulder outside the candlelight. There was a dark street with waving torches, moving forms, and a sense of the shrill shouts of boys. The scene passed by, a misty reflection from the sight of yesterday — but now suddenly with an unbearable addition. Had it been present in reality? Had she seen it with her eyes, but re-

[185]

fused permission for the appearance to be registered in her brain? Or was it a private nightmare of distortion, conjured up to undermine her courage and destroy her happiness? For this time in the procession of the jeering boys there were two dummies, two fair-haired figures, rising and falling in the torchlight to their cries.

Robert stopped speaking. With an effort Caroline recalled herself from the darkened street and tossing shadows. Robert had placed his confidence in her. He had told her of a humiliation, speaking against his pride, which had been, almost visibly, counseling his silence.

"This is your bad time, Robert," she began. "These are the days when there is a cloud over your star. I can see some of your difficulties, and I know there are others which I can't see. These are the times when it is hard to do anything right; and if you do do it, it will be misunderstood. You must seem to yourself like a person in a mist, which distorts all his movements, and even twists his face into strange shapes . . ." And as Caroline began to speak she saw that she had embarked on the struggle of the evening. The battle was joined. She had taken upon herself to give him comfort; it was now quite necessary that she should succeed. She had to impress her own mind and her own attitude upon him, changing his. She must manifest the power, not only to console, but vitally to transform his mood; and the transformation must last when she was gone. It was not simply that she must leave with him this evening a picture of herself which he would cherish. That was commonplace and obvious enough. She had to do what was far harder, to give Robert a new and satisfying imprint of himself, in place of the one he had for a long time found disturbing, and was now, she thought, beginning to detest. She must conjure up out of herself that image of him which she so closely cherished, and make him comprehend and accept the likeness as his own.

Caroline talked. At first she had to force herself to talk. Her words fell awkward and constrained, but she went on. She told him of the troubles she saw in his life, of the gifts and qualities she felt in him. She went over the short times they had been together, showing him how he had done this and thought that, revealing new and still new sides of himself, recalling words he had forgotten and gestures he never knew he made, pleading, arguing, brushing objections away, speaking and refusing to fall silent.

She was like a child running at speed down a slippery track above a river. The impression of the next few yards comes up before the mind with absolute distinctness, and while the feet fly over the selected footholds the eye is already ranging far ahead, and again the feet jump and pause and fly with the assurance of memory, not vision.

Caroline saw before she reached them the explanations that would be difficult; she knew exactly how deep to go in touching on the things that would disturb him most: she enjoyed for those few moments a seventh sense of understanding, with a flow of passionate speech and argument.

And at last, as she talked, she began herself to feel how convincing was everything she said. She had received so vivid an impression of this man that, once she was able to bring it out as words at all, it carried, by its own clarity and force, the certainty of being true. Other people might have other views of Robert and his talents: to some he might seem a henchman or stand-in to some vanished Leo. To Caroline he stood out in his own right a radiant being — and who had ever seen so clearly, or thought so much about him, as had she?

When she ceased speaking, something had happened in the room. There was a sense of danger. Robert did not look at her, or thank her, or get up and touch her hand. He said nothing at all. But she was suddenly aware of him in a new sense. She was aware of him as a physical being. When she spoke again, she had, in the silliest way, to exercise control to prevent her voice from shaking. The sound shook, and the words did not come out as she had intended. All she said now was entirely trifling and artificial, but it was necessary to talk because he said nothing — and there was a painful tension in the air which was only to be relieved by speech. Her throat was dry, and the points of her breasts were painful to her.

When she referred to the book she had seen on her first visit, meaning to ask — in sheer groping for a subject of discussion — if he had studied it further, she said "your eyes" when she meant "your book of eyes."

If she managed to utter the words she had in mind at all, they came out with a quite different effect. She was telling him of the evening before, of how the musicians had played her home through the streets, then she had got quickly ready for bed, and stood at the window while they played her a last song. To the three men playing in the shadow two soldiers had come up, and argued with the little singer for disturbing the night's peace — until he put an arm round each of their shoulders, and all three went singing off together. That was the story as she told it; but it was not to the men singing in the street that their minds turned, it was to the girl standing sleepy in the window, and when Caroline tried to say what she could see from the window "in the night" she said "in the nightdress" instead.

Was it possible, Caroline wondered, that only five minutes ago she had been speaking to this man as she had never spoken to anyone before? At this moment it seemed hardly possible to exchange a word. She had thought and spoken of him "as a friend." As she looked at him now he did not seem like a friend at all. He bore no resemblance to a friend. A friend is familiar. This man was altogether strange. Altogether strange was his fine gold hair, which stirred in every draft from door or window. Strange was his sunburned skin. The chest that showed through the opening of his white silk shirt was unfamiliar. Unfamiliar was his narrow waist. His quick decided movements were strange and even foreign. His manner of pouring out wine, drawing the curtains, closing the door fast, had something strange. When he spoke there was a tremble, "shake" was the word that came to her, in his strong voice. It annoyed her, this shake. What had his voice got to shake about?

And yet, though all this disturbed her, Caroline understood quite well inside herself the meaning of their thirsty aimlessness. She understood, if he did not, why the conversation strayed and staggered, and the glasses continually ran dry. All this was well. It was all in order, like herself. What was not quite in order, what was not quite beautiful and in the scheme of things, was a feeling she had, and could not describe, a feeling that centered not on her, on Robert.

It was as though she were entirely occupied and present with all her faculties, dispersed and not quite in control, yet present to her very fingernails — but the same was not true of him. Robert was not so present in the moment — not utterly, not down to the last fine hair of gold. Something that should have been there, particularly there, was not. He was like a picture very slightly out of focus. How did she know it? In what did it consist? Only in nothings. A pause too long in finding an answer — though sometimes indeed she herself took half a minute to collect her thoughts. A shade too much awareness of her comfort and convenience: he noticed so much to do with her that clearly he had not lost himself.

With another man the reason for so much attention would be obvious — he would be following a plan, acutely on the watch; from Robert it had the opposite effect, as though he were keeping himself up to the mark. There, that was it. There was occasionally, and for only a vanishing second, an impression of something strained and forced. And when, risking everything, Caroline ventured to say a word of Leo — breaking her own rule and intention because somehow to have no mention of him had become more artificial than to speak his name — Robert answered, at once and with a smile, blocking the question.

"Had he any news of Leo?" she found herself asking. He "did not expect to hear anything from him for some days" was Robert's not quite direct reply, given so quickly that it seemed to have been prepared. Prepared no doubt it had been; clearly it was

evasive; but even in evasion she could feel the candor
and directness that she loved. For it troubled him to
use even this shade of deception. His eyes looked
darker and the skin of his forehead made a faint unconscious movement.

The meal was over. The table had been cleared.
Robert had gone into the alcove where the oven
stood to make some coffee. Caroline, glad of a moment to herself, went over to the window. In spite
of the uneasiness she felt in Robert, she had no doubt
that everything would turn out as she hoped. She
had ceased now to have a conscious plan, to try to
control their talk or the movement of events. They
had reached the smooth water that precedes the
waterfall. She simply stood. She stood by the window, looking out from a corner of a curtain onto
the thickening night, the stretch of street falling
away down to the sea, the glow from doorways of
the lighted lamps, the crisscross in the road of indistinct and shrouded figures, which might be children
close at hand or men and women down beside the
water. In her eyes were the movements from outside.
Her ears were filled with noises from the room: the
flare-up of the stove, the clash of cups being put
ready, the lighter jingle of the teaspoon — she knew
there was only one — being dropped into her saucer.

Through the gap between the curtains her mind
traveled out, over the four days' journey she had

come between this country and the land where she was born. She saw the whole waste of water, from the estuary out of which the ship had carried her ten days ago, to the coast a mile away where she had nearly drowned. Different countries, but the sea united them, the sea which, being without shape and of one substance and density throughout, expresses most perfectly the idea of space. The sea, united under the gathering night, was simply so many hundred miles of shadowy space, the distance she had traveled to arrive at this moment in this room. She had come a great distance in order to get here, and she had come a great distance in her mind as well. She saw, with perfect clarity, the state of feeling in which she had first visited this room; she recognized, without the knowledge disturbing her at all, that she had hoped for a casual love affair with Robert, as a distraction from her own worries, and because it would be so appropriate, so obviously romantic, having been rescued by him from the sea which brought her here.

She saw how, already after the first evening, her original idea had vanished. Robert was now a person in his own right, not a distraction. Later, in further meetings, in consideration by herself, in talks with Bettina, she had come to realize the curious and complex position in which he found himself, distracted by confusing loyalties, sapped by humiliation rooted in the thing he cherished most. As she understood Robert better, as she called into play for him her powers of feeling and imagination, as she overcame in herself the tendencies to be shocked or frightened by what she learned, overcoming them so that she could more fully understand, and by understanding help — so Robert had grown in importance for her; but his value as a refuge or pastime had withered and disappeared, till now, as she stood and looked out into the night, she realized that the tables had been completely turned. She had wanted something from him, and she knew now that she was quite likely to get nothing. She had looked for some kind of solace for her own unhappiness. She felt herself now content to double, or to multiply that unhappiness, if it would bring comfort or benefit to him.

Suddenly, as she stood there, the sound of one of the songs they had heard the night before floated up from below, from the stable where Caroline could hear the horses stamp. The sound of the horses, the unexpected presence of a stranger, gave Caroline a cold shiver of surprise.

As he saw her shudder, the shade of anxiety fell from Robert's brow. He looked at her in amusement and delight. Setting down his tray of cups, he put his arms round her.

"You're frightened, little one," he said. "Could it be the horses? They do not come upstairs, you know."

"No, Robert," said Caroline. "I'm not frightened at all, only happy. The horses can come upstairs if they want to." She put one hand up and touched his fine gold hair. In a foreseen but still mysterious excitement, they clung to one another — in an excitement, in a frenzy, in a swirling dream.

It was not, Caroline admitted to herself, an altogether happy love-making, but first love-makings are seldom altogether happy. At least it had been a love-making. They had found and met each other. Next time would be more direct, more certain. They would have the peace of knowing they had met to love — a tension free from strain.

As she lay beside Robert with her dark hair flowing over his arm and chest she experienced a deep content. She had taken the risk on his behalf and had not failed him. They had only to hold on, and the future would open out before them. The danger and bitterness of disaster were behind. Immense problems lay ahead. There was the question of how she should get him to England and to safety. But practical difficulties are nothing to the difficulties coming from within. If she had brought Robert to be her lover, if Robert, against such forces fighting the other way, had loved her, environment and laws would not keep them apart. A government, after all, is made up of human beings. Laws and regulations — with the many exceptions to them — are enforced, or allowed, by individual men and women. Caroline felt prepared at this moment to tackle whole cabinets and parliaments, one by one, if it were needed to get her lover into safety. Caroline felt something which went beyond anything she had known, earlier this evening or at any other time. Then she had the knowledge that, even if things went wrong, the struggle would have been worth while. Now for a moment she lay bathed in the certainty that they would go right.

The certainty did not last long. As she looked up at Robert to try and convey to him a small part of what she felt, she saw Robert's face fixed in a set stare. She thought for a moment it was herself that he was looking at, with his eyes cold and an expression almost of horror. Then her heart missed a beat. She saw that he was looking beyond and over her. She thought the door had opened, and someone had come in without her noticing. Appalling as the idea was, she summoned her forces in a second to outface it. She would use this horrible event to show still more her confidence in Robert.

But the horrible event was not what she expected. Following his look, she saw now what held Robert's eyes. He was gazing at the clock. The hands showed a quarter to twelve. She felt his body stiffen, and he turned his eyes down to her with a look that banished illusion like the hand of death.

In a second he was out of bed and putting on his clothes. He said nothing. He explained nothing. Caroline needed no explanation. It was the bus that Robert had to meet; the bus that might be bringing Leo back to Marinha.

XV

THE FRANTIC SEARCH

IT was six o'clock of the following evening and Caroline, pleading a headache, had not yet left her room, when word was brought to her by the waiter that there was a Senhor below who wished to see her. Caroline tidied herself to come down to meet him. She felt sure that it was Robert, and that he had come with an apology. No apology could make matters right between them. No apology could even begin to touch the wound she had received, a wound in the deepest, tenderest part of her woman's nature. It was a deadly stroke, too deep for her yet to feel it fully. She felt like a man fallen on a mountain side, who wakes out of stupor, not yet to blinding pain, but to the slow perception that the snow around is colored with his blood, and that those bruised objects close beside him are his limbs, which somehow before long he must contrive to use again.

She went downstairs. It was Robert who was waiting. He looked as she had never seen him look. He was unshaved. His hair uncombed. He wore a pair of broken sandals, and his beret was screwed up tightly in his fist. Any idea that he might have come to apologize was soon removed.

"Why are you still indoors? What are you doing? You must come down. You must come out with me at once. There is no time to waste."

"Why? What's the matter, Robert?"

It appeared soon enough that the matter was Leo. During the morning Robert had rung up Estoril half a dozen times, trying to get in touch with him. He had not succeeded. In the afternoon he had called at the house of a Portuguese doctor he knew slightly, and got him to phone the hotel at which Leo had been staying. The clerk bluntly replied that the person they were asking for had been gone for several days, and they had no record of his whereabouts. They might inquire from the police. It was that word which had given the finishing touch to Robert's anxiety.

Robert was convinced that all this was the result of his own "harsh words" to Leo — this was the first Caroline had heard of any harsh words between them — and that, unless he found Leo soon, the end would be disaster. He saw already the figure stretched out on the carpet.

What did he want of her? Caroline asked. Surely

that must be obvious. She was English, wasn't she? And she had a good reputation. The word in Caroline's ears had a painful ring. She could get the police to make inquiries which they would not make for him. She could ring up the police in Estoril, and ask them if they knew anything of Leo. She would ring up the British Consul. No! It would be better not to do it from the hotel, where everybody would be listening. He would take her to a public telephone, and she could phone from there. All he asked was that she should hurry.

The incredible nature of this suggestion, that she should now be fetched out of her room to help him recover Leo, was clearly not apparent to Robert in any degree. He was — or seemed — completely unaware that she could have any feelings in the matter. He was simply demanding her help, not even as from a friend, but in the name of common decency for someone who happened to be in need. His whole manner implied that he was asking the least that could be expected. By such an attitude, at this moment, Caroline at first was utterly bewildered. What right had he to ask anything of her at all; above all to ask anything on Leo's account? Was he without common perception? Was it simply a piece of cold-blooded insolence? His behavior seemed the one thing needed to break down her resistance altogether.

Then her pride, which had carried her through so many things in the past, came to her rescue. If Robert could ask this, she could give — and she could see it through. By granting everything he asked she would shame him, if he were accessible to shame at all. If not, she would at least prove herself untouched, superior to what had happened. She walked straight out of the hotel with him, in the clothes she happened to have on.

They went first to the post office, where Robert's Portuguese seemed to be even more limited than she had supposed. He had difficulty in making it clear that they wished to telephone. When he repeated the number of the British Consul the woman failed to understand. He had to bring the book and show the number to her. To Estoril was a trunk call, likely to take ten minutes to come through.

For much more than ten minutes Caroline waited. When it got to twenty minutes Robert expostulated, and the woman replied that she had told them in the first place, it would take ten minutes — what were they complaining of? Caroline found herself staring, in boredom even greater than her misery, at a notice which showed a man in peasant dress firing a shotgun, which discharged clouds of smoke and small visible bullets at the pot insulators on the telegraph poles. She translated to herself the writing underneath the picture: "It is not the act of a well-bred gentleman to shoot at the insulators, which are the property alike of Government and people."

Robert complained again of the delay, with petulance. Getting no reply, he turned to Caroline. "It is impossible," he declared, red with fury, "to get the simplest thing done in a backward country such as this."

As he spoke, a man in the far corner of the post office, writing a telegram, lifted his head, glanced over towards them, and then quickly went on writing. Caroline was convinced that he had heard and noted. She realized in a flash what had kept Robert and Leo, what would always keep them, from the havens where they wished to be. For to Leo's doubtful reputation would always be added Robert's honest tactlessness. He would always be outspoken with officials, and then surprised they did not go out of their way to help him. He would lose his temper with them, quite justifiably, tell them a few harsh things in perfect truth, and then be surprised that later his wishes should mysteriously be crossed. Perhaps such words as these, "a backward country," forgotten by him as soon as spoken, had prevented their being in South America long ago. Perhaps they would one day do more to prevent the renewal of a visa than all the scandal Leo caused.

The phone was ringing. Caroline went to it. The voice was far away. It spoke in Portuguese. Caroline had to have the sentence repeated several times before she could catch a word known to her from her phrase book . . . *fechada*. The Consul's office was closed for tonight. It was already seven o'clock. The office staff had gone home.

As they came out into the street, Caroline could feel a paralyzing tiredness and headache; but it seemed her task was still only beginning.

"Since we cannot get the Consul," declared Robert, "we must speak to the police in Estoril. The people in the post office are impossible: I have found that many times. All people in post offices are impossible. It is necessary, therefore, that we ring up from a telephone outside. It will be easiest if we go to a fishermen's café on the shore."

It seemed to Caroline that it would, on the contrary, be most difficult, and most embarrassing. However, she held her resolve to do whatever she was asked.

They went down to the shore, to the café which Robert said was "the quietest." It was full of fishermen, of noise and smoke. The telephone was behind the bar. When Robert had made clear what he wanted they were allowed to pass through — with no specially good grace, she thought. The man asked what number they required; when Robert told him, argument arose.

Caroline guessed at once what was the trouble. The

owner of the café recognized the number, and was refusing to have a call to the police put through on his own phone. He did not like the police. His customers did not like the police. Anyone who wished to make contact with the police should make it somewhere else. He did not intend to have his café used for purposes like that.

Red-faced and furious, Robert broke into argument. It was a public instrument, he declared. The man had no right to dictate what calls should be made on it.

The instrument might be public, the café owner answered, but his café was private. He could not forbid anyone to talk to the police on the public instrument, but he forbade them to talk to the police inside his café. If Robert wished to use the public telephone for such a purpose, he must take the telephone away into a public place. Caroline could guess the way the talk was going from the gestures of the owner and the laughter of the fishermen who had gathered in the doorway. To be involved in such a scene would, in the ordinary way, have made her awkward and confused. Here, at this moment, she had no feeling about it whatever. She didn't care if Robert or the café owner won the argument. She didn't mind in the least whether they got through on the telephone or not. She didn't care if the whole fishing population gathered laughing in the doorway — provided no one of them should actually touch her with his finger. At the the slightest touch of a hand she would, she knew, scream out loud, but just to be jeered at had no longer the slightest meaning to her.

The café owner was now speaking to her. He was addressing her in the execrable French used by the hotelkeepers. Caroline was surprised to find that she understood him perfectly. He was saying that Mademoiselle was indeed welcome to his telephone, and to anything in his café, providing she would, as an act of courtesy to him, avoid having any speech with the police, whom he and his friends happened very naturally to detest.

The faces of the fishermen ceased to smile, for they no longer knew what was being said. Robert, it seemed, did not follow the conversation either; perhaps, thought Caroline, the French was too bad for him to understand.

They appreciated the great courtesy of the Senhor, she replied, but her companion particularly wished to telephone the police to inquire after a friend who had disappeared, and that being so, they would not inconvenience the Senhor any further.

The owner accompanied her to the door with polite smiles, and Robert followed. It gave her the fleeting shadow of a triumph. It was the only triumph she would get tonight. Two more cafés full of faces had to be entered. Twice more, requests for permission to use the telephone had to be made. Once they were roughly told that it was not for use, and, on pressing the question, that it was out of order. At the last, they held the receiver for ten minutes without getting a reply.

Robert was growing desperate. Darkness was closing down. Caroline felt she could scarcely stand up any longer, let alone walk round the town attempting to secure favors from the hostile.

"I think," she said, "that we should go to Bettina and Quinta and see if they can do anything to help." Though it was clear to Caroline afterwards that this was the obvious first step they should have taken, they did not wonder about it at the time. It seemed to them at this moment that the suggestion to call in Quinta and Bettina was an excellent idea which had somehow got mislaid, and which Caroline, fortunately, had recovered. Robert almost smiled at her when she suggested it.

Bettina and Quinta occupied a large flat on the first floor of a house not far from the central square.

"It could be," said Robert, as they walked round, "that Bettina and Quinta will not yet have returned. They have been staying in Estoril for the week end."

A ring brought Quinta to the door. His commonplace brown face wore a troubled look; troubled inside himself, thought Caroline, and troubled again at sight of them. He led them upstairs to a large room furnished like a sitting room in a bad French hotel. The only signs of Quinta's occupation were a leather dispatch case, a set of mathematical instruments, and a catalogue of machinery. Bettina's portfolio leaned against the wall. There were a pair of her shoes on the mantelpiece and a whisky bottle on the table. Whisky in Portugal is a luxury drink.

"Bettina," called Quinta from the doorway. "Here are Robert and Caroline come to see us."

Bettina did not appear actually to have been in bed, but her hair was ruffled, and she was buttoning up her frilly blouse as she came in. She looked physically distracted, but her eyes were even brighter and more wide awake than usual. She glanced quickly at Robert and Caroline in turn, then pulled up a chair as if she saw they were in for a long talk.

"We have come," said Caroline in a flat voice, "to know whether you have any news of Leo in Estoril. Robert is worried about him, because Leo has not come back and he has not heard from him. He thinks you may perhaps have seen him in Estoril, or that Senhor Quinta may possibly be able to find out something on the telephone. We have been telephoning ourselves all evening, but we have not been successful."

In these words and by her appearance, Caroline knew well, the whole of her story was disclosed. Bettina did not look at her at all. She took one long look

[207]

at Robert, a remorseless look, and then Quinta caught her eye. He was visibly asking Bettina how much they should tell.

"Well," said Bettina at last, "we did see Leo in Estoril," and she stopped. Caroline had the feeling that everyone in the room felt in some sense guilty before everybody else, that even Bettina had something to conceal.

At the mention of Leo in Estoril, Robert began to take charge. He leaned forward, concentrated: "Well, what did you see?" It was clear that he meant to have the truth.

"On Sunday night," said Bettina, resolving to come out with it all, "we went to the Casino. We had had dinner, and we went there to have some drinks and play a little. We were dancing in the ballroom when suddenly we caught sight of Leo. You know how tall he is," she explained to Robert. She seemed to be speaking defensively, deliberately spinning out her story. Every now and then she looked for confirmation to Quinta, who nodded back. "At first we could see only Leo's head. Then when he got closer we could see that he was dancing. He was with a woman. Rather a common woman, very much painted."

"A whore," said Quinta.

"Leo is dancing," Bettina went on, "and we are on the far side of the room. Suddenly there is shouting. We can see Leo only over the people's heads. He is calling out and striking with his fists. He seems to be fighting with two men. Then suddenly we cannot see Leo any more. We go towards the door, and we see Leo taken past. He is bleeding from the head, but he is walking, and he is being led by some police. The police of the Casino have come, and are taking him away."

Caroline's tiredness had left her. Her headache served only to show her the picture with a painful sharpness. She saw not only Leo, every detail of his appearance, and the woman with whom he had been dancing; she saw the despair which had led him to a dance floor, for him of all places the most meaningless and futile. She saw the start of the quarrel with the two men, the uneasy protectiveness of the whore, whom she saw as angrily shaking off the fighters when they tried to hold her back, and pressing after the police to see what happened.

She saw the source of Bettina's own defensiveness and of Quinta's guilty hesitation. He had not intervened, and she had concealed from Robert these happenings for two days. Bettina had gone to Estoril, Caroline felt certain, in order to persuade Leo, in Robert's interest, to stay away from Marinha. She had gone to plead with him to give Robert the chance which was really in Bettina's mind, his own last hope of being able to enter a safe country. Had Bettina actually spoken to Leo? Was it the things she told

him which had produced in him this incredible reaction, his taking a public woman to a dance? Or
was Bettina then still waiting for a chance to speak?
Had she simply accepted what fate offered? She had
gone to Estoril to get Leo to stay. Seeing him carried
off by the police, had she decided on the spot that that
would do as well?

Guilty as she might be towards Robert for concealment, Caroline was convinced that towards Leo
Bettina would be absolutely clear. Whatever she did
had been done wholeheartedly for him.

"The police will not keep Leo long," Quinta was
saying. "It was on Sunday that he was arrested. Probably he is already free."

Robert leaned forward on the table. His face had
lost its color. He did not appear even to be angry any
more. "That was the same thing which has happened
the night Leo try to kill himself," he said. "That night
also he has been out with a street woman."

Bettina turned to Caroline. "Quinta will take Robert to his friend the police officer," she said. "Together they will ring up Estoril."

Obediently the two men rose and went towards the
door. As she heard them go upstairs Bettina turned
to Caroline.

"It's time you were in bed, my pet," she said.

XVI

SURVEY OF THE BATTLEFIELD

WHEN Caroline realized once more where she was, she was lying in Bettina's bed. She had drunk the best part of a tumbler of whisky and swallowed a couple of tablets which Bettina gave her with the remark that they would be "bad for her, but very pleasant."

She came to herself with the feeling in her ears of a regular sound, like that of a train going over rails, or the breaking of waves down on the shore. The noise, it came to her at last, was neither of these. It was Bettina's crying. She was sitting at her dressing table with her arms out in front of her, shaking with sobs.

"Good Lord!" cried Caroline, flinging back the bedclothes and beginning to climb out.

Bettina looked up, caught sight of Caroline, rushed over to her and flung her arms tightly round her. "My poor child; my poor, poor child. I liked you so, why do I have to get you into such a mess? Why did you ever get mixed up with all of us? Why couldn't you stay where you were? Why did you come to this bloody place at all?"

Bettina's storm, the sign that someone realized what she had been through, had on Caroline a most comforting effect. She stroked Bettina's hair. "It wasn't your fault at all," she said. "All you did was *not* to stop me doing something I always meant to do. You really can't blame yourself for that."

Bettina clung to her. "I could have kept you out," she said. "I could have done, and didn't. I thought with your help we might get things straight. When you walked into the room this evening I felt like a murderess. I could see everything that had happened in your face. If you want to fall asleep or vomit, do," she went on kindly. "Things like that I do not find disturbing. Yes, I can see everything that happened. But there is one thing I must tell you."

"What is that?" They were sitting side by side against the pillows like two children.

"It is something I really only saw this evening, so I could not have told it you before. When we talked in the castle I told you truly everything just as I saw it. I wanted you to stay, it's true, but I did not lie to you or hide anything from you I knew then. Only I did not know this thing. I see it only now." She spoke pleadingly.

Caroline smiled, for the first time today, and

pressed Bettina's hand. "What have you only just seen?"

"I said there was one chance in five for you and Robert. There was *never* the least chance at all."

"You mean it wasn't my fault . . . I didn't . . . it would have been . . ."

Bettina cut her short almost savagely. "Your fault indeed! Listen to me. I'll tell you what I see now, and should have seen long ago. I thought that underneath all this muddle, Robert was either one thing or the other, either an ordinary man or . . . something different, just as Leo is. I see now that he is not one thing or other, he is double. And it's not because he's attracted both ways, but because he is repelled. He is divided in himself, and reacts always *against* the thing which is and wants the thing which is not. Look at him tonight! He is mad — mad against you, because he has loved you. To bring you out like this to help him in his absurd chase after Leo — what is it? It is not kindness, and it is not sense. Leo has been gone a week, ten days. How is it Robert did not start telephoning for him a week back?"

"I don't know," said Caroline wearily. "How is it?"

"He did not look for Leo before, because he did not want to find him. He was always expecting Leo, going off to the bus to meet him, talking about when he would be back, but he did not *want* him. He was waiting, in his mind, for something else. He wanted something else, that thing he was waiting for, to happen. Now the something else has happened, so he turns against it. Even this evening, even this whole time he has been rushing up and down with you, he has not really been looking for Leo. He thought he was, of course, but he was not."

Everything Bettina was saying, the actions she was describing, seemed to Caroline to be happening at an immense distance from herself. She followed them with mild interest, and no personal concern.

"What *was* he doing?" she asked to keep the cinema in motion.

"He was punishing you, my darling. He was making you suffer for a crime which he imagines he and you have committed against Leo; a crime against Leo, to be avenged by making you do things for Leo. It is guilt," cried Bettina, "guilt which directs the life of this poor Robert. Before, it was guilt over Leo. Now it is guilt over you. Whatever is, is wrong — it will always be wrong, and must be paid for by himself and everyone about him. One chance in five, indeed! The only hope with such a man is to be the thing which he rejects, never that which he accepts — then he will still be drawn towards you, and you can always keep away. I have given you bad advice, my darling, and somehow or other I shall pay for it."

"I don't want you to pay for it," said Caroline, who was beginning to experience a sensation of extraordinary lightness and release. It was not simply that her head had ceased to ache. It had floated away entirely from her shoulders, giving her a freedom she had never known before. "I don't want anyone to pay for anything."

"What do you want?" Bettina asked.

"Only one thing, and I hardly dare to ask it."

"What?"

"I want to know the source of the trouble you take for Leo. Why do you do it? For you, everything comes back to him. Yes, I know you were honest with me. I believe that through and through. You felt there was a chance, that for me it was one worth taking. If you hadn't believed that, you'd have warned me off. All that I accept. But it wasn't to my advantage you were looking. I never thought it was, and you must have known I didn't think so. And it was certainly not to Robert's. You don't even very much like Robert."

"I like Robert," said Bettina, "but I have no patience with him. I think it a pity that in taking some of the qualities of men and leaving others, Robert should have chosen to keep the denseness of a man. He is so gifted; and at critical moments he does always what is wrong. He is honorable, courageous, intelligent, devoted. If only he weren't always wrong."

"So," went on Caroline, from the beautiful aloofness which the drug conferred on her, "I knew from the first that it was Leo for whom you were concerned. But why are you so concerned for him? Of all the things I have heard about him since I came here, there isn't one I like."

"Nobody likes the things they hear of Leo," declared Bettina. "Nobody likes the things he does. But everyone loves him when they see him. Even you, with all the cause you have to hate him, will love him, just like everybody else. He will come back tomorrow or the next day. You will know all the things about him which you do know, and some other bad ones which he will do before he comes — and when you see him you will love him. That is his nature, to give and to take love."

"It sounds a very curious nature."

"There is also another reason why I care for Leo, which I told you the first day I saw you, though perhaps you did not notice, or perhaps you did not think it was important. He is an artist. I am not an artist, but I am not entirely a fool. I know the good thing when I see it. Leo's poetry is the good thing. Of all the artists and poets and sculptors I have known, Leo is the one who has the secret. In the world there are a few people only who can do good work; and there are only a few people, too, who know good work when they see it. I know only one real artist — Leo. I know him, and he knows I know him. With me, out of all the people that he meets, he is entirely free. I never ask anything of him. I don't even ask him to do more work. If he wants my money, or for his house to be cleaned, or to have my bed to sleep in — he can take anything he likes. When he does things which people say are stupid or cruel or unjust — or immoral, which is what they say most often — I say nothing, nothing to him, and to the people who repeat these things, I either say 'It is a lie' or I say nothing — till they become silent and stop saying them. From Paul and his friends I was away a whole week because of something they had said about Leo — something which is true, but about which I say to them, 'It is a lie.' After a week Hélène comes to me and says, 'Bettina, it was a lie' — and we are friends again."

Caroline turned towards her. "So everything from the beginning, Robert and me and Paul and Hélène and Quinta — everything that's happened while I've been here, or is going to happen till I go — is really part of your plan for Leo."

"No," answered Bettina. "Not all things, but most things. I brought Paul and Hélène here, for reasons which I told you. They brought Maxim, without asking me. When you began to fall in love with Robert, I was happy. I had thought for a long time that the two had a better chance of life apart. Those who will help and care for Leo do not want Robert. Those who would do something for Robert are frightened and upset by the things Leo does. Paul and Hélène even might still do something for Leo by himself."

Caroline thought of intervening, but did not. All that could be gone over later. Just now she could not bear to leave her cloudy doze.

"Leo is a poet," Bettina continued. "If he has a little success in England, which perhaps could be arranged, they will be only helping a distinguished exile. But for Robert they will do nothing. They have quarreled with him, and they know that he does not forget. He is against them for good, because he thinks he can no longer trust them. Leo trusts everybody always, because he forgives everybody when they do him harm. People can injure Leo, and still go on loving him and being friends, because they know that he forgets all the bad things they have done to him.

"I had even thought" — Bettina paused, and then continued — "I had even thought it possible that, if there is love between you and Robert, the scandal about Robert and Leo will die down. It is even possible that the police record can be expunged. The police officer said to Quinta: 'That is a thing which has sometimes been arranged.' "

"My God," said Caroline, marveling at the way their minds had run side by side. "How deep you go! And suppose I hadn't happened to fall in love with Robert?"

"In that case you would have been no use," said

Bettina — "unless you had happened to fall in love with Maxim."

"I don't see how that would have helped."

"Neither do I," said Bettina, examining her slim ankles which were cocked up on the bed, "but then I haven't thought about it yet. Everything that happens can be used somehow."

"And Quinta, is he also part of your love for Leo?"

"No," declared Bettina. "Quinta is just what you always thought he was — my Portuguese passport. In all the foolish things I have done, there is one I have never done — that is to get married. That is my last card, and I shall only play it when there are no others left."

"I think that is very delicate of you."

"You need not sneer at me, my darling," Bettina said, without the least sign of ill-feeling. "If I do marry Quinta, I shall try to be fair with him. I shall never be a good wife, but I shall try at least to keep the bargain equal, so that he gets something that he wants and is not made ridiculous before other people of the same sort as himself."

"I think you give Quinta a great deal."

"No. I get much more from Quinta than I give."

"Chiefly the help of the police chief, I think."

"Partly that," Bettina admitted. "Quinta knows everyone. He talks to the bus driver and he talks to the mayor. He calls in for a drink with everyone.

When he comes back tonight he will know everything Leo did in each minute of the days he has been gone."

"And now your plan has failed," asked Caroline, sitting up in bed, unable, despite herself, to keep a tinge of bitterness out of her voice, "what are you going to do next? Robert has let you down, and I have let you down. Robert and Leo are still together, and there are more bad marks on the police record for fighting in Estoril. What happens now? Where do you go from here?"

"From here, my darling, I do not know," Bettina answered. "But I know where those two go to in the end, and I think now that they will go together, and nothing I can do will save Leo, any more than you have been able to save Robert."

"Where is that?"

"Twice in Paris," Bettina said, "Robert went to see fortunetellers, different people in different parts of Paris. Each time the same thing happened. The person he had gone to see refused to tell him anything at all. At last, when he argued and pleaded, each one said the same thing to him: 'I see a hand pushed into your gold hair. I see your head jerked up — and then the bullets.' That was what each one said, and that is what I think is coming. There will be a war. Robert and Leo will be driven out of here. Somewhere, I don't know where, they will be captured by those who have for a long time been looking for them. Then they will be shot. That will be all. It was perhaps because of that that I was crying when you woke up tonight, which is something I have not done for many years."

As Caroline flung her arms around Bettina, they could hear downstairs the two men opening the door. Quinta was fumbling with the lock. They could hear his thick kindly voice speaking the nasal English which he used with Robert. "In the presence of the stars," he was saying solemnly, "does not one feel how small are the troubles of the human beings?"

The two girls clung together crying.

"At least," sobbed Caroline, "he is kind."

"At least," said Bettina, "he does say funny things."

XVII

THE WANDERER'S RETURN

QUINTA might be inclined to platitudes, but he knew just how to handle a situation such as this. His reluctance was always to get started. From each of his acquaintances he could ask only so many favors in a year – nicely related to the number he was able to confer — and since taking up with Bettina he had the feeling of having rather strained his credit. However, as soon as it was clear that this was a case in which he had got to act, he took it up with a good grace, managing matters skillfully to escape attention and avoid conflict with authority.

"If only Robert would take a few lessons from Quinta in how to get round people in high places — " said Bettina.

" — or important people in low places — " put in Caroline, thinking of the post office.

" — they would both have been in Chile long ago."

They were sitting outside a café on the square,

watching the glow lift off the town, light up the cliff, and die out of the sky, just one day later, on Caroline's last evening in Marinha.

All Quinta had done the night before had been to ring up the hotel in Estoril at which he and Bettina always stayed, and get through to the manager. An influential English lady, approved by the government and having important interests in Portugal, he told him, wished to know what had become of a certain young German poet, who had had a minor encounter with the police a day or two before. She had intended ringing the police direct, but he had advised her that in such matters it was wiser to ask some man of honor in a public position to make for her those inquiries which he could carry out so easily, and which in her case would be certain to attract attention.

Quinta had then simply waited by the telephone for half an hour. At the end of that time he knew in which cell Leo had spent the night, how he had slept, what the official said to him next morning, where he had gone on leaving the police station — with the information that he would be arriving in Marinha on the bus the following evening.

Quinta thanked the manager profusely, and assured him of the distinguished lady's gratitude, but added that the young man had been expected on the bus for several days, so that it was quite likely he would not arrive next evening after all.

"On the contrary," he was told. "It is certain that he will arrive in Marinha, tomorrow by the midnight bus."

This very night, therefore, Leo was expected. As the time of his arrival approached, Caroline could hardly control a growing curiosity as to what kind of man this Leo would be who, without appearing until she was about to leave, had exercised so large an influence over her affairs. After sleeping the night in Bettina's bed, she had spent much of the past day with her, and there had been one question which a hundred times she had been on the edge of asking, and each time had stopped herself because it seemed so personal and trifling — even, in her position, so absurd. It was simply the question of whether Leo knew of her existence, or not. Each time she had checked herself, but each time it remained, until at last, unable to get rid of the idea, but determined not to ask, she had tried to find out for herself why it should interest her at all. Why should she care whether Leo was aware of her being in Marinha? Did she want him to know, or didn't she?

The curious thing about it was that she saw at once that she *did* want him to know. It might be supposed that, defeated as she had been in a remote and mysterious encounter with him, she would have wished to escape his knowledge altogether. That was not so at all. Her unexpected fear was just the opposite, that on his return — for which everyone, even Paul, Hélène, and Maxim, were now openly waiting — all the rest would be known and accepted by him, and she would be left, the one stranger outside the party. To such an extent had the attitude of everyone, and particularly Bettina, influenced her that she had not the slightest fear of Leo in any way triumphing over her. Her concern was that she might be overlooked, and perhaps be rather in the way.

As the evening changed to night, a night which did not close down on Marinha, but into whose coolness the little town opened like a flower, the whole party was assembling in one of the cafés on the square. Bettina and Caroline had had dinner there with Quinta, whose gently boring quality Caroline found restful, and after dinner Paul had arrived with his depleted army, Hélène and Maxim.

"You should have had dinner with us tonight, Caroline dear," he began as soon as he came in. Caroline cast about in her mind for the right excuse, imagining Paul was going to reproach her for leaving them on her last evening. She was relieved when he went on: "We had a most delicious goose, and Maxim brought a bottle of champagne which was sent him by his family. Excellent! Delightful! The best dinner we have eaten since we dined with the Lucignys at Cannes. We very much wished you were there," he added graciously.

"I am glad you have come here now," said Caroline, smiling at Hélène and Maxim. She had dressed with care, and was pleased to see Hélène looking at her with approval. She knew the approval showed kindness on Hélène's part, but she realized that it was genuine as well, and was glad on both accounts.

Maxim went over to a mechanical organ on the far side of the café and poured a handful of change into the machine, which began to play. Quinta ordered drinks, and Paul recommended to everyone, not what he fancied they would like, but drinks he had once enjoyed himself, or would be interested to see tried again.

The drinks arrived and disappeared. They were powerful and mixed, and the glasses were soon refilled. The organ had an exciting brassiness and valor. They were in a café they had never visited before, and the proprietor, pleased with such lavish custom, was paying them particular attention. The now assured arrival of Leo was a relief or an excitement to them all. Even those who had been glad of his going were now openly anticipating his return. Every trace of the quarrel from which so much had started seemed now to have entirely disappeared. Hélène, content and reassured by the past ten days, shared in the general expectation.

Suddenly a feeling of mutual gaiety descended on

the little party. Quinta, with a polite bow, invited Caroline to dance. Maxim held his hand out — with what seemed an open and forgiving gesture — to Bettina. Paul looked a little hurt at not having been consulted, but was soon dancing with Hélène. Others in the café joined in. The tiled floor was crowded. Passers-by in the square came up and lined the window; a few fishermen lounged at the doorway.

So far from resenting it, the slight sense of being a public spectacle seemed to Caroline the one thing that could get her through the evening. Even the appearance of Robert did not upset her. He sat down at their table, dusting a chair first with his screwed-up beret, and his presence was covered by the talk in which everybody joined.

"Excellent! Delightful! Splendid people!" exclaimed Paul, beaming happily round at the company who revolted him so much every morning on the bathing beach. "How nice it is to see so many of them!"

Quinta and Maxim made sure that every glass was well supplied. Paul, from time to time, would get up and go over to the bar to see if there were any kind of cake or sweet which he had not yet sampled. Hélène, who had not a strong head, quickly became maudlin. Everything she said was now quite aimless and silly, but it was natural, and everyone liked her better on account of it. Robert told them of his latest dispute with the man who kept the horses, in which he, Robert, had locked the door of the stables downstairs when the man was out, and the man had brought one of his horses up by the outside steps in order to put it in Robert's room, only to find that he had fitted a new padlock to the door, and the horse, which had come up, would not go down.

"I see how it is," thought Caroline, observing herself and Robert, who exchanged remarks, but indirectly and without looking at each other: "When one is falling in love, one looks at the other one, but does not speak. When it is over, one speaks to the other one, but does not look."

Bettina, observing that Caroline had fallen silent, at once promised that if Maxim would go back and fetch the last bottle of his father's champagne, she would dance her famous "sitting-down rhumba" in the middle of the café. Quinta looked disconcerted, but Maxim went for the champagne.

Meanwhile, whether because they liked her company or by secret contrivance of Bettina, Caroline was never without someone asking her to dance, and her glass, which had always just been filled, was always empty. Hours moved fast, as they do when one is constantly occupied and partly drunk.

In the first pause that happened since they assembled at the café — the champagne had just arrived, and everyone was helping to put it into a bucket of ice behind the bar — Caroline, with a swimming eye but mind still clear as glass, found herself gazing out onto the square. There was a certain activity at the upper end which she was watching with mild interest. On the curb a tall figure waited until the driver reached up for his case . . . in a flash she realized what was happening. The midnight bus had arrived, and this was Leo. There was no mistaking him. He was fifty yards away, but the lamplight shone on his gold hair, neither long like a woman's, nor like that of a man whose hair is allowed to grow, but of a length and cut between the two.

He stood on the curb, elegant, a little aloof, but altogether friendly, waiting for his bag to be lifted down. When he took it, she missed something, a customary movement of the hand. He had not given the man anything; but the man had turned away quite satisfied. Caroline guessed at once why there had been no tip. Of the two thousand escudos there was nothing left.

And now began an infinitely prolonged half-minute. The party were still clustered round the bar, offering advice as to how more ice could be packed into the bucket. Leo, starting to walk along the square, looking in for them no doubt at each of the cafés, had disappeared from her line of vision. In a moment, led by the noise and fuss, he was certain to arrive at the café. Meanwhile she was the only one who knew that Leo had come back to Marinha and that, in a matter of seconds, his face would look round the door, and he would himself be in the room.

The bucket was filled. The group by the bar broke up. They rushed back to the table and sat down to order a drink that would keep them going till the champagne was cold enough to be uncorked. In that moment Leo had come in.

Perhaps because of the drink, perhaps because of the drug she had swallowed the evening before, Caroline took in the whole of his appearance in one look. He was present in his full nature and completeness. Her first thought was the single one: "So they were all quite right."

He had eyes of a brilliant childlike blue, but what impressed one most was their curious roundness. The pupils were round and clear of the eyelids. The shape of the eyes was round, and so large that they would have seemed protuberant had they not been set well into their sockets.

The face was built on a noticeable bony structure of forehead, jaw, and cheekbones — but it was overlaid with the smooth contours of a woman. The ears were neat and fitted closely to the head; one was invisible under the falling wave of hair.

By far the most extraordinary feature was the mouth. The eyes and brow gave the head authority and strength; its extraordinary air of sweetness came directly from the lips. The central line of them was perfectly straight, but, above and below, the lips arched back in lines of unbelievable delicacy and fullness. It was not a classic mouth. It seemed to have no forerunners. It was its own original, giving an effect of firmness and courage, coupled with extreme sensuality and sweetness. It seemed both to make up to, and to bless, whomever it addressed.

It was from the mouth, thought Caroline, that there came to the mind of everyone who tried to describe Leo the same banal suggestion — of an angel, a spirit loving, generous, and solely benevolent to man. Such an idea was at once dispelled by the nose. It was well-modeled, but short, with quite unusually full and open nostrils, open to snuff up the wind of life. Though only a slight feature in an astounding face, they could not, once noticed, be forgotten or overlooked, for in them showed plainly the reverse side of the image. The channel connecting nostrils and upper lip was deeply chiseled. The chin was firm, and even heavy.

In physique Leo showed the same doubleness implicit in his face. He was well-built, even athletic. His strong arms and legs and shoulders were those of a swimmer, and could be powerful in a fight, as Robert had many times declared, but the roundness of his hips, accentuated by his well-cut flannels and dark blue shirt, was soft and womanish. His clothes altogether, with his small gold wrist watch on a bracelet and his jeweled ring, were the extreme that elegance permits, and his movements had a contour and airiness that could not pass as unconscious.

But what affected Caroline most, and what she imagined must affect everyone who met Leo, was not his good looks at all — though there was something about them which made every other face in the room seem either flat or cheap: Paul's showed the handsome self-satisfaction of the suburban tennis court; Hélène looked like a peevish cover from a fashion magazine; Robert, for all the real quality of mind apparent in his face, had become a squire, or man-at-arms. What was moving and affecting about Leo, what, at this moment, and in spite of everything, shafted to her heart, was the air of detachment which hung round him like a mist. It was as though he did not quite belong — as though, in spite of all the efforts he made, in spite of the most intimate contacts and a power of the deepest sympathy with others, of active suffering upon their account, he was still not one among other men. He could not ever forget, or lose, himself. He conveyed to every seeing eye a haunted feeling, the tooth mark of the hidden worm. Leo had been born with the fox inside his shirt, the murdered albatross about his neck, that would never, do what he would, slide off into the sea — until one day it would drop with a dull echo but without a splash, and carry him down with it. He was a being possessed and driven, for purposes he had not chosen and which he could not comprehend, towards an end only too vividly foreseen.

Caroline saw now what Bettina meant when she told her that she could not only forgive Leo anything he did, even the most sordid crime, but that she would utterly overlook and disregard it. Whatever he does, or fails to do, thought Caroline, comes out of a hidden conflict greater than any of us has power to judge. Elderly savages on benches, frozen and be-wigged, may thumb their books of precedent and sound a judgment; the humans wonder and keep silence.

Doubly impressive and delightful in view of this was the way in which Leo put himself at once in close and separate touch with all the party. He gave a warm glance to Robert and another to Bettina, though he did not speak a word. His expression conveyed: "We old friends know each other: we can do our talking later on." He smiled naturally at Paul and Hélène, laid a hand in passing on Quinta's shoulder, an unexpected gesture which gave Quinta visible satisfaction, and then in a second he was standing directly in front of Caroline.

She looked straight into his eyes, making no at-tempt to conceal what she felt towards him: pity, the recognition of one human spirit for another, the readiness to accept him and their situation — with, behind it but unconcealed, an equal readiness to stand up for herself and fight it out. To Leo, as himself, she would concede anything he needed; as an enemy, still less as a defeated rival, she would not give an inch. All those present were aware in some degree — and Bettina with a burning sympathy — of the tension in this second.

Then with a quick and graceful movement Leo picked up her hand and kissed it. "This is the one I have come specially to see," he said. "After all I've heard about you, I wanted to welcome you myself." For a moment everything hung in the balance. Caroline had no idea how to reply: she needed some further clue. Bettina stepped in quickly.

"If you'd waited another day, Leo," she said, "you'd have missed Caroline altogether. She's going back to England tomorrow."

"Then we must see a lot of her tonight," said Leo, and he took the chair beside her while Maxim went for the champagne.

For hours Leo sat with them and talked. He had clearly no sense at all of having given anyone any trouble, or if he had, he had too much tact to embarrass them with apologies. Instead he rejoiced with them over his own return, and entertained them with his spirits. From the way he spoke, it would seem that his sole purpose in going to Estoril had been to collect anecdotes that would amuse them. He told them about his arrest, his night in the cells, his interview with the police officer next morning, in which he had refused to give his name or answer any questions until the police had apologized to him for the theft of his beret — which he later found inside his shirt, where he had stuffed it for safekeeping the night before.

He had a special story for Bettina about an old man and a dancer at the table next to him at dinner. The girl, conscious that Leo was listening to every word they said, had rapped the old man on the knuckles with her fork for something he was whispering.

"Don't you ever have a decent thought?" she asked.

"Only when I am with my family," answered the old man.

For Hélène he brought accurate reports of everything that was being worn, the things that should be worn and the things that shouldn't. He was perfectly well aware of the least details of fashion, and Hélène was obviously delighted to discuss them with him.

He flattered Paul by telling him that the babel of different languages at the Casino reminded him of a party they had gone to together once in Lisbon, a party of every nationality known, where Paul had said something to each present in his own language. To Robert he only said: "I suppose we shall find horses in all our rooms when we get back." He was clearly aware, down to the details, of the movements of their life while he was absent.

Most curious to Caroline was the effect of Leo's presence upon Robert. The effect was double. It put Robert back into the shade. He talked far less and uttered few opinions of his own. He was inclined to fuss over Leo, to fetch him coffee and ask him if he had slept. Far down, below all the fuss and behind the suppression of his own abilities and feelings, Caroline perceived a deep restfulness and satisfaction. Leo was back. They were together. That, then, was the thing he had been really waiting for. A wave of weariness and misery flooded up inside her. This was the end of the holiday she had looked forward to so long, the holiday that was to change everything for her. Tomorrow she would go back, and all her life would begin again — the old life she had grown so sick of. The remembrance was like a dull blow in the region of the heart.

As often happens when one person is preoccupied, Caroline's silence soon spread to all the others. In the pause Leo began to fumble in the pocket of his trousers. He brought out what looked like a ball of tissue paper and laid it down before him on the table. The gesture with which he did it made it seem that this was the whole purpose of the evening.

"Caroline is leaving us tomorrow," declared Leo,

"I should like her to take something that will remind her of Portugal, and of her friends."

With a movement that came strangely from him, a movement of diffidence and hesitation, Leo laid the package in front of Caroline.

As she began to unwrap the tissue paper, the others leaned close across the table to see what it contained. The silence spread out to other tables, even around the bar there was a moment's quiet. Everyone, it seemed to Caroline, was looking at that tissue-paper package which must contain for someone there the secret of life or death. Caroline pulled away the last fragment, and set down on the café table a small silver box. It was obviously of great age, and had an air both sumptuous and elegant. It looked as if it were made to hold wafers for a cardinal, or sweets for the mistress of a royal admiral. Its four small legs were prancing dolphins, its belly chased and embossed with those ornate images of the sea which enrich buildings of the high Manuelline period — a heavy twisted cable, short-stocked and thick-fluked anchors, sea flowers, trees, and weeds, writhing in the profusion of a deep-sea garden. The patterned lid curved up to a knob or boss, bearing the triumphant symbol of the girdled globe which, from the days of Prince Henry the Navigator, has formed part of the arms of Portugal. Caroline opened it. Inside was gilt, and the tiny floor was paved with rough seed pearls, seeming to have been pressed into some soft metal while it was still warm. It was a treasure such as Caroline had never dreamed of, and the little group round the table gazed on it astonished.

Caroline opened the box, closed it, opened it again, set it down in front of her, and still could not speak. She did not know what the present meant, or why she had been chosen to receive it. She did not know whether she should accept it, or refuse. All she knew was that this was the most beautiful little object she had ever seen, and that there was some meaning in the present, if only she could understand it.

As she looked and wondered, Caroline found herself gazing, for the first time that evening, into the eyes of Robert. She understood his look as a request of some kind, a request to be forgiven, to be thought of without horror and distress, a request the whole meaning of which she could think out later. For the moment it was certain, a request to accept the present offered to her by Leo.

Caroline struggled for words. She doubted for a moment if she could speak at all. At last — "I shall keep it as long as I live," she said.

XVIII

"TAGUS, FAREWELL . . ."

THE ship was beginning to gather speed. For hours which seemed to Caroline as long as weeks they had slid slowly through the close Tagus mist, the bows hardly rippling the estuary water, or lain swinging to anchor in mid-channel, hooted at by invisible ships on every side. At one moment the sound of the sirens would come faint, as if from the far side of a mountain range; and then, after the shortest interval, the same siren would crash out menacingly near, and their own would reply in shuddering blasts that shook the mists down in drops onto the deck.

Fretting to get away, Caroline had walked up and down all the late afternoon, unable to remain still until her mind could settle, unable to settle down in mind until the ship should be really on its way to England and the too near past separated from her by space as well as time.

All the hours she had leaned over the side she had

seen nothing, nothing but a few sea gulls that blundered upon the ship and sheered away; a melon bobbing past them on the ebb, dropped overboard from a barge unloading upstream in the docks. Once too a fishing boat, so crammed with men as to leave no room to stow a catch if they had made one, swerved suddenly out of the mist almost underneath Caroline as she leaned over the dripping rail. One second a mere shadow, the next the boat gained not only form but color, her hull and the men's tanned faces making a bright momentary patch in the gray photographic world of mist. Her motor, inaudible till this instant, hammered loudly on the ear. As she cleared the ship's side by a yard, Caroline could see the boat heel over to a hard-forced tiller and the men on her gunwales swing in unison, one row inboard, the other out to keep her trim. For a second she was almost touching, the next she had disappeared and the sound of her motor folded in behind her.

And now the evening was coming on, the mist was thinning, and the throb of the ship's engines was beginning to speed up, a rapid rhythm much faster than a pulse which flung a wave far out from the bows and left a wake as far as could yet be seen astern. To Caroline the broadening, lengthening wake was the sign for which she had been waiting.

She had set off that morning very early. On everyone except Bettina she had practised a deception.

They had expected her to leave by the ten o'clock
bus, and made plans to come down and see her off.
Instead she had ordered Senhor Branca's car for
seven o'clock, and caught an early train from Vallado
to Lisbon.

The party had continued late the night before. It
was three when they left the café, and four by the
time she finished her packing and got into bed. At
five, unable to sleep, Caroline had got up and stood
beside the window in her nightdress. An enormous
moon was floating slowly down into the sea, making
a pathway of light that led directly to the shore and
towards her window. A little to one side of its track,
the red leaping of a fire showed where a group of
fishermen were cooking themselves a late or early
meal. Behind them every minute or so a sudden line
of whiteness would appear and vanish, like a smile,
and then a moment after it had passed came the
sound of a wave exploding softly into the steep sands.
Soothed by the rhythm and comforted by the coolness
of the night, Caroline stayed by the window, crying
softly to herself. She was not crying out of misery, but
for relief. Except for the evening with Bettina, she
had not cried at any moment in the last two years.
And even now she was not crying actively: the tears
just formed themselves in her eyes, to overflow down
her cheeks; and other tears ran after them.

Through her watering eyes she became aware after

a time of a figure seated in one of the doorways between her and the shore. She thought nothing of it,
paid it no special attention. After a time the light
of the sliding moon touched the figure, giving it for
the first time an outline. It made a shape of such
despair that Caroline caught her breath and the tears
stopped of their own accord. She turned and got into
bed. As she lay down, the impression of the figure
came before her mind again. For the first time it
occurred to her that the figure could be anything
more than a resting fisherman or homeless creature.
She jumped out of bed and ran quickly to the window
to see if her impression had been right. The figure
was no longer there.

The minute her head touched the pillow Caroline
began to dream. She dreamed like a stunned person
wandering, rather than a sleeper. She was out on the
sea, trying to sail a boat. It was a beautiful boat with
sails so bright they seemed to shine like gold, and two
large eyes painted on the bow. The boat was ex-
quisitely made and fitted out, but, try as she would,
she could not make it sail. It would begin to move,
and then, just when it should have bent to its work,
it would come up into the wind and stop. The shining
sails would fill, but they would not draw the boat.
Caroline worked the tiller desperately, for there was
a crowd of people watching — she could recognize
her own parents in the shapes of Hélène and a

bearded fisherman — and she was ashamed to fail in front of them. Besides, she knew that if she could not sail the boat they were going to take her home and make her live in a cupboard on the stairs where you could hear all the noises of the house; and she would have every day to clean the shoes of her brother, Hilary. Still she struggled; sometimes she was in the boat, sometimes in the water. At last, to her horror, the tiller actually came off in her hand, and she was convinced that her own awkwardness and stupidity had broken it. At the same moment her eye caught sight of the boat's name painted on the stern. The name was *Crab,* and she realized then what she had done wrong. The boat would only move sideways, and she had been trying to make it move forwards. "It's all my fault," she told herself, "anyone else would have known that at the start. But since I have changed my name, I have lost my own identity, and so I cannot recognize things and people any more."

At once all the people on the shore began to laugh, and a crowd of fishermen who had been hiding in a big villa in the town came rushing down into the sea for her with sticks. In terror she sprang into the water, meaning to drown, but when her feet touched bottom she found that it was paved with pearls, and she heard Bettina, who was wearing the dress belonging to her earliest school friend, say: "Don't mind the fishermen, darling. It's not you they're after."

[243]

Comforted by these words, Caroline fell into a real sleep. She did not wake until the car was beneath her window. As she got in the driver handed her a note. She opened it and read *"Think of me sometimes, too — Bettina."* The note, which Caroline found curious and touching, the small difficulties of her journey, with the worry as to whether she would catch her ship, had filled Caroline's mind all morning. In the afternoon she was haunted and preoccupied by the ship's delay. She regarded with all the terror of a refugee the possibility that it might put back for a few hours to Lisbon to allow the mist to clear away.

Against the ship's side the sea was swirling away now at gathering speed. The air, sucked underneath her hull as she drove forward, came slowly up through the sea in tiny bubbles, like smoke on a still day. Caught, before it could break surface, in the long curl of water turned back from the ship's traveling side, it vanished before ever it had come to birth. In the moist and thickening air of evening the handrail and everything about the deck were sticky to the touch.

Caroline crouched back into a corner where the canvas cover of a lifeboat gave her some protection. They were going back to England. Her holiday was over. What lay ahead of her when she got back? Of one thing she felt certain. The sensitive noses of the little band she had left behind — stranded on one of the westernmost points of Europe, no more able to

cross the ocean into safety than if they had lived before the New World was discovered — had been right.
They had snuffed the air, smelled blood, and foretold
war. The war was coming. For herself she no longer
cared. She would find something to do and do it. As
for those she had left behind, she had tried her ut-
most to help them in the way that had seemed best.
If any new way came to her, she would try that as
well. She did not think it likely that it would. She did
not think it likely that she would ever see Leo again.
To the innumerable rifle cracks that would ring out
across Europe during the next years, that golden
head — among so many other golden heads — would
be jerked up, or would fall forward. The gift of the
silver box was, she believed, a parting gift. And
Robert too, for at last it was possible to think of him
directly, what would become of him? Far more bitter
to her, far more salt upon her tongue, was the thought
of his doom than of Leo's. The reason was double. Not
only had she loved, did she still desperately love,
Robert — but Leo had a secret salvation Robert could
never have. Leo had faith. In the world of ordinary
men he had never entirely belonged. He was a
stranger and a sojourner in the homes of human
beings. He had the air of having come upon this
earth at all only by accident, or in mistake for somewhere else. Whatever might be done to Leo, his
essence was out of reach. But Robert was by no means

a creature from another world. He was a human, born into this world, of this world. Only he had lost his way. It had been beyond her power to help him, but that did not mean that he was outside human aid, and if she had failed, it seemed to Caroline that either she was unequal to her task or else she had gone about it the wrong way.

That was the fact against which Caroline continually came up. That she had failed. Had her whole attempt been crazy, a flying-in-face of the common sense known to every woman from her cradle, treasured by some, possessed by all, flouted by her alone? She did not think so. Bettina, whose judgment she relied on, had encouraged her — and, as she thought of Bettina, another idea came into Caroline's mind, and brought a shred of comfort. Bettina, in her intense and passionate concern for Leo, had given her, she felt, a lesson in love, and set her — casually, and quite unaware that she was doing it — a standard by which she would know how in future years to test other people's boasts and her own claims to "love" this one or that. In face of this, it was at least a comfort to remember her failure had not been due to greed. Her love might have been foolish, but it had nothing disreputable about it. The object was real, and the feeling was not something different, passing itself off under the name.

Caroline knew that this, and far more painful prob-

ing of the kind, was the task she had got to face, if
she was to learn anything from the past two weeks,
and not either cherish her own sickness or deny the
truth of her own feelings and experience. The
grownup, like the child, grows from what it can take
into itself, and loses by what it rejects, or fails to break
down and assimilate. Though at times a flood of
shame came over her, making her long to hammer her
head against the metal fittings of the lifeboat as a fool,
yet from it all she knew she could still be the gainer,
if, like the child, she could bring herself to swallow.

She could be the gainer, and somehow, some day,
Caroline knew already that she would — but Robert,
whom she loved, would not gain from what had happened, and nothing she could ever do would make
him gain. He had acted, not out of love as she had,
but from fear, an instinctive, overwhelming fear —
but a chilling, narrowing fear as well. He had behaved callously towards her, and his punishment
would be self-supplied. His divided nature would
grow after her in separation. Absence would increase
her hold upon him, as her own interest and concern
grew less. She would become a symbol, the other
hand of the signpost, pointing the way he had not
followed. From now on, at every setback and ob-
struction in his life, perhaps even at mere resting
points, Robert would pay, in the attraction of a course
he had not taken — and yet would never know the

relief of full regret, remorse admitted and acceded to, for remorse requires first the confession of wrong done. Robert's mind — intricate, curious, restless, and despairing — would, as time went by, invent still new ways to torment itself in fruitless self-justifications and accusings.

The night was closing down onto the sea. Caroline looked out across gray wastes of water to the last glow left by the sun in its race for the Americas and safety. The ship shuddered to a steady rhythm. The seas were drawn away faster past her sides. The domes of water churned down by the screws burst up further and further behind her as she raced along, surfacing like huge jellyfish, from whose glassy backs the sea rolled down in all directions.

Suddenly, from under the canvas cover of the lifeboat by her head, a moth flew out. Far back in the warm countries it had come aboard, in some port where the ship had touched at night, for in Lisbon she had docked in bright midday. There, in the corner where she was hiding, the cool evening air had reached and touched her. She crept out of her hiding place, flew up from the ship's side, out over the water, and was gone, fifty miles or more from land.

Out over the sea a small dark bird was swooping. It flew low over the water, cutting out arcs to left and right with swerving flight. Suddenly it swung in, passing almost over Caroline's head. It was a little nondescript bird that would not draw a second glance in any hedge, and it was flying with the same broken, flipping flight that hedge birds use, which are not accustomed to long journeys, but just flit over the barn and down to the tree at the bottom of the field. Caroline expected the bird to land, was preparing to pick it up, but it dodged round a ventilator, sheered up against the funnel, and was gone.

Along the corridors of the ship a gong was sounding and a voice was calling. The sound rose and fell like the flight of the small bird that had vanished. It was dark, it was cold, and Caroline was hungry. It was time to go below and eat.